# THE

# DARK

# STAR

**Andy Lloyd**

*Original Artwork:*
*Andy Lloyd*

*Cover Design by:*
*Bruce Stephen Holms*

© 2005 Timeless Voyager Press
PO Box 6678
Santa Barbara, CA 93160

*www.timelessvoyager.com*

THE DARK STAR

TIMELESS VOYAGER PRESS
PO Box 6678
Santa Barbara, CA 93160
1-800-576-8463

I would like to dedicate this book to Fiona, and our two boys, Chris and Robbie, whose light fills each and every one of our days.

# Acknowledgments

My very special thanks go to my best friends, and colleagues, Dave and Martin Cosnette, without whom I would never have embarked on any of this. From an inspirational chat over a cup of tea, we three set about creating one of the world's best-loved UFO websites, "Cosmic Conspiracies". Also thanks go to my great friends, Simon Faulkner for the Dark Star inspiration, and to Pete Scott, for the T-shirt.

Lee Covino deserves special thanks for all the hard effort and time that went into editing this book, not to mention the persistent urging to find a publisher. I would also like to express my gratitude to my publisher, Bruce Stephen Holms, for believing in the merits of this project, and to Peter Gersten, without whom that opportunity would not have arisen.

The long road to "The Dark Star" has been made a great deal easier by the help and encouragement of many people. In particular, I have been inspired by Zecharia Sitchin, greatly encouraged by Lloyd Pye, believed in by Monika Myers, and actively published by Joan d'Arc and Al Hiddell, of Paranoia Magazine. Their support and guidance has been invaluable throughout.

I am also very grateful to the following people, who have helped along the way (with apologies to anyone I've forgotten): Rob Astor, Anthony Austin, the late John Bagby, the late Graham W. Birdsall, Tom and Kerry Blower, Shad Bolling, the "Clockwork Team." (Parameshwaran Ravindranathan, Samit Basu and Jaideep Undurti), Frank Cordell, William Corliss, Al Cornett, Maurice Cotterell, Roger Cunningham, Richard Day, Kathy Doore, Dr. Richard Fitzpatrick, Robert Frola, Mattia Galiazzo, Dr. Brett Gladman, Andy Goldie, Dr. Matthew Holman, Holger Isenberg, James Arthur Jancik, Greg Jenner, David Jinks, Allene Keller, Theo Kermanidis, Dr. Marc Kuchner, John Lee, Lystra Maisey, Dr. Mark Marley, Ed Massey, Marshall Masters, Dr. John Matese, Ralph McConahy, Brant McLaughlin, Dr. Mario Melita, James Monds, Dr. John Murray, James Oberg, David Pearson, Enrique Pérez Porter, Dr. Alice Quillen, Angel Rapallo, John Rockley, Rick Savard, Robert Sepehr, Robertino Solarion, Pat Thomas, Barry Warmkessel, Michael Weinberger, Phil Whitley, Dr. Daniel Whitmire, and Roel Wolfert.

# Table of Contents

# *Introduction*

It is human nature to accept certain apparently self-evident facts as fundamental truths.

We live comparatively short lives, and the education we receive as children and fledgling adults, for many of us is the only education available in a lifetime.  Most people in the world have no time for books. Their televisions are their sources of knowledge, perhaps aided and abetted by newspapers. So what is taught in schools is what is taken to be truth, often for the rest of a person's life. Yet our science and our understanding of the world change over time, often very rapidly. Academics must spend a lot of time just keeping up with the changes of knowledge in their own fields of expertise.  And there are thousands of fields of expertise...so what real hope is there for the rest of us to access the latest thinking of science and the arts?

This is where books have a unique role to play. Through 300 pages or so we can immerse ourselves in modern knowledge and thought, and extend the rudimentary understanding of our world imparted to us through school. Sometimes we must 'unlearn' as well, as what was once taught as fact becomes an historical mistake. Yet people don't readily unlearn. They don't readily throw off cherished beliefs or theories to accept those offered by a new generation. This leads to conservatism within academia and society as a whole.

A kind of cultural constraint is evident within the field of science, as it is in our religious and educational establishments. That is not to say that scientists do not consider weird and wonderful new theories, as many of them are open-minded and liberal. However, the institution of science has itself become rather conservative, and there are certain lines of inquiry that are as heretical to modern science as witchcraft was to the medieval church. The British Egyptologist David Rohl has highlighted the ultra-conservative consensus that plagues modern scholarship (1). He argues that most scholars lack the imagination to really take on the big unanswered questions, and that the vacuum is filled by non-academic thinkers, who lack the resources and critical training to balance their work.

We live in an ultra-sceptical world where new ideas are derided as a matter of course. It seems as though modern science has achieved the begetting of the central tenets of its knowledge, and is happy only to tinker with the peripheral details. The major problems that remain are ignored, and scholars who chose to tackle them are often sidelined, or even publicly ridiculed.

It is a cultural norm to laugh at suggestions that our origins are from the skies, not the seas; or that evolution through natural selection might not actually provide a cast-iron explanation for the development of humanity, or that 'Others' might live in our own cosmic backyard, while our SETI scientists peer over the fence into the cosmic fields beyond in search of extra-terrestrial life

As odd as it may seem, the often stiff upper-lipped Victorians and Edwardians were far more open-minded about the possibilities of life in our solar system than we. We live in an age of high technology, space exploration and global communication. These are great, if not monumental achievements in the history of our species, but what has been lost recently is the speculative form of science that the Victorians indulged in when considering such things as the possibility of life existing on other planets.

The hope that we are not alone took a bit of a battering. If life was not to be found on Mars or Venus, then the next best possibility was life around other stars. The distances involved and the physical limitations of space-travel, mean that this possibility is far less dramatic, or even relevant. Hence the relative sterility of the scientific debate regarding extra-terrestrial life. This debate has become fringe science, yet this has not subdued its general popularity. Such a position can be infuriating for scientists who perennially find themselves pouring cold water over popular speculation about alien life.

It is said that a change in human understanding of some fundamental 'truths' takes not years, but generations. Historically, great leaps forward in science, such as the identification of the sun as the centre of the solar system by Copernicus (1543) and Galileo (1633), were not accepted overnight (2). Quite the contrary, the Western religious institutions that wielded such power over our ability to reason fought tooth and nail for hundreds of years to prevent these ideas from catching on. Carl Sagan analyses this intellectual intransigence in terms of the psychological craving we have to be the centre of the Universe. Each stage of scientific progress that exposes our ordinariness in the eyes of the Cosmos knocks our concept of self-importance, and humanity seems to always reject it, at least to start with (3). Often in the past this has been because of religious sensibilities about our rightful place in the Cosmos.

Sagan may be right. But on the subject of ET life, it is not the religious establishments that have stifled debate, but the scientific Establishment itself. Scientists have been banging nails into the coffin of 'ET life in the solar system' for decades. But the contents of that coffin are about to be resurrected. There is another incredible possibility, one that is so remarkable that it has quickly caught on among interested parties surfing the Internet. Since 'The Dark Star Theory' first proposed this new possibility, the growth in visits to the site has been rapid. Why? Because it gives a clear and plausible argument for the possibility that life could evolve elsewhere in the solar system. A planet beyond Pluto need not be cold and lifeless! Astronomers know this. This is not controversial for them. They understand what brown dwarfs are, and they realize that they provide enough heat and light to provide habitable environments on planets orbiting these failed stars. They know that one might well be circling the sun, in the comet clouds that make up the bulk of the solar system's volume. They recognize the difficulties that detecting such a body present. But where the Victorians would have indulged in a little hopeful speculation, the modern mainstream scientists remain stubbornly mute, afraid to cross that boundary into what has become fringe science.

So instead of reading of these ideas in scientific journals, that in turn would be reported on in mainstream media outlets, you, dear reader, are instead reading an 'alternative science' book. What I like to refer to as 'alternative astronomy'. This book will be dismissed and ridiculed by the intellectual establishment, insofar as it even moves above their horizon of interest. Even so, I can promise you something; you will discover in these pages a reasoned and scientific debate, one worthy of open scientific enquiry. I hope that this book re-kindles the debate about extra-terrestrial life in our solar system, and the environments that such life could inhabit. It throws the tremendous repercussions of the potential discovery of a brown dwarf in the solar system into the public domain. In this way, it paves the way for the astronomical discoveries of the future, and the way they will bring change to the way we understand ourselves.

When we were in school our physics teachers told us that there are 9 planets in the solar system; Mercury, Venus, Earth, Mars, Jupiter, Saturn, Uranus, Neptune and Pluto. They may even have added that Pluto may not really be a planet anyway. What they didn't tell us was that that knowledge is not cast into stone like Moses' Tablets. This is because our scientific knowledge is necessarily limited at the moment by our ability to detect distant dark objects. We simply cannot say with certainty that we have discovered all of the planetary bodies that orbit around the sun.

One day we may understand our solar system more fully, and be able to draw up our own Tablets of Knowledge. When we do it seems that there will be ten entries as well, just like there were with Moses. But at the moment we are missing a crucial commandment...

1. D. Rohl  "Legend: The Genesis of Civilization" p50 Arrow 1999


2. P. Moore  "Atlas of the Universe" p12, George Philip Ltd. 1999


3. C. Sagan "Pale Blue Dot" Headline 1995

# The Extended Habitation Zone

Our investigation starts with a look at our current understanding of where life can be found in the solar system. In years gone by, scientists and fictional writers speculated that life was common on other planets and that alien civilizations existed on Venus and Mars, our nearest neighbours. When Humanity began to explore the planetary environments in more detail with space probes, it became apparent that life was a rare commodity in the solar system, and perhaps throughout the galaxy as well.

Life needs liquid water, and water takes its liquid form through a relatively small range of temperatures. Most of the planetary environments in the solar system have more extreme environments than we enjoy here on Earth. Mercury, the sun's closest planet, is hard-boiled and baked, its surface blasted by the heat of the sun.

Venus, planet number 2, maintains a thick atmosphere which has been made highly acidic by what is thought to be a runaway green-house gas effect. Temperatures on the surface of the planet are extremely high, air pressures intolerable, and the combination of these factors means that lead melts on the ground there. Not very promising for the search for life, although it may still be found high in the atmosphere.

The Earth, however, is just the right distance away from the sun, and basks in the sort of medium-range temperatures that allow liquid water to exist across most of the surface of the planet. This has been the case for billions of years, and life has had a firm foothold here for most of that time. Earth is in the sun's 'habitation zone'. If the sun was bigger and hotter then that habitation zone might have been on the next planet, Mars.

If the sun was smaller and cooler, then Venus might have enjoyed a more profitable relationship with life. But only Earth enjoys that exalted, and possibly unique position. The discovery of life further out in the planetary solar system remains one of the great unanswered questions in science.

## Is There Life on Mars?

We still don't know for sure whether there is life on Mars, and by implication whether there is life elsewhere in the solar system, or Universe beyond. The Viking landers searched for signs of life in the 1970s, but the results of the experiments on soil samples on the Martian surface were said to be 'inconclusive' (1). The famous meteorite ALH 84001, discovered in the Allan Hills of Antarctica in 1984, seemed to contain evidence that life once existed on Mars (2). These findings remain controversial, and provide the merest threads of proof of extraterrestrial life. But those strands of hope are enough for many people to maintain their hopes that the rest of the solar system is not barren.

Confirmation of the existence of alien life has been inextricably entwined with the search for life on Mars, mainly because it seems to offer the second most hospitable environment in our solar system. Its atmospheric conditions are certainly deadly for most life-forms currently dwelling on Earth, but under the regolith of its barren plains may lie lakes and even seas of frozen water. Surface features of the red planet tantalizingly suggest the movement of liquid water during the distant past, or possibly more recently.

Thousands of enthusiasts scour over detailed images of Martian terrain sent back by NASA probes hoping to find conclusive proof that the surface of the red planet plays host to life. Others are intrigued by the trace amounts of methane detected in the Martian atmosphere, which may allude to micro-biological activity occurring under suspected ice packs. Their motivations may be driven by the fear that Mars is the last hope; that beyond this cold world the solar system may be truly devoid of life.

# Far Beyond the Sun

But there are other possibilities elsewhere, much further from the sun. This is where the conventional notion of the 'habitation zone' starts to break down, and new possibilities open up.

The asteroid belt beyond Mars is simply a collection of orbiting rocks, devoid of life like our Moon. Scientists have been able to rule out life on the gas giants, Jupiter and Saturn, and the frigid outer giants Uranus and Neptune. These huge worlds have no detectable solid surfaces below their immense pressurized atmospheres, and even if they did the internal pressures would surely rule out the emergence of life in any recognizable form. Pluto, at the far reaches of the planetary zone, is a frigid Moon-like world far too bleak to harbour the chrysalis of life.

So, by a process of elimination we are left with just two candidates among the recognized worlds orbiting our sun: Mars, and the Earth. This is the classic argument supported by the notion of the 'habitation zone'. But there may be nooks and crannies on other planetary bodies that could hold liquid water. As implausible as this may first seem, we must consider the moons of the outer planets.

The vast majority of these distant moons orbiting the gas giants are barren rocks. However, we now know that several of them have features suggestive of frozen oceans. This has provided an extension of the solar system's 'habitation zone' to the realm of the gas giants Jupiter and Saturn. Life could readily await discovery on one or more of their numerous moons.

The chances for future discoveries of life have increased because biologists have been able to show that life is able to withstand extreme conditions with unexpected ease in parts of the Earth once deemed "uninhabitable" (3). The discovery of veritable 'oases' of water scattered widely through the solar system has increased the potentialities further: where there is liquid water, there is the potential for life.

The 4 major 'Galilean' moons of Jupiter are 'warmed' by the gravitational influence of the gas giant itself, and, among them, Europa almost certainly boasts a liquid water ocean below its icy crust (4). The tidal effect produced by the parent planet internally warms Europa and shows that our traditional assumptions about what is thought to constitute the habitable zone around a given star have been 'oversimplified' (5). Distance from the sun is not the only factor at play, even if it remains the most important.

## Moons of Life?

The Galilean moons of Jupiter offer good conditions for the emergence for life because the vast bodies of water under their surfaces are warmed by gravitational and tidal effects induced by their massive parent.  Io is the closest moon to Jupiter, and the effect is extreme enough to make this moon highly active volcanically.  Europa is the best candidate for life, and a deep ocean seems to lie below its frozen surface which may contain twice as much water as all the oceans of Earth combined!

Europa looks like a scratched and colourful billiard ball from space, and NASA plans to explore the geography of this moon by radar and probes (4). The two further Galilean moons, Callisto and Ganymede, may also be hiding secret oceans below their frozen surfaces.  Yet these worlds are five times further away from the sun as the Earth.

Is it possible to move even further away from the sun and apply the same principles to moons of the more distant, and colder, planets?

The main moon of the beautiful ringed planet Saturn is Titan, a smoggy, cold world covered in hydrocarbons.  We now know that Titan has oceans of liquid hydrocarbons on its surface, mostly consisting of methane.  It also has landmasses and coastlines, familiar features to us on Earth.  Liquid methane goes through a similar dynamic process there as water does here; evaporation, precipitation, run-off and drainage occurring below Titan's surface (6). Scientists speculate that there may be water buried beneath the surface of Titan, warmed by Saturn's tidal forces.  It's perfectly possible that water might 'geyser' up into the organic molecule-rich oceans, and allow the building blocks of life to emerge (7).

One day, when the sun begins to wind down and expands to a red giant, Titan will become the most valuable real estate in the solar system.  For a short time Titan will become the new Earth, warmed by a massive red sun that has already driven off all of the waters of the Earth (8). We have 4 billion years to wait before that happens, though.

But at the present time, Titan seems too inhospitable a climate for complex life, despite the presence of liquid water. The dark atmospheric smog and great distance from the sun will stop photosynthetic reactions taking place, preventing a meaningful eco-system from developing on the surface of Titan. But there may be the presence of 'extremeophiles': Life that can evolve and exist at the limits of environmental conditions. After all, the building blocks for the formation of life exist on Titan, and a dynamic environment may have already created the spark that is needed for life to begin.

The major moon of the very distant planet Neptune is called Triton. It has no atmosphere to speak of, and lies at the edge of the planetary zone around our sun. Its surface is laden with dark organic materials and nitrogen ices, some of which appear to have occurred as snowfall near the equator. It is simply too frigid at this distance for Triton to hold onto an atmosphere, despite tidal warming by Neptune.

Any atmosphere it might once have, had precipitated out onto the surface as ice (9). At this distance there is simply too little heat to create the conditions for life, even with the tidal warming effects by Neptune. Liquid water is not available out here, and even the most optimistic commentator must doubt whether the extended habitation zone goes as far as Neptune, some 30 times the distance of Earth from the sun (known as 30 Astronomical Units).

## Comets

This seems to mark the boundary for the potential for life in the solar system. Beyond Neptune and Jupiter lie two collections of comets. The first is a belt very similar to the asteroid belt between Mars and Jupiter, which surrounds the planetary zone. It is known as the 'Edgeworth-Kuiper Belt', and the discoveries that are taking place about its nature will form the basis for some of this book.

The second collection of comets is a far more distant one which surrounds the solar system. This 'Oort Cloud' is a deep spherical layer of comets which are finely distributed, some of which occasionally fall back towards the sun as long-period comets. There appears to be a substantial gap between the Edgeworth-Kuiper Belt and the inner Oort Cloud, where few comets trespass. Again, an explanation for this can be found in this book.

It has been argued that comets carry with them the seeds of life, and this may well be so. Such ideas form the basis for Panspermia, a theory that involves the universal spread of life via such intra- and inter-stellar travellers. But even if comets hold onto bacterial spores, they do not provide conditions for that life to actually get started. Instead, 'life' rests here in a state of suspended animation.

Our knowledge about what celestial bodies might lurk beyond the orbits of Neptune and Pluto is still in its infancy. As the distances from the sun become ever greater, our ability to detect dark bodies 'out there' diminishes rapidly. The Harvard astrophysicist Matthew Holman recently noted that a Mars-sized planetary body could easily have escaped detection even if it was located as close as 200AU away (10). Given that one Astronomical Unit (A.U.) is the distance between the sun and the Earth, then this is a considerable distance indeed. An undiscovered planet could be orbiting the sun beyond this point and we could still be none the wiser, despite the advances in detection methods.

This is because the brightness of an object depends on its distance from the sun to the fourth power (11). The luminosity of an object rapidly falls away with distance. This is why the immense planets Uranus and Neptune cannot be seen in the night sky with the naked eye. As the distances increase further, into the Edgeworth-Kuiper Belt and beyond, the potential for a substantial undiscovered planet increases with it.

The reason why this is an important question is that there is a possibility that our extended habitation zone could find itself out among the comets. If something is out there and is significantly massive, then it may generate its own heat. A planet that size would have to be more massive than Jupiter.

Common sense would lead us to believe that scientists should surely have discovered such a world by now. But that is not necessarily the case. Remember, luminosity drops off sharply with distance, and finding anything 'dark' among the comets is a real challenge for astronomers, even with the largest telescopes.

Such a massive planet has been proposed before by various scientists, and their ideas considered seriously by the scientific community. It is not the realm of the fantastic at all.

# The Perturber

There is indirect evidence that a body greater in mass than Jupiter is orbiting the sun. It has been termed the 'Perturber', because of its alleged effects upon comets within the distant Oort Cloud. It may be sufficiently large to fall into the category of 'failed stars' known as brown dwarfs (12, 13, 14). These bodies are too small to have become stars, and may have been splintered off-shoots of stellar matter ejected from primordial star systems. They burn brightly when young, and are termed 'light-emitting planets' in the early stages of their lives (15).

Over time they become dark planetary 'embers'; warm bodies that emit little or no light. The astronomers who have speculated about the existence of a small brown dwarf circling the sun consider it to be similar to Jupiter, although several times more massive. This is not the stuff of science fiction, but of very real scientific speculation.

Little is known about these bodies as so few have been directly detected elsewhere. Their warmth and ability to emit light remains a controversial subject, but as their mass becomes greater they become more star-like, and less planet-like. In the midst of this murky area of knowledge lies what I have termed a 'Dark Star', a hybrid planet/star whose warmth can incubate life whilst simultaneously remaining difficult to detect (16).

Since astronomers first started detecting and studying brown dwarfs directly, their stellar properties have proved surprising given their relatively small size (17). To give some indication of how our knowledge has progressed, it is interesting to note that it was once thought that life could exist actually on a brown dwarf (18). This idea has been discredited, but it has been acknowledged that life might be possible on a moon orbiting one (19). The brown dwarf's moon would be warmed by gravitational tidal effects as well as the warmth emitted directly by the failed star itself.

The implication of this is dramatic. If the 'Perturber' were to be detected directly it could open a new chapter in the search for life in the solar system. Even at the distances from the sun involved, a small brown dwarf among the comets could provide a habitable environment on its own moons. This is not dissimilar to the picture provided by the moon Europa orbiting Jupiter. But a brown dwarf's moon has the added advantage of basking in the ember-glow of this failed star.

This is a crucial point to take on board. When we looked at the case of Europa we considered how life might exist in a liquid ocean under its surface. This ocean was warmed by Jupiter, and not just the sun. Yet, Jupiter is just a regular planet.

Out in the comet clouds the sun's warmth is practically negligible. In order for life to exist on a moon orbiting a Dark Star, the brown dwarf itself would not only have to be more massive than Jupiter, but it would need to emit its own heat as well to warm its inner moons. Yet, it couldn't be too big or its electro-magnetic radiation would be readily detectable from Earth.

It would have to be warm, but fairly dark. Yet, it may still glow enough to light its own moons, rather like the glow of the embers of an old fire can dimly light a room in winter. Because, as we know, luminosity drops off with distance. Beyond its system of moons, the Dark Star would become all but invisible in the night sky.

This concept is a central plank of my Dark Star Theory. It raises the possibility of extending the habitable zone into the comet clouds, and adds a sense of urgency to the otherwise rather academic pursuit of discovering planets beyond Pluto. The hunt for Planet X becomes the hunt for life.

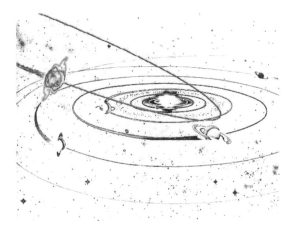

# Detecting Planet X

Although such a planet has so far evaded direct detection in our solar system, similar entities have been found orbiting neighboring stars. How can this be, given how much further away those stars are? Surely, if we can find these bodies around distant stars, we should be able to see one very clearly around the sun? Strangely, perhaps, it is the other way around; the planets located around other stars are easier to spot. This is because they are detected in a different way.

The means of detecting dark planetary bodies around other stars involve indirect techniques. These include the measurement of the star's 'wobble' in space, as its position is influenced by the massive body interacting with it. This wobble may be very slight, but it is enough for the modern astronomical techniques to detect. Calculations based on these observations can then give information about the size and orbit of the planetary body orbiting the star in question. Sometimes the light of the star will be seen to dim slightly, and this is attributed to the planet moving between the star and us, effectively blocking out a miniscule amount of the star's light.

These can be conclusive observations, enabling astronomers to confidently claim the existence of giant worlds around neighboring stars in the Milky Way. But the same techniques cannot apply to our own sun. If the sun is wobbling in space because of its companion, then the effect is negligible because of the Dark Star's immense distance from it.

This contrasts with discoveries of extra-solar planets whose orbits are all similar to the inner planets of our solar system. We know that the sun is moving in a slightly odd direction compared with its neighbours. It is heading towards the Solar Apex, near the star Vega in the sky, and this may turn out to be coincident with the position of the Dark Star. But, this does not provide evidence in itself for the existence of this possible 'binary companion'. So, to find such a body around our own sun we must rely upon different techniques, even though it is much closer to us than the stars studied by planet-hunters.

Often, the orbits of the extra-solar planets, or 'exo-planets' are eccentric. Yet, they can remain an intrinsic part of stable planetary systems (20). This was a surprising discovery, but is in keeping with long-standing speculations about the nature of our own Planet X. These speculations stem from some rather remarkable theories generated in the second half of the 20th Century.

Certain researchers, including Immanuel Velikovsky and Zecharia Sitchin, proposed that we could learn a lot about ancient astronomy from ancient myth. Their theses worked on the principle that before writing was developed, scientific knowledge was already being handed down from generation to generation -- but that it took the form of myth. If one then worked backwards from the myth, and understood the 'gods' to be equivalent to cosmic bodies, like the sun, Moon and planets, then the myth would indicate ancient models for creation of the solar system.

Careful scrutiny of certain ancient myths shows a fairly precise understanding of the solar system among ancient peoples, possibly reflecting advanced observations thousands of years ago. But the myths also contained additional elements that did not equate with our current knowledge of the solar system. An important planet was missing from the myth, one that stood as a central pillar in the creation myths. I believe that this body is a Dark Star, which means that the sun has a binary companion, albeit a rather diminutive 'kid brother'.

The possibility that such a body has a highly eccentric orbit would readily explain how it is currently very difficult to detect, yet has been observed in the sky during history and prehistory, becoming an established part of humanity's mythological inheritance.

A planet the size of a small brown dwarf might approach the outer planets, or move through the distant Edgeworth-Kuiper Belt, without causing orbital mayhem. In times gone past, it may even have moved among the planets nearer the sun, perhaps through the Asteroid Belt; a zone which may once have been the home of another, long-destroyed world. This may seem incredible, but it has been shown that a small brown dwarf could actually move directly through the solar system without disrupting the other planets.

Computer simulations have shown that a planet as massive as 10 Jupiters would have no discernable effect upon the other planets if it moved among them (21). This surprises many who would naturally imagine that the passage of a large planet through the solar system would have a catastrophic effect on the other planets, including Earth. However, this is not necessarily the case.

Even though this is a possibility, I now doubt that the Dark Star moves through the planetary solar system during our current era. Instead, it treads quietly through the more distant Edgeworth-Kuiper Belt during the closest approach of its orbit. It seems to be leaving the cosmic equivalent of dirty footprints in the snow out there. It may bring with it other planets, though, that do move closer to us and become observable. This is another theme we shall be exploring in this book, one that will allow us to integrate science with myth in a rather elegant way.

The creation myths that we have spoken of here indicate that this Dark Star did move among the planets in the distant past, and that the effect of its transit among these familiar worlds was, in some cases, catastrophic. Again, there is anomalous evidence in the solar system to support such a contentious argument. It seems that its catastrophic incursion a billion or so years ago was confined to that brief, but traumatic period, and that it has migrated out to more tranquil waters since.

The strong-headed god who stormed the solar system soon after its creation has wizened up and now keeps its distance. Yet, the glory days of its youth are evidenced every time we look at the Moon in the night sky. Armed to the teeth, our fiery young god brought with it a devastating array of weaponry.

## Mythology and the Dark Star

Let us imagine for a moment that a brown dwarf moved through the solar system billions of years ago. We can consider this seriously because of the evidence in the solar system that multiple catastrophic events occurred about 3.9 billion years ago, about 500 million years after the birth of the solar system. The Earth and Moon were literally pounded by massive bodies, whether asteroids or comets.

The Moon still shows the scars of this event long ago, which is known as the 'late, great bombardment'. This is because the surface of the Moon is extremely ancient. Other similar bodies in the solar system also show this traumatic pattern of cratering.

There are many theories as to why there were so many impacts over such a short period in the history of the solar system. No one knows for sure. But it is quite legitimate to speculate that another cosmic body invaded the solar system at that time, causing mayhem. And the bigger the body, the more likely it is that we can explain the sheer magnitude of the calamity that befell the inner planets around the sun.

If we were to try and describe what happened at that time in non-scientific terms, how would we go about doing so? What would this invading Dark Star with its own system of planets have looked like as it crashed through our sun's territory?

Young brown dwarfs shine with a red flame, despite their name. Theoretical observers on Earth might see this red star's corona or 'halo', which would be subject to the driving force of the Solar Wind, and would thus be swept back from the sun. Perhaps this would give the brown dwarf the appearance of a bright red fire-bird in the sky, its swept-back corona appearing as wings.

Like the mythical Phoenix, the normally invisible brown dwarf binary would have been re-born to enjoy a fleeting movement through the heavens, before returning to the darkness of the comet cloud. Unless this planetary Phoenix approached too close to one of the other planets, life would go on in the solar system as if nothing had ever happened. If it did cause cosmic calamities, then anomalies would have been created that remain, even today, mysteries. Like the fact that Uranus spins on its side, or that Pluto's orbit is eccentric, or even that the Earth has water!

For several years, I have undertaken studies to prove the existence of a 'Dark Star' orbiting the sun from a dual perspective: mythological and scientific. The two studies are deemed to be mutually exclusive by mainstream academics, making my research unacceptable at their level, but I believe that there is increasing overlap between the two disciplines for anyone who cares to look. Certainly, the scientific evidence for a binary companion is becoming more voluminous, and these startling new findings will form the basis for some of this book.

## Zecharia Sitchin

The mythological aspects of this study expand upon research conducted by Zecharia Sitchin 25 years ago regarding the writings of the ancient Sumerians of Mesopotamia (22). He offered an intellectual argument for the existence of a mysterious planet termed 'Nibiru' that was observed from Earth during historical times and venerated by many cultures. Its meaning is 'the Ferry', implying its nature as a crossing point between two places (23). This is a rather enigmatic name, and one that I don't think Zecharia Sitchin ever satisfactorily explained, but the meaning should become clear during the course of this book.

Zecharia Sitchin

Sitchin equated Nibiru with the Babylonian god Marduk from the Creation Myth called the 'Enuma Elish'. I think this Marduk was the Dark Star, the sun's binary companion. Marduk was the ambitious young hothead of a god who decided to take all the other gods on in a titanic struggle for cosmic dominance. He is the 'Son of the sun', a phrase that finds a real meaning in the binary Dark Star. This planet was described by the Babylonians as a 'red star...that bisects the heavens' (24), and as the 'Celestial Lord' greater than all the other planets.

How could the ancients have known of such a planet if it had not passed through the solar system during historical times? They had no advanced telescopes to seek out distant planets among the comets, and were reliant upon either their own historical observations, or the receipt of information about this 'Nibiru' from elsewhere. This is where Zecharia Sitchin becomes highly controversial. He claims that Nibiru is the home of the gods of Mesopotamia, in a flesh-and-blood sense.

His maverick ideas have been almost universally dismissed by the academic establishment. However, I believe that the core ideas presented by Zecharia Sitchin are correct, but in need of some technical modifications. This book sets out to argue that case.

A massive planet in a comet-like orbit is actually consistent with modern science, and could offer conditions on its moons conducive to life, but not in the way originally envisioned by Sitchin. Even so, his claim of an undiscovered planet is fundamentally sound, and I believe that it is awaiting discovery. And what a monumental day that will be! The future discovery of the Dark Star will provide us with a greater potential for life than Mars ever could. If Sitchin is right, it may also give us new insight into our own origins.

This book will provide extensive evidence to suggest that the Dark Star's presence among the comets is a reality. It will look closely at the nature of 'Nibiru', and show how it can be rationalized scientifically. It brings both myth and science together as a cohesive whole.

But before we start to piece the puzzle together we must first explore many of the ideas expressed in this first chapter in more depth. We will start with the ideas of Zecharia Sitchin, and then look at the general history of the hunt for Planet X. This will provide an excellent grounding from which to proceed.

## Chapter 1 References

1. P. Moore "Patrick Moore on Mars" Chapter 11, Cassell 1998

2. I. Wright & M. Grady "Focus: Life on Mars" Astronomy Now Oct. 1996, pp39-46

3. 'Horizon' BBC2, "Snowball Earth" Shown on 22nd February 2001

4. M. Milstein "Astronomy" p38-43 "Diving into Europa's Ocean" Oct. 1997

5. D. Kalk "Alien Haven" pp32-5 New Scientist Sept. 1999

6. S. Battersby "One Hour on Titan, Forever Bathed in Glory" New Scientist, 22/1/05, pp6-8

7. Redding.com, Seattle (AP) "Mysteries of distant moons await earthly oceanographers" 15/2/04, http://redding.com/news/national/stories/20040215nat048.shtml

8. T. Radford "Titan, Mystery Moon where it Rains Liquid Methane" The Guardian, 22/1/05, p6

9. C. Sagan "Pale Blue Dot" p140-141, p127 Headline Book Publishing 1995

10. J. Kelly Beatty "Big-orbit Object Confounds Dynamicists" <http://www.skypub.com/news/news.shtml#bigorbit> , 5th April 2001

11. A. Quillen, D. Trilling & E. Blackman "The Impact of a Close Stellar Encounter on the Edgeworth-Kuiper Belt" arXiv:astro-ph/0401372vl, 2004

12. J.B.Murray Mon. Not. R. Astron. Soc., 309, 31-34 (1999)

13. J.J. Matese, P.G. Whitman and D.P. Whitmire, Icarus, 141, 354-336 (1999)

14. The Economist Newspaper Ltd. "X Marks the Spot" http://www.economist.com/editorial/freeforall/16-10-99/st7748.html 7th October 1999

15. http://news.bbc.co.uk/hi/english/sci/tech/newsid_957000/957518.stm 5/10/2000 "Mystery of free-floating 'planets'"

16. A. Lloyd "Winged Disc: The Dark Star Theory", 2001, http://www.darkstar1.co.uk © 7th February 2000

17. K. Leutwyler "Bright X-rays, Dim Dwarfs" 17/7/2000 http://www.sciam.com/exhibit/2000/071700dwarf/

18. C. Sagan "Pale Blue Dot" p392 Headline Book Publishing 1995

19. Correspondence from M. Marley, 28/1/00

20. Associated Press "We Prefer Not to Call It a Failed Star. We Call It a Specially Challenged Brown Dwarf" http://www.aci.net/kalliste/ 9th January 2001

21. J.G. Hills "The Passage of a 'Nemesis'-like object through the Planetary System" The Astronomical Journal, 90, Number 9, pp1876-1882, September 1985

22. Z. Sitchin "The Twelfth Planet" Avon 1976

23. G. de Santillana & H. von Dechend "Hamlet's Mill" App. 39, pp430-451, http://www.apollonius.net/trees.html Thanks to Robertino Solarion

24. B. Van der Waerden "Science Awakening II" pp66-68 Oxford University Press 1974

# The Sumerian 'Nibiru'

The essence of the Dark Star Theory is that certain ancient myths regarding our solar system are accurate, and that modern science is fast catching up with them. Those myths have become vague and misinterpreted over time, but they point in the direction of a series of specific astronomical events that have shaped the world we live in today.

The ancient myths in question originate from the first historical civilization, known as Sumer, which crystallized dramatically in Mesopotamia 6000 years ago. Its ruined ancient cities now rest in what is now Iraq, and this area is rightly referred to as the 'cradle of civilization'. Its origins are mysterious, not least because the development of Sumer seemed to appear out of nowhere. Scholars are in disagreement as to whether the Sumerians migrated to the land between the Tigris and the Euphrates, or whether they were an indigenous people (1). But changes in the geography of the region played a part, as the waters of this region receded back to the Persian Gulf, leaving a 'fertile crescent' from which the Sumerians created a 'garden paradise'.

Sumer seemed to burst into life, fully-fledged about 6000 years ago. The first Sumerian cities were highly organized affairs with centralized governments and social class structures. Each city was populated by up to 10,000 people, rising to 50,000 by 2700 BCE. Agriculture still took up the time of the majority of workers, but this created a stable enough supply of food for the cities to allow its other citizens to work as masons, bakers, weavers and other tradesmen, overseen by a municipal bureaucracy. The age of the specialist craftsman was born (2).

One should not underestimate the achievements of the Sumerians during this period, which pre-dated the rise of Dynastic Egypt. They produced 'superb painted pottery' and 'magnificent' stonework, were the 'first inspired builders of monumental architecture' and produced exquisite epic poems (1). Their creation myths formed the basis for many of the accounts in the Old Testament, through the migration of the Sumerian patriarch Abraham to Egypt. Yet Sumer was just one step removed from the Stone Age. The Danish-American Sumerologist Thorkild Jacobsen considers the transition to be linked to the invention of writing, almost

The Author in the Louvre

'overnight' (3). He expressed his wonder at how the blueprint of an advanced society could have been achieved so suddenly. Perhaps, then, it should not surprise us that so many scholars puzzle over how ancient Sumer came into existence, and probe into the mystery of where its people came from.

The impact on the world of this emergent civilization cannot be underestimated. Despite being only one step removed from its Neolithic hunter-gatherer predecessor, Sumer managed to put into place most of the fundamental aspects of a civilized society as we would recognize it today.

## Sumerian 'Firsts'

The Sumerians can be accredited with inventing writing, political and religious infrastructure, and the building of complex buildings, such as Ziggurats, high-rise buildings and archways. They also invented metal-work, involving smelting, refining and alloying; the use of bitumen as a fuel and for waterproofing, caulking, painting, cementing and moulding. They had advanced understanding of medicine and surgery as well as veterinary science. Their agriculture was well developed, including extensive irrigation by canals. Their astronomical knowledge was remarkable, and they were the first to establish a calendar. They had a formal system of education, where schools taught not just language and writing, but botany, zoology, geography, mathematics and theology. They were civilized enough to develop a complex legal system. Last, but by no means least, they developed a refined and complex system of mathematics, called the sexagesimal system (4).

The sexagesimal system does not appear to be an obvious choice of mathematical method for a fledgling society emerging from primitive times. It is a complicated form of base 12, and this seems to reflect an early categorization of the zodiac by the Sumerians into 12 houses. Their calendar was based on 12 lunar months with an intercalary month inserted periodically to adjust the calendar back to the solar cycle.

Records of the Sumerian zodiacal system stem from at least 3800BC, the time of Sargon of Akkad, a remote period long before the emergence of pre-dynastic Egypt. In 1903, Plunket described the then emergent knowledge of the Akkadian and Sumerian astrological works:

"That the constellations of the Zodiac were from a remote age recognized by the dwellers in Mesopotamia is scarcely to be doubted. We find on the boundary stones in the British Museum representations of several of their figures. The Bull, the Tortoise (in lieu of the Crab), a female figure with wings, the Scorpion, the Archer, and the Goat-fish, are all portrayed, not only on boundary stones, but also on cylinder seals and gems." (5)

The Sumerians thus created the Zodiac, an arbitrary division of the constellations that lie on the ecliptic, an invisible line drawn across the heavens along which the sun appears to traverse. These same 12 houses of the Zodiac crop up throughout history, and we still have them today, although some alteration has occurred to several of them. This is remarkable, not just from the perspective of the Zodiac actually having been developed by the first civilization to emerge from Neolithic times, but that this contribution to astronomy has stayed with us for the next 6000 years.

The scientific knowledge required to explain the advanced knowledge of the Sumerians far exceed what they should have been capable of, if one is to presume a linear evolutionary development of knowledge. Like all of the remarkable achievements of the ancient Sumerians, their knowledge appeared as if out of nowhere, including astronomical knowledge of the Precession of the Equinoxes. This particular scientific understanding rests on careful scrutiny of the sun's apparent backward shift along the ecliptic, and through the Zodiacal houses, over time.

This movement is slow, shifting only one degree during the lifetime of a human being. It is only over a period of about 2150 years that the sun is able to shift fully from one Zodiacal house to another, presaging the Dawn of a New Age. Such knowledge is not acquired through study of astronomy during one life-time, but becomes apparent only after many, many generations. One would expect such knowledge to emerge later on during Mankind's development, not to be accepted science right from the start of our first civilization!

So we can see that the Sumerians had an exceptional grasp of astronomy and cosmology.

Like so many of the Sumerian 'firsts', this points to an inheritance of knowledge from a period before Sumer emerged. The texts they have left us imply something quite extraordinary, however. They tell us that their science and laws were given to them by the gods.

The Sumerians left us vast quantities of written material, in their particular style of 'cuneiform' script. Much of this material was written on clay tablets, then preserved by baking. Furthermore, they developed the use of 'cylinder seals' for imprinting these tablets. The Sumerians were great keepers of records, and left us a legacy of written work, including the famous 'Epic of Gilgamesh', the story of one of their semi-divine rulers.

Their cultural legacy was handed down to the later Mesopotamian civilizations of Akkad, Assyria and Babylon, as well as Persia, Egypt and, arguably, India. In their many accounts of their past and present, they were quite clear about how their advanced knowledge was attained. It came from the 'gods', who, it is said, lived among them, and who bequeathed them the gift of civilization.

Given the remarkable culture that formed the spring-board for so much of mankind's development in the following millennia, how is it that so few people are even aware of the historical existence of the Sumerians? After all, the ancient Egyptian culture has gained a strong foothold in the popular psyche. Part of the solution is historical. Western culture has traditionally considered itself to have been developed from scratch by the Romans and Greeks.

Our ancient languages were Latin and Greek, and these cultures were the European super-states of their time. They represent the modern Western ideal of cultural dominance and imperialism. Furthermore, the Church developed through the Romans, and all official learning through the Dark Ages, Middle Ages, the Reformation and beyond was directly controlled by this institution, using Latin as its holy language. The idea of European and North American intellectual dominance is ingrained within modern scholarship.

So, although the Greeks clearly obtained a great many of their religious and intellectual ideas from the Egyptians, we still consider the Greeks as the original philosophers and cultural creators. We marvel at the technical abilities of the Egyptians, yet choose to ignore the impact they had on the development of Western culture. The Mesopotamian civilizations are one step further removed still. The Biblical passages dealing with the Babylonians tend to have been from the perspective of a subjugated people, the Hebrews, who were held captive in Babylon in the 6th century BC. As such, the Babylonian (hence Assyrian, Akkadian and Sumerian) culture is generally seen in a more negative light. The far older Sumerian culture didn't stand much of a chance of establishing its true place in history when it was unearthed over the last two centuries.

Part of the problem was the growing realization amongst scholars that the creation stories in the Old Testament found an earlier equivalent in the Mesopotamian literature, rendering the Genesis account in the Bible as a later development of Sumerian and Akkadian culture. This was deeply offensive to many Christian and Hebrew scholars, who continue to ignore these controversial findings.

When Assyriologists began to work through very ancient clay tablets that had been unearthed from the Akkadian cities 150 years ago, it became clear that Akkad had been derived from an older culture with a wedge-shaped writing that was unlike anything yet discovered. These very ancient writings revealed the secrets of the sudden development of Sumerian civilization from nowhere. The Sumerians claimed that they had been taught all they knew by a group of powerful gods who lived among them, whom they called the Anunnaki.

The Sumerians served their masters and described in detail their very Earth-like activities. In many respects, the Anunnaki were just like us, but more powerful and remarkably knowledgeable. All of the crystallizing development was accounted for by direct intervention of these enigmatic 'gods'. Furthermore, these gods, or Anunnaki, were subject to death like mortal humans, implying a temporal existence. Yet, scholars have wrapped the gods of Mesopotamia in the cloak of myth.

## The '12th Planet'

An alternative approach to the study of Mesopotamian myth was made in the 1970s by Zecharia Sitchin, who made a personal study of Middle Eastern languages and archaeology whilst working as a journalist in Israel (6). Sitchin read the ancient texts and came to a rather different conclusion about the origins of Sumerian civilization. He proposed that the Sumerians weren't alluding to mythical allegory when they spoke of their gods; they were literally describing flesh and blood characters who were historically contemporary with them. Their service to their gods was less religious, more day-to-day work to support an infrastructure that centred upon these powerful beings.

After some study, Sitchin had in his mind a complex and far-reaching exposé of the historical development of civilization, one that turned the tables on the standard versions of events. He set about collating this magnum opus in a series of popular books known as the 'Earth Chronicles' (7). The running theme of the books was based on the conceptual framework of the 12th Planet, the home world of the gods. Sitchin wrote that this new planet was known to the Sumerians as 'Nibiru', and to the later Babylonians as 'Marduk'.

Sitchin's rather unique way of thinking is based upon a rather literal interpretation of the texts, particularly the Babylonian "Epic of Creation", the "Enuma Elish". Many critics voice their disquiet with Sitchin's mode of interpretation, and he is utterly dismissed by mainstream Sumerologists. To some theorists, there may be some good reason to be cautious about some of Zecharia Sitchin's claims. But, it is undeniably true that there are clear references in ancient Mesopotamian texts which mention this enigmatic Nibiru as a red star that moves through the heavens.

In their classic book 'Hamlet's Mill', Giorgio de Santillana and Hertha von Dechend explored the mysterious nature of 'Nibiru' in 1969, and showed that, at that time, no scholarly theory adequately explained its celestial nature:

"The plain meaning of "nibiru" is "ferry, ferryman, ford" – "mikis nibiri" is the toll one has to pay for crossing the river – from eberu "to cross". Alfred Jeremias insisted that Nibiru "in all star-texts of later times" indicated Canopus, taking this star for the provider of the meridian of the city of Babylon. There have been other identifications– the summer solstice, or the celestial North Pole; the opinions and verdicts collected by Gossmann show clearly that Nibiru remains an unknown factor for the time being." (8)

Most scholars now believe that Nibiru is simply the planet Jupiter, but that rather simple explanation is cast into doubt by the mention of Nibiru's color: Red. Jupiter is a rather boring looking white color. There is still a real mystery here, 36 years after 'Hamlet's Mill'. The focus of this mystery is the name 'Ferry'. We shall return to this at a later point.

Sitchin claims that the ancient Sumerians were aware of all of the planets circling the sun, both observable ones and those detectable only by use of a modern telescope. He maintains that the Sumerians counted the planets from outside in. The Earth was thus the 7th planet. This is said to reflect the appearance of the solar system from the perspective of travellers from outside, in other words, the space-faring race of Anunnaki.

Only the five planets nearest to the sun are visible to the naked eye. Uranus is observable under extremely good conditions if one knows exactly where to look. Neptune and Pluto are both non-starters.

Is it possible that these ancient peoples, barely out of the Stone Age, were able to detect distant, invisible planets? Robert Temple has shown that many ancient peoples possessed lens technology, and were thus theoretically capable of creating rudimentary telescopes (9). But, even so, it is surely beyond the realm of possibility to imagine that Neptune could have been discovered by Mesopotamian astronomers in the 3rd Millennium B.C.E.!

Well, indeed. Except that Zecharia Sitchin is not claiming that the Sumerians independently discovered these far-flung worlds. He argues that the knowledge was handed down to them by their gods, becoming an astronomical science, and that it was later corrupted into astrology by the later civilizations. We now understand that early science as pure myth and dismiss the possibility that the Sumerians understood our solar system as well as us. Or perhaps even better!

The concept that the planets should share the names of the gods is not a new one. After all, the 'English' names for the planets and other heavenly bodies are derived from the pantheons of Greek and Roman gods and goddesses. This follows an age-old tradition, and it is certainly not that strange a claim to associate the gods of ancient Mesopotamia with astronomy. The difference with Sitchin's work is that he has taken things to their logical conclusion and has seen the Enuma Elish to be an accurate representation of the physical creation of the solar system.

However, the tale that emerges from this important Babylonian creation myth is somewhat different from our own understanding of the solar system. This epic tale speaks of events on a cosmic scale, with a fierce battle between two great planets, or Gods, that presumably occurred 4 billion years ago. But neither of the two combatants are known to us. We can recognize many of the planets, but not the two key players known as Marduk, and a 'watery monster' called 'Tiamat'. Both do battle on a catastrophic level. It is this difference between the account in the Enuma Elish and what we now scientifically know about the solar system that lies at the heart of the Sitchin's 12th Planet Theory.

## Son of the Sun

According to Sitchin's interpretation of the Babylonian 'Enuma Elish', there was no planet between Venus and Mars in the early, primordial solar system, where the Earth now resides. In the beginning, Earth was absent from the orbital position we currently take for granted; the classical 'habitation zone'.

Also, Pluto was a moon (or 'counsellor' and 'emissary') of Saturn, and there was a 'watery monster' of a world called 'Tiamat', the "maiden who gave life" between Mars and Jupiter. It had a major moon called 'Kingu'. This configuration was not stable, and the noise of the Gods implied erratic orbits. Then along came an outsider, a planet that was not born of Apsu, but one that attempted to join the throng of the celestial gods. In other words, a wandering 'planet' entered the solar system, with catastrophic results. It attacks the watery planet Tiamat and subdues her with terrible weapons. From this cosmic battle, Marduk becomes the centrally important god of Babylonian myth.

His birth is described in the Enuma Elish, and although he is described in anthropomorphic terms, like the other gods, his dominance of them is clear. This powerful description, when applied to a planet, gives the distinct impression of something massive and fiery:

> "Greatly exalted was he (Marduk) above them, exceeding throughout.
>
> Perfect were his members beyond comprehension,
>
> Unsuited for understanding, difficult to perceive.
>
> Four were his eyes, four were his ears;
>
> When he moved his lips, fire blazed forth.
>
> Large were all four hearing organs,
>
> And the eyes, in like number, scanned all things.
>
> He was the loftiest of the gods, surpassing was his stature;
>
> His members were enormous, he was exceeding tall.
>
> "My little son, my little son!"
>
> My son, the Sun! Sun of the heavens!"
>
> Clothed with the halo of ten gods, he was strong to the utmost,
>
> As their awesome flashes were heaped upon him."

Tablet I, 92-105 (10).

Notice also the allusion to the little 'Sun of the heavens', another clue that leads us towards the Dark Star. Marduk is given 50 names, the 49th of which is 'Nibiru', or 'Nebiru'. This name clearly indicates the appearance of an actual star in the heavens, one that is centrally important to the movements of the planets in the solar system:

> "(49) NEBIRU shall hold the crossings of heaven and earth,
>
> So that the gods cannot cross above and below,
>
> They must wait upon him.

*Nebiru is the star which in the skies is brilliant.*

*Truly he holds the central position, they shall bow down to him,*

*Saying: "He who the midst of the Sea restlessly crosses,*

*Let `Crossing' be his name, who controls its midst.*

*May they uphold the course of the stars of heaven;*

*May he shepherd all the gods like sheep."*

Tablet VII, 125-133 (10).

Marduk is instrumental in setting up the 'stations of heaven', possibly by influencing the Earth's orbit and tilt. As part of this he creates the 'station of Nebiru':

"He founded the station of Nebiru to determine their heavenly bands,

That none might transgress or fall short." Tablet V, 6-7 (10).

As planetary gods go, Marduk was a colossal specimen that seemed to breathe fire. It was red in color, and sparkled from his 'eyes'. It had a tremendous 'halo' surrounding it, the equivalent of that of 10 gods. If Sitchin's logic is followed, then the above descriptions of Marduk describe a fiery planet without equal. It is certainly self-evident that Marduk was strongly associated with the enigmatic phenomenon that is Nibiru, described in unmistakably astronomical terms in the Enuma Elish.

But, that association falls short of the two names being completely interchangeable. Where Marduk seems more strongly associated with a dominant and powerful god, Nibiru is evidently a celestial phenomenon observable from Earth. This complicates matters somewhat.

## The Cosmic Battle

According to Zecharia Sitchin, Marduk rampaged through the planetary solar system, pummelling the watery planet Tiamat with one of its moons (called the 'North Wind'), and later cleaving Tiamat into two. This may have been a direct hit, or it may mean that much of the waters of the primordial Earth were shed as a result of the encounter with the Dark Star. The 'North Wind' is presumably also lost. In the description of Marduk above, we learn that he had four eyes and four ears, perhaps indicating 8 moons initially. This is speculation, of course, but it seems as though the Dark Star ended up with seven 'moons', the eighth having been lost in this traumatic encounter.

The major remaining part of Tiamat became the Earth, the smaller debris was flung out to form the celestial bracelet that is now known as the asteroid belt. Most of this debris was water from Tiamat's great oceans. Hence the 'division of Heaven and Earth' in the Bible, as the 'Lord' passed over the waters of the Primordial World.

The wounded Tiamat migrated into a new orbit as a result of this encounter, that of the 'habitation zone'. Tiamat becomes the Earth. It somehow managed to retain its major moon, now over-sized compared to the host planet 'Earth'. The Moon was thus denied the possibility of becoming a planet in its own right.

Marduk itself migrated into a new orbit as a result of this melee with Tiamat, flung into an eccentric orbit that carried it into the comet clouds. Many of the comets were formed as a result of these events, themselves debris from Tiamat's oceans. During the 'battle', Nibiru also caused a moon of Saturn, Pluto, to be swung away from its host planet and take on its eccentric orbit at the boundary of the realm of the planets.

The Enuma Elish describes Nibiru as an enormous, fiery world. However, Sitchin also claims that Nibiru was the home-world of the Anunnaki. The implication is that the Anunnaki came from a massive, fiery world which is described as the 'son' of the Primordial Father, the sun. How could a terrestrial home-world be an enormous, fiery planet?

## A Stellar Character?

An Akkadian description of the visit of the god Anu to Earth, thought to have occurred in 3760BC, describes the appearance of the 'sun disks' in the plural, a point emphasized by Sitchin himself:

"Enlil and Enki were waiting Anu at the 'golden support', standing by or holding several objects; the Akkadian terms, whose precise meaning remains elusive, are best translated as 'that which opens up the secrets', 'the sun discs' [plural!] and 'the splendid/shining posts'. Anu then came into the courtyard accompanied by gods in procession." (11)

Does this mean that Anu came from another 'sun' appearing in the skies? I have argued that this additional sun is the Dark Star. I used to think that this massive fiery planet became visible in the skies during perihelion, therefore fitting the description of Nibiru.

But now, I think that the observable phenomenon of Nibiru is merely associated with the Dark Star, which may itself remain

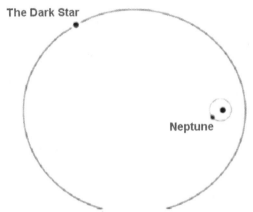

**The Dark Star**

**Neptune**

unseen during its distant perihelion passage. Nevertheless, the indication of 2 suns in the sky indicates to me the perihelion transit of the Dark Star, and it makes sense that this event is associated with the return of the gods to Earth; in this case the visit of the god Anu. This description also gives us one date for Nibiru's visible presence in our solar system; 3760BC.

## A Homeworld Amongst the Comets

One of the central criticisms levelled at Zecharia Sitchin was aimed at his claim that the gods are 'flesh and blood' and live on a planet, Nibiru, that moves among the comets. This seems quite impossible. There is not enough heat in that part of space to warm a planet sufficiently to support any kind of life at all.

Consider the outer rocky planets. They are so far away from the sun that their atmospheres, if they are able to retain them at all, are desperately cold. Rocky planets do not have significant internal heating due to their relative small size. So their outer mantles are frigid. Most gases precipitate out as ices.

Triton, for instance, the largest moon around Neptune, seems to have a surface laden with dark organic materials and nitrogen ices, some of which appear to have been snow-fall at the equator. Triton's atmosphere is very thin, entirely due to its great distance from the sun. If it were to be moved closer to the sun, say around Saturn, then these ices would evaporate and form a rich atmosphere, similar to Titan.

Triton shows us what happens to the atmosphere of a rocky world that is extremely distant from the sun; its atmosphere becomes surface ice. At this distance the sun's warmth is so diminished that it is singularly incapable of warming Triton sufficiently for it to retain an atmosphere. Instead all of the atmospheric gases become locked onto the surface of this Neptunian moon in the form of volatile ices. If the Earth was suddenly moved to Neptune it would suffer the same fate; not only would the oceans freeze, but the air would freeze also, precipitating out to create a layer of nitrogen and oxygen snow ten metres thick across the entire surface of the planet. Our atmosphere would be gone, exposing the surface of our world to the intense cold of space (12).

Which begs the question, how could Nibiru retain an atmosphere out in the comet clouds? The warmth from the sun would be practically nil. Which means that Nibiru would have to be generating its own heat. Yet, a rocky world generates insufficient warmth in its core to retain an atmosphere without an external heat source such as the sun.

The gas-giants generate plenty of internal heat, however, at least all of them but Uranus. But their massive atmospheres create severe pressure problems for potential life-forms. These planets also lack surfaces to speak of. At the cores of Jupiter and Saturn, the pressures are so intense that the very air, consisting mostly of hydrogen and helium, becomes metallic.

In contrast, Uranus does not appear to exhibit the same outflow of heat from its interior, despite being very similar to Neptune. Uranus is also anomalous in that it has been turned on its side, but this does not necessarily explain why its internal heat supply has been turned off. In some ways, this air of mystery prevents planetary scientists from claiming that they understand the mechanisms that are at play in the interiors of the gas-giants, and this leaves a little lee-way for Sitchin.

Could not a terrestrial-sized planet have some internal heat source that is currently not well understood? Might its atmosphere be self-luminous in some way, allowing the evolution of complex life forms? This conjecture is what 12th Planet theorists put forward to extricate themselves from the various difficulties discussed above. However, we move into the realm of science fiction with these ideas, not science fact. Not only that, but there is a better solution.

## When Is A Star Not A Star?

The size of Marduk was described as greater than all the other gods, which we interpret as planets, yet Sitchin's Nibiru had to be a world that was itself habitable. A planet large enough to create its own heat would end up with atmospheric pressures that would destroy terrestrial-based life. Yet, if Nibiru was to be understood as a far smaller planet, then the lack of internal heat would cause its atmosphere to precipitate out as ice, only to re-evaporate once every 3600 years as Nibiru achieved perihelion around the sun. Like a planet-sized comet.

Marduk's appearance was said to be fiery; his 'halo' the equivalent of ten gods. Yet that self-same atmosphere had to be capable of supporting oxygen-breathing humanoids; the Anunnaki. Nibiru would have to be a strange world indeed, self-heating, self-luminous, yet terrestrial. Is it any wonder that so many consider the concept of a cometary planet supporting life ridiculous?

Let us go back to those accounts and start afresh. Let us try to unravel the mysteries of Marduk and Nibiru.

The Sumerian word 'MUL', meaning 'celestial body', could be used to describe both a planet and a star. The equivalent word in Akkadian, 'Kakkab', has the same dual meaning (13). Either this means the Sumerians weren't sophisticated enough to differentiate between stars and planets, which seems highly unlikely given the general level of their knowledge, or else they were more insightful about the nature of 'celestial bodies' than we give them credit for.

# Red Star Nibiru

Sitchin's astronomical interpretation of the creation myth in the Enuma Elish is supported by corroborating evidence found in a Babylonian astrolabe, as cited by Van der Waerden:

"The red star, which when the stars of the night are finished, bisects the heavens and stands there whence the south wind comes, this star is the god Nibiru-Marduk" (14).

This is an explicit Babylonian record denoting Nibiru/Marduk as a red star, a description that clearly differentiates it from white Jupiter. The reference implies that this star is seen as a bright early morning object in the south. This is important because it differentiates this object from a reddened heliacally rising planet such as Venus or Jupiter, which would naturally be seen in the east. The Babylonians included it in a star list, as can be gleaned from the "12 stars of Elam, Akkad and Amurru" in APIN, BM 86378 col. 1, 36-38:

"When the stars of Enlil have disappeared the great faint star, which bisects the heavens and stands, is Marduk-Nibiru SAG.ME.GAR; he changes his position and wanders over the heavens." (14)

The Babylonians astronomical knowledge is widely recognized as being considerable. Nibiru-Marduk was clearly understood in astronomical terms, yet its description does not readily lend itself to any known celestial body that astronomers recognize today. These passages also show that Sitchin's interpretations of the ancient texts were neither fraudulent nor misguided, as many have claimed.

The passages also present us with evidence that Nibiru/Marduk appeared to the Mesopotamians as a red star during historical times, and that its heavenly passage was unusual. It was faint, red, stood still in the sky and then wandered like a planet. This is highly unusual, to say the least. It is no wonder that the nature of Nibiru remains controversial.

The closest match to these observed accounts of the appearance of Nibiru is that of an unknown and rarely seen celestial body. A comet would be an obvious choice were it not for the red color. It would have to be a very special comet; one whose color is red. But even then there would be problems.

When we look at comets, we see only the material being blasted off its surface by the heat of the sun. Its actual body is lost to sight within this huge stream of gas. But if the cometary body was big enough -- perhaps the size of a planet -- the gases driven off would be relatively less. We would start to see the world itself.

So Nibiru seems to be a massive comet of planetary proportions, one whose gravity retains relatively more of its volatile gases as it moves among the more familiar planets. Its surface is red, which is in keeping with many of the bodies in the outer solar system whose surfaces are strewn with reddish organic material. Yet it also appears as a comet.

This would make sense of the ancient Mesopotamian myths. Except that Marduk seems a rather more sizeable god than is implied by this description of a reddish planetary comet. Marduk is described in monumental terms; the 'Sun of the Heavens'. To my mind, this implies a body that generates its own heat; a brown dwarf that is the sun's binary companion. That ability to produce heat out among the comets is crucial to the sustainability of an atmosphere, liquid water and life.

It is clear that Nibiru is a planetary comet, but I now doubt that Nibiru is absolutely identical to Marduk of the Babylonian creation myth. Marduk 'created' Nibiru in the heavens, and takes the name as one of fifty. But are they they entirely the same?

I believe that the answer to this riddle is that Marduk is the binary companion, the Dark Star that orbits the sun like a comet. Marduk crashed through the solar system and caused great chaos some 4 billion years ago, as described by Zecharia Sitchin. It then migrated out into a larger orbit as a result of its encounters with the sun's other planets.

What the ancient Mesopotamians saw and recorded in their astrolabes and star lists was one of Marduk's moons, or planets, appearing among our planets for a short while, and behaving very strangely.

This is a complex explanation. The reason I have opted for it after many years of research is because of the scientific evidence. To understand Nibiru, we cannot just read myth.

We must also understand how that myth might fit into physical reality. Science has learned an awful lot about the outer solar system in recent years. That new knowledge needs to be incorporated into the hunt for Planet X. That knowledge, I believe, points towards the explanation I have presented here, and this book will present the logic that lies behind it, which I believe to be compelling.

At this stage, it would be very helpful to look back over the history of the search for a tenth planet, and to then bring forward that new scientific knowledge. We must leave the myths and legends of ancient Sumer and time-travel to the last century, and consider the data emerging from just the last few years.

# Chapter 2 References

1. D. Rohl "Legend: The Genesis of Civilization" pp29-31 Arrow 1999

2. "The Cassell Atlas of World History" Cassell 1997

3. C. Sagan & I. Shklovskii "Intelligent Life in the Universe" pp456-463 Holden-Day Inc., 1966

4. Z. Sitchin "The 12th Planet" p245-246 Anon Books, 1976

5. E. Plunket "Calendars and Constellations of the Ancient World" p8, John Murray, London 1903

6. L. Lawhon "Nephilim. The Theories of Zecharia Sitchin" http://ufos.about.com/science/ufos/library/weekly/aa010801a.htm

7. Z. Sitchin "The 12th Planet" Chapter 7 Avon 1976

8. G. de Santillana & H. von Dechend "Hamlet's Mill" App. 39, pp430-451, http://www.apollonius.net/trees.html Thanks to Robertino Solarion

9. R. Temple "The Crystal Sun" Century 2000

10. The Babylonian "Enuma Elish"

11. Z. Sitchin "When Time Began" pp110-2 Avon 1993

12. C. Sagan "Pale Blue Dot" p140-141, p127 Headline Book Publishing 1995

13. Z. Sitchin "When Time Began" p161 Avon 1993

14. B. Van der Waerden "Science Awakening II" pp66-68
Oxford University Press 1974, with thanks to Pat Thomas

## Planet X, Past and Present

The idea that there is a massive undiscovered planetary body orbiting the sun is almost 100 years old now. It is certainly not a new idea, but is one whose popularity has fluctuated down the years. At the moment, it is a possibility that is regaining a certain amount of scientific credibility. An idea, perhaps, whose time has arrived.

Our science and technology seems to progress at an accelerating rate, and this tends to make us all a little complacent about what remains to be discovered. It seems common sense that any scientific endeavour lasting 100 years would have certainly reached a conclusion by now, as the means to discover the answer has improved. Yet, many of the most important scientific questions remain unanswered: a cure for cancer; a renewable energy source; a unified field theory in physics, to name but a few. These problems remind us that our knowledge of the cosmos, the Earth and ourselves is far from complete, and that science has much to learn.

And so it is with our knowledge of the solar system. Because we are looking further and further into space with larger and more technologically refined telescopes, we have a tendency to assume that everything in-between has been discovered, catalogued and understood. This is far from the truth in reality.

Astronomy is only as good as its ability to pick up light sources, or sources of other types of radiation, and distinguish them from other similar sources. Our eyes, searching the heavens at night, perform the most simple form of astronomy, detecting the light from distant stars. Yet we cannot see closer objects, including the outer planets of the solar system beyond Saturn, nor the asteroids and distant comets.

Even so, we know that these objects are there, because they have been detected and photographed by our telescopes and spacecraft. We don't need to see them with our own eyes. Similarly, we cannot see far more distant objects than our neighborhood stars, for instance distant galaxies. Yet telescopes, and sometimes just binoculars, allow us to see these incredibly distant swirling masses of stars. Because we can clearly 'see' so far, we think that our knowledge of the heavens is nearly complete.

However, we are dependent upon light for our knowledge. Almost all of the objects in the sky that we can see emit their own light. A few simply reflect sunlight, like the Moon and the five planets visible to us as we look up at the heavens.

As these planets become more distant from the sun, the amount of light they reflect dwindles such that the massive outer planets Uranus and Neptune are too faint to see. This brightness deteriorates very rapidly as you consider objects in the outer solar system. So although we can easily see thousands of stars light years away, it becomes extremely difficult to detect even planetary-sized bodies beyond the orbit of Neptune.

Astronomy is rather like looking down a long garden at night-time. You might be able to see the light from the house behind your back fence, but beyond a small distance your own garden is in darkness. It is within this darkness that our knowledge of the outer solar system resides, even after 100 years of peering through the gloom.

Just because we can see the lights over our back fence, does not mean we should assume we know what's prowling about at the bottom of our own garden. The extent of our sun's gravitational influence may be about 50,000 Astronomical Units, or 50,000 times the distance from the sun to the Earth. Our current knowledge of solar system objects includes only those within about 50 AU, which is just 1/1000th of the distance to the edge of the sun's influence.

Continuing my analogy, if our nocturnal garden is 100 metres long then our current view out of the window at night takes in just 10 centimeters of the patio! Beyond that we have no clue what's out there beyond inference and theoretical considerations.

Yet, for some reason, we think we can assume an excellent knowledge of what's out there beyond Neptune. We can't.

For many years, people have speculated that other planets lie beyond Neptune and Pluto, waiting to be discovered. Some evidence has emerged to back this conjecture up, and some arguments have been levelled against such an idea. The result is that the current scientific consensus is that we have a pretty good idea about what the other 999/1000th of the solar system looks like, without ever having seen it, and that there are no more big surprises in store. Anyone who thinks there are are is thought to be fantasizing, or is labelled a 'crank'.

Well, I beg to differ. There is plenty of astronomy-based evidence for a so-called 'Planet X', and plenty of good reasons to remain open-minded about the possibilities. Not only that, but there is the potential here for great science.

## Pluto and Planet X

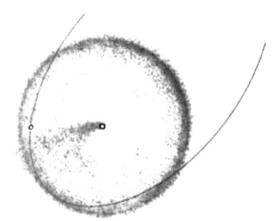

The term 'Planet X' was first coined by Percival Lowell, who founded the Lowell Observatory at Flagstaff, Arizona. Lowell is also famous for his interpretation of perceived markings on the surface of Mars, his 'canals'. But, despite the tarnishing of his reputation (which resulted from his belief in intelligent life on Mars, creating such marvels of extra-terrestrial engineering), Lowell was a great scientist.

Originally, the scientific speculation about Lowell's undiscovered Planet X was built upon observed 'wobbles' in the orbits of the outer planets, Uranus and Neptune, based upon data gathered over the previous century by astronomers. At that time, it was not considered unlikely that more planets remained to be discovered. Science seemed to be enjoying a golden age and great discoveries were changing people's lives for the better. Nothing seemed impossible. This massive perturbing influence at the edge of the solar system was just a new challenge beckoning for yet another great discovery.

As it turned out, a new planet was discovered -- but not the one anticipated. Clyde Tombaugh's discovery of Pluto in 1930 was made while he searched for Planet X at the Lowell Observatory. Tombaugh was a young amateur astronomer who had been recruited by Vesto Slipher, the director of Lowell Observatory. The ex-farmboy from Kansas pored over hundreds of photographic plates searching for Lowell's Planet X, a time-consuming and laborious process.

Eventually, he was rewarded on 18th February 1930. However, it turned out that Pluto is too small to have been the object perturbing the outer planets. Tombaugh continued his search for another 13 years, but failed to find Planet X. His sky searches were, by the end of those 13 years, so comprehensive that astronomers assumed that no Planet X could still await discovery (1).

The claim that Planet X is still out there has always been a very controversial one among astronomers, and all hope that it may have a grounding in fact seemed to have been killed off by E. Myles Standish, Jr. at NASA's Jet Propulsion Laboratory (JPL) in Pasadena, CA. Standish publicly expressed his doubts that there had ever really been problems with the orbits of Uranus and Neptune. He argued persuasively that previous anomalies over the past two centuries were explainable by "...systematic errors in the observations, and, in some cases by faulty data reduction and interpretation" (2).

Standish wrote a paper in 1993 outlining his theoretical work, based upon improved measurements of the masses of the outer planets during the Voyager spacecraft fly-bys. He claimed that the effect described by Lowell could now be negated, and that Lowell had been quite wrong to attribute the alleged wobbles to a massive undiscovered planet (1). Yet, Pluto had been discovered in the location predicted by Lowell for Planet X, in the zodiacal constellation of Gemini, even though it was evidently not the sought after massive planet. This was simply coincidence in the eyes of Standish and others, and the thoroughness of Tombaugh's sky searches 60 years before was seen as further evidence that Planet X was dead in the water.

This opinion has held sway since Standish's influential paper in 1993 (at least until relatively recently, when new anomalies emerged). However, before 1993, many scientists had continued to ponder openly upon the possibility of a Planet beyond Pluto.

The late Carl Sagan, a popular and brilliant scientist from Cornell University, described the potential for a dark sister companion orbiting the sun back in 1985. Sagan acknowledged the speculation surrounding a proposed Nemesis 'star' orbiting the sun at a great distance. He even proposed a fictional scenario where ancient peoples mythologized this 'Death Star' as the sun's Dark Sister (3). The 'Death Star' -- presumably taking its name from the equally fictitious moon-like battle station of George Lucas's Star Wars trilogy -- could periodically bombard the solar system with comets when its elliptical orbit caused it to brush through the comet clouds. This, in turn, could create a periodic extinction cycle.

This idea was not a particularly new one, even in 1985. A controversial article in Newsweek (28th June 1982) described the possibility that there may be a binary dark star at some considerable distance beyond the orbit of Pluto. Furthermore, a tenth planet might be orbiting around this binary system:

"A 'dark companion' could produce the unseen force that seems to tug at Uranus and Neptune, speeding them up at one point in their orbits and holding them back as they pass...(John) Anderson (of JPL.) thinks the best bet is a dark star orbiting at least 50 billion miles beyond Pluto, which is 3.6 billion miles from the sun. It is most likely either a brown dwarf – a lightweight star that never attained the critical mass to ignite - or a neutron star, the remnants of a normal sun that has burned out and collapsed" (4).

Catastrophism was enjoying a revival in the early 1980s. It was around this time that the world was coming to grips with the notion that dinosaurs had been wiped out by an asteroid or comet impact, as proposed by Luis and Walter Alvarez (5). It was a phenomenal notion, based upon the remarkable quantities of iridium found at the K-T boundary. In 1984 two paleontologists, David Raup and John Sepkoski, then proposed that there was a pattern to extinction events on Earth (6). A cycle of 26 million years appeared to have emerged from their data.

This seemed to call for some kind of cosmic-scale periodicity to explain it. The idea of a 'Nemesis' dark companion orbiting the sun every 26 million years was proposed in Nature by two independent teams of physicists; Daniel Whitmire and Albert Jackson (7), and M. Davis, et al (8). The orbit of this massive companion, a 'black dwarf', might pass through the Oort Cloud periodically, showering the solar system with comets, and causing a clockwork extinction pattern in tune with Raup and Sepkoski's data (9).

## IRAS

One can see the amount of speculation about Planet X, and/or a distant 'Dark Star', was quite considerable in the mid-eighties, prior to the sceptical paper by E. Myles Standish. But doubts about the proposed Nemesis object were already widespread among many mainstream scientists, and the catastrophists were in a minority to begin with. The fact was that such an object had not been discovered by the 1983 IRAS survey, which had methodically scanned the heavens in the infra-red band seeking invisible, but warm objects. This sky survey, it was widely argued (and still is…) should have found any undiscovered planets.

After all, the infra-red telescope which was carried by IRAS (the Infra-Red Astronomical Satellite) was quite capable of seeing 'through the dust and gas that obscures stars and other objects when viewed by optical telescopes' (10). One would have expected Planet X, if it was out there, to shine like a beacon in the dark.

In fact, news did break at the time regarding a 'sighting' of Planet X by the IRAS team, but nothing ever seemed to come of it. The Washington Post science team broke the story, declaring that "a heavenly body possibly as large as the planet Jupiter and possibly so close to Earth that it would be part of this solar system has been found in the direction of the constellation Orion by an orbiting telescope called the Infra-red Astronomical Observatory" (11).

According to JPL's Public Relations Office, which was contacted by Zecharia Sitchin in 1984, the finding had been ambiguous. Presumably, was that their way of accusing a reporter from the Washington Post of overstating the case? This report in the Washington Post has been reproduced many, many times over the Internet, and has indeed become the focal point for many who believe that knowledge of a tenth planet exists within official circles, but has been withheld from the public.

Part of that belief no doubt stems from a misguided understanding of the efficacy of the IRAS sky survey. This has not been helped by members of the mainstream astronomical community, sometimes talking up the failure of the IRAS study to detect another solar system planet. This perceived failure is seen as definitive by many, tolling the death knell for Planet X.

Tom Chester, who worked on the IRAS project and who has a sceptical attitude towards the existence of Planet X, once informed me that the coverage of the infer-red sky search was 95% complete. Taken on face value, this appears to create a big problem for a potential sizeable body out there. Patrick Moore tells us that IRAS discovered no less than 200,000 infra-red signatures in the sky (12). Given this extraordinary amount of data, it is tempting to conclude that a thorough search for Planet X was essentially completed by IRAS.

But the disappointment of the IRAS survey could well have been a "false negative". John Anderson, a distinguished scientist formerly of the Pioneer programme and the Jet Propulsion Laboratory, argued that the survey could easily have missed Planet X. He explained that there were many objects in the sky that had infra-red signatures similar to those of planets. To truly pinpoint a possibly unseen planet, its proper motion would have to be determined. If the motion across the sky of a distant planet were very small over a period of weeks, or months, then IRAS could easily have missed it (2).

Recently, I have been informed that this opinion is also shared by the renowned expert on brown dwarfs, Professor J. Davy Kirkpatrick. He seems optimistic that a brown dwarf could be discovered between our sun and the nearest known star, Proxima Centauri. The IRAS survey didn't detect such a body, of course, but that doesn't mean it's not there. A fellow researcher, John Lee, often working under the 'handle' of 'Rajasun' agreed that a dark mass with an insignificant proper motion across the sky could not have been distinguished from a stationary object by IRAS. More surprisingly still, he cited an article (1) that described how any detection of a possible object with a notable motion across the sky would have been dismissed as questionable data!

These researchers consider the best chance for the future discovery of a binary brown dwarf to be NASA's Wide-field

Infrared Survey Explorer (WISE) mission. It may surprise the reader to learn that the hoped-for discovery of a brown dwarf closer than the sun's nearest stellar neighbor is actually one of its main mission goals (14)!

The commitment of funds for WISE flies in the face of the general negativity among scientists regarding the prospects for a massive solar companion. This future mission, scheduled for launch in 2008, will be specifically searching for such an nearby brown dwarf. It is possible that a brown dwarf might be discovered as a free-floating object in the interstellar space beyond the solar system, or a cold object could possibly be found actually orbiting the sun.

Another positive remark about the potential for an undiscovered planet orbiting relatively closely to the sun emerged when an astrophysics group from Harvard released details of an anomalous Kuiper Belt Object known as 2000 CR105. One of the team, Dr. Matthew Holman, indicated that this object's bizarre orbit might be the result of a massive perturber in the comet clouds beyond the planetary zone. He went on public record as saying that a Mars-sized body might "easily" have evaded detection as close as 200 AU (15). This clearly flies in the face of the opinion that the IRAS sky survey's failure to detect Planet X means that there is no Planet X.

So, there is a lot of scope for being open-minded about the existence of Planet X. While it evidently does not orbit the sun as close as the outer planets Neptune and Pluto, you don't have to move too far away from the sun before its existence again becomes an open question. There are theoretical considerations of course, because many astronomers dismiss the existence of a massive planet out there, because it would cause some problems for our current models of solar system formation. But the tide is turning as new discoveries come to light about other star systems.

I recently had an opportunity to ask the space historian and sceptic James Oberg about NASA's current attitude towards Planet X, and his reply was illuminating. He suggested that there probably wasn't an official position towards the subject, but that it is considered when relevant to specific missions, like the proposed Pluto-Kuiper probe. He had seen a renewed interest in the discoveries in the outer frontier of the solar system in recent years, which we will dwell on shortly, and was personally excited about the possibilities emerging (16).

It seems that even commentators who are often labelled as sceptics are being won over to the idea that Planet X could be out there. But that doesn't stop astronomers from being very cagey about what they say on this subject. To openly promote the idea of a major undiscovered planet or brown dwarf in the scientific literature, is to invoke the wrath of many sceptical scientists.

I don't know why this is particularly, but it is evidently true. The science of astronomy and cosmology can be quite bold and speculative at times, so one would expect that such ideas -- if properly presented in the literature -- would be welcomed in the same way as, say, new thinking on black holes. Alas, this does not appear to be so. One can only surmise that the mere suggestion of the existence of a Planet X suggests greater consequences than just the advancements of scientific knowledge about our outer solar system.

## The Dark Star Discovered

In 1999, two researchers presented findings that might indicate the existence of a small brown dwarf orbiting the sun. One of them, Dr. John Murray of the Open University in England, initially found it difficult to even get his paper published. Perhaps that was because he wasn't an astronomer, but an Earth scientist. More likely was the nature of his proposal, which subsequently brought much criticism his way. As well as a lot of publicity, because any suggestion of an undiscovered planet in our solar system is inherently newsworthy. Popular interest and academic disdain often go hand in hand.

John Murray looked at the trajectories of long-period comets and analyzed them to see if any patterns emerged (17). Long-period comets are thought to originate in the Oort Cloud, an hypothetical, but generally accepted spherical distribution of comets beyond about 2000 Astronomical Units (18). The comets in question emerged from the outer Oort Cloud, which extends from about 20,000AU onwards to the very limit of the sun's influence. These are very considerable distances indeed.

In his paper, John Murray explained why he thought a very massive planet might be orbiting the sun out among these distant comets: the comets had arrived from points in the sky that indicated a pattern to their origins. He noted that whilst other explanations for this were possible, the cometary orbits were most likely to have attained these configurations because of the presence of an unknown distant object circling the sun between thirty and fifty thousand astronomical units away (17). This is an immense distance and a great circular orbit around the sun out there would take millions of years to complete.

He made a strong case for the following argument: The Oort Cloud should have a random, but spherical distribution around the sun, rather like a very thick skin on an orange. Assuming comets are dislodged randomly from the cloud to move into the planetary zone of the solar system, then the sky locations from which they came should be randomly distributed, as well as their original distances from the sun. His analysis showed that this was, in fact, not the case, but that there was a statistical aberration. That clustering calls for another influence affecting the comets that were disturbed from their meandering distant orbits around the sun. A likely contender appears to be a massive 'Perturber' among these distant comets.

Dr. Murray then predicted an approximate sky location for the massive planet, or brown dwarf, based upon its perceived retrograde motion around the sun. When I read his paper I was amazed. This position was somewhat north of Sagittarius, in the small constellation of Delphinius. The planet appeared to be acting in a very similar way to the orbit described by Zecharia Sitchin for Nibiru.

It was moving the wrong way around the sun, compared to the other planets. It was inclined to the plane of the planets by 30 degrees, as proposed by Sitchin. And it was in the right part of the sky. To my mind, this 'Dark Star' of Dr. Murray's was Sitchin's Nibiru. He had found physical evidence to show that this fabled planet exists.


## Myth and Reality


My excitement was compounded by the fact that I had already independently proposed that the way in which Nibiru was described in the myths correlated well with our understanding of a brown dwarf, or failed star. In the Enuma Elish, the Babylonian 'god' Marduk, whose 49th Name is Nibiru, was described using words that have a strong cosmological flavour (19). The description seemed to tally with an extraordinary and massive planet which emitted fire and lightning. In other words, it was a planet more massive than Jupiter with certain stellar characteristics.

Its dramatic incursion into the myth seems to indicate to us that Marduk had once entered the solar system for the first time, blazing with fire and shining like the sun. There is an even clearer reference to Marduk's sun-like attributes in these lines, and is quite literally called the "Son of the Sun":

*"MARDUK, as Anu, his father, called him from his birth;*

*Who provides grazing and drinking places, enriches their stalls,*

*Who with the flood-storm, his weapon, vanquished the detractors,*

*And who the gods, his fathers, rescued from distress.*

*Truly, the Son of the Sun, most radiant of gods is he.*

*In his brilliant light may they walk forever!"*

Tablet VI Lines 124-9 (20).

I believe this designation as the 'Son of the Sun' is of great significance. If the 'Dark Star', which seems to be synonymous with the Babylonian god Marduk in the Babylonian creation myth exists, then our solar system is a long-standing binary system, whose smallest 'star' is now old and cold. But at the time of its dramatic entry into the sun's domain, it was a radiant and powerful planet whose stellar attributes are clearly described. The planet represented by Marduk seemed to have once shined like a small star, becoming the 'Son of the Sun'.

Sumerologists and sceptics in general argue that the Enuma Elish should not be interpreted in terms of an astronomical framework, that the gods described in the Creation Myth are not synonymous with stellar deities, whether in the form of planets, stars, or constellations. They take issue with Zecharia Sitchin for making this connection (21). Yet, the Enuma Elish is packed full of cosmic descriptions, in keeping with the advanced knowledge of astronomy of the Babylonians.

This is an old argument that has raged for many years. Although many of the gods of the ancient pantheons are directly related to planets, the sun and the Moon, scholars generally don't interpret that as meaning that the ancients were trying to tell us about the physical nature of the solar system: myths are myths, nothing more.

Alan Alford

Yet, we are becoming more aware of the remarkable astronomical knowledge of ancient peoples, through the complex archeo-astronomical alignments of many of the monuments dating back from megalithic times (22,23). The myths seem to be an excellent vehicle for the transmission of an oral tradition about the astronomical knowledge that the ancient people all round the world clearly exhibited. Such an argument lies at the heart of an illuminating thesis by the scholars Georgio de Santillana and Hertha von Dechend entitled, "Hamlet's Mill" (24).

These ideas have become part of my own approach to understanding what the myths can tell us about our solar system, and I believe we still have more to learn from them than our present scientific knowledge suggests. To my mind, the existence of an undiscovered planet of massive proportions was suggested by many different legends and traditions, which have been chronicled across the globe (25).

## Synchronicity

Just months before the release of John Murray's paper, I had reviewed a lecture given by the British researcher Alan Alford, and had used this short review as a vehicle to formally propose the connection between Sitchin's planet Nibiru and a brown dwarf. Alan had once entertained the ideas of Zecharia Sitchin and had written a very popular book on the subject (26). He then retracted those ideas, and had made his criticisms of Sitchin's work apparent during a lecture he gave in Gloucestershire in the summer of 1999.

The criticisms included, quite rightly in my opinion, the difficulties that Nibiru would have sustaining life in the solar system beyond Neptune. In a letter published by the British newsstand publication UFO Magazine, I discussed Alan Alford's lecture and suggested that Sitchin's dilemma could be solved by Nibiru's planetary status being upgraded to that of a small brown dwarf, thence allowing life to exist on its attendant moons:

"Here is the crux of the problem – the world's most ancient race, the Sumerians, said that the gods came to Earth from a planet, describing a comet-like orbit around the sun. To generate sufficient heat to have liquid water, the planet must either be too massive gravitationally, or too radioactive to support life. Case closed.

But modern astronomers are trying to grapple with the facts that the solar system exhibits too much gravity, and that there is a huge amount of missing mass in the universe. Brown dwarf stars have been proposed to account for both anomalies. If our sun has a tiny sister star that is too faint and distant to have been detected, then maybe this star is the twelfth planet.

So why would the Sumerians call a star a planet? In fact, they already included the sun as a planet, as well as our Moon. That's how they arrived at the number twelve as the total number of planets in the solar system. They also said that the Twelfth Planet had a number of 'attendants', which we could then consider to be the brown dwarf star's own planetary system. They said that the Twelfth Planet was glorious to behold, with a great halo. Well, maybe they were describing a brown dwarf that became visible to the naked eye as it traversed the outer solar system as part of its eccentric orbit around the sun." (27)

Although I would have written this somewhat differently now, the basic points continue to stand, and formed the basis of later articles released over the Internet that would change many people's notions about the nature of Sitchin's Nibiru.

The reason for including this here is to demonstrate that the ideas behind the Dark Star Theory were published two months before John Murray's paper on his proposed Planet X, which was described by him as being large enough to potentially be a small brown dwarf. We were tackling the problem from different angles, certainly, but coming to similar conclusions at the same time. Of course, the first mention of a 'Dark Star' orbiting the sun as a binary companion was made as long ago as

1982, so none of this is entirely new! But at the time, in 1999, this development seemed newsworthy.

There was a synchronicity at play there, certainly, but I would also like to emphasize the fact that I had not taken John Murray's paper and used that to re-write Sitchin. Rather, I had independently thought through the 'habitable planet' problem, come up with a viable solution, and then discovered later that the basis for that idea could corroborate Dr. Murray's scientific work.

Had my letter not been published in UFO Magazine in the late summer of 1999, I would have difficulty proving this course of events, and I have always been grateful to the late Graham W. Birdsall for its inclusion in his magazine at the time, as well as a major follow-up article a couple of years later (28).

## John Matese and Daniel Whitmire

A second synchronicity also occurred at that time, because it was not just John Murray who had been looking closely at the patterns of long-period comets. In the United States, John Matese's research team had carried out a similar analysis, and independently come to a similar conclusion. His paper was published at exactly the same time as Murray's, although the details of their work varied somewhat. John Matese is a Professor of Physics at the University of Louisiana at Lafayette, and he was joined in this research effort by Patrick Whitman and Daniel Whitmire. The latter famously co-wrote the 1984 Nature paper on the proposed 'Nemesis' body, and its link to the 26 million year extinction cycle.[7]

Like John Murray, they concluded that a massive planet or small brown dwarf could be orbiting the sun, sending comets our way. Unlike Dr. Murray, they stopped short of postulating a possible location for the object. Other details were different too, including the approximate distance, and the orbit. They also considered it likely that the effect supplemented that of the galactic tide, which was the dominant feature in the statistical aberrations (29).

In the paper it was also speculated that the orbit of this planet, which they call the 'Perturber', would, on occasion, bring it fairly close to the outer planetary zone. This was because an orbit that was at the distance of 25,000AU was not one which could be sustained for the life-time of the solar system, a point also conceded by John Murray (17). Citing a very interesting paper by Jack Hills from 1985 (30), they noted that any orbit in the outer Oort cloud was liable to be altered by the action of the galactic tide over hundreds of millions of years (29).

As the sun rotates around the centre of the galaxy, it bobs up and down through the galactic plane rather like the horse on a fairground carousel ride. The periodic changes to the orbit of the perturber, known as 'oscultations', are related to this motion with relation to the galactic plane, and, according to Dr. Matese's calculations, could at times lead to a minimum distance from the sun of just 125AU. This is an important point. Let us say that the sun was formed in conjunction with a distant binary brown dwarf that initially formed at the sort of distances that comets are now located at. Over several hundred million years the action of the galactic tide would cause the brown dwarf to drift inwards towards the planetary zone of the sun.

This is precisely what I think took place 3.9 billion years ago, some 700 million years after the formation of the solar system. The sun's binary companion fell down towards the sun as a result of the galaxy's gravitational interaction, destabilizing its orbit. It then swept catastrophically through the solar system as described by the Babylonian myths, before migrating out towards the comets once again.

Furthermore, Dr. Matese argued that this situation would repeat itself over time, without significantly destabilizing the orbits of the other planets in the solar system (29). Incredible, isn't it? The mathematical calculations carried by Dr. Matese and his colleagues created a model to describe how a distant binary companion could, on occasion, end up wandering near to the sun.

If a small brown dwarf sometimes approaches the planetary zone to within 3 times the distance of Pluto, even though for the vast majority of the time it is located much further away, then it would significantly affect the minor planetary bodies of the Edgeworth-Kuiper Belt. As we shall see, this is exactly what has been observed in the last few years. Where the brown dwarf has wandered, there is an absence of comets known as the "Kuiper Gap".

Finally, it is clear that a brown dwarf in a loosely bound orbit around the sun is subject to other external factors that can change its orbit. Indeed, to have even arrived in the outer Oort cloud in the first place, the Matese team were speculating that the brown dwarf had accreted, or formed from proto-planetary disc matter, closer to the sun -- and then migrated out as a result of stellar impulses over the history of the solar system (30). There is a dynamic process at play that complicates matters.

If the orbit of the Dark Star fluctuates over time then, the binding relationship between it and the sun within the binary system also changes over time. This potentially has dramatic consequences for the rest of the solar system. I will argue that dynamic process creates a unique mechanism for Catastrophism here on Earth, including the ebb and flow of the great Ice Age eras.

## Critics in Both Directions

These considerations opened my eyes to the potential room for manoeuvre in the outer solar system. The orbits of the solar system brown dwarfs, as described by the scientists, were in the order of several million years. Yet, Zecharia Sitchin's planet Nibiru was said to orbit the sun in a relatively short time period of 3600 years. These two situations were not readily convergent, even if many of the rest of the findings seemed to tie in superficially.

Dr. Matese and his team were aware of the comparisons which I had been making between their work and Zecharia Sitchin's controversial ideas. Their main concern with such a link was that their brown dwarf occupied an orbit and periodicity that could not in any way be compared to Sitchin's 3600 years. John Murray voiced similar objections. I think it is fair to say that their concerns did not arise from a dogmatic scientific stance, nor was it a knee-jerk reaction to an unwanted association with alternative science. Simply put, they thought the two theories could not be linked because the data would not support such a notion.

One should also put these objections in the context of the heat emanating from the scientific community in general, which was less than pleased about the resurrection of the Planet X debate. Both of these researchers had been getting some difficult feedback from their peers about their ideas, which were not generally well received in scientific circles (the media, in contrast, loved it). The influential solar system dynamist Brian Marsden was invited to comment upon the possibilities by The Telegraph, and was cool about the idea:

"It's possibly suggestive," comments Brian Marsden, associate director for planetary sciences at the Harvard-Smithsonian Center for Astrophysics in Cambridge, Mass. "I don't want to bet on it. We're certainly not going to name it" (31).

But other, more difficult questions have been publicly raised about John Murray's research, such as by Harold Levison of the Southwest Research Institute in Boulder, Colorado. When he was interviewed by 'Discover' magazine in 2001, he argued that "tinkering" with the comet data would make the anomalous effect simply disappear (32).

It must be remembered that John Murray is not an astronomer. Although, his paper clearly met the approval of the Royal Astronomical Society, in order to be accepted for publication by this prestigious body. But he is somewhat "out-ranked" by an acknowledged expert on the Oort Cloud. However, such objections from the scientific community have been met head-on by Professor Matese, who cites other scientific researchers analyzing long-period comet data who have had a more positive outlook (33). The possibility of a Jupiter-mass companion seems alive and well.

In fact, the Matese team continues to analyze long-period comets and continues to find the non-random clustering, suggestive of the brown dwarf's presence. And they continue to stand by their work. However, they see no reason whatsoever, that their proposed object might lie closer to the planetary zone in the guise of Sitchin's mythical Nibiru (34).

With respect to them, I'm not so sure. Their discussion of the "oscultation" effect, whereby their brown dwarf spends some of its time in an orbital configuration that approaches the outer solar system, is very interesting. The fact that the great circular orbit at 25,000+AU is "unstable" over long periods of time, suggests a migratory pattern for the brown dwarf. Then, as we shall see, there's the large gap between the Edgeworth-Kuiper Belt and the inner Oort Cloud, where no comets are seen to emanate from. I can't help but think this is because this "gap" marks the territory of a massive perturber that has swept the region clean of cosmic debris.

This leads me to argue that the brown dwarf currently resides closer to the sun than the Matese team suggests. It is in the small print of the Matese paper from 1999, that a mechanism for a closer passage near the solar system becomes a distinct possibility.

## Chapter 3 References

1. J. Davis "Beyond Pluto" pp9-10 Cambridge University Press 2001

2. (Ed) J. Shirley and R. Fairbridge "Encyclopedia of Planetary Sciences": 'Planet X' by John D. Anderson, Chapman and Hall, see http://dosxx.colorado.edu/Pluto/PlanetX.Anderson.html

3. C. Sagan & A. Druyan "Comet" pp300-6, Headline 1985

4. "Does the Sun have a Dark Companion?" Newsweek, 28/6/82, p83, with thanks to Greg Jenner

5. W. Alvarez "T. Rex and the Crater of Doom" Penguin 1998

6. R. Corfield "Architects of Eternity" Ch 6, Headline 2001

7. D. Whitmire & A. Jackson, Nature (1984) 308, 713

8. M. Davis, P. Hut & R. Muller, Nature (1984) 308, 715

9. D. Raup & J. Sepkoski, Proc. Natl. Acad. Sci. (1984) 81, 801

10. P. Moore "Atlas of the Universe" p195, George Philip Ltd, 1999

11. Z. Sitchin "Genesis Revisited" pp319-24 Avon 1990

12. P. Moore "Guide to Stars and Planets" p100, Chancellor Press 2001

13. Hogg, D. W.; Quinlan, G. D. & Tremaine, S., 1991, "Dynamical limits on dark mass in the outer solar system", AJ, 101, p2274-2286

14. Private correspondence from J. D. Kirkpatrick, shared with me by John Lee, aka Rajasun and various other aliases 9/6/03

15. J. Kelly Beatty "Big-orbit Object Confounds Dynamicists" http://www.skypub.com/news/news.shtml#bigorbit 5th April 2001

16. Correspondence from Jim Oberg, 13th January 2002, www.jamesoberg.com email: joberg@houston.rr.com

17. J.Murray "Arguments for the presence of a distant large undiscovered solar system planet" Mon. Not. R. Astron. Soc., 309, 31-34 (1999)

18. J. Oort "The structure of the cloud of comets surrounding the solar system, and a hypothesis concerning its structure" Bull. Astron. Inst. Neth. 11, 91-110 (1950)

19. Enuma Elish Tablet I, Lines 87-105

20. Enuma Elish Tablet VI Lines 124-9

21. "Waiting for the Apocalypse" Documentary Video, 2003

22. E. Krupp, (ed.) "In Search of Ancient Astronomies" Doubleday & Co. 1978

23. E. Krupp "Echoes of the Ancient Skies: The Astronomy of Lost Civilizations" Oxford University Press 1983

24. G. de Santillana & H. von Dechend "Hamlet's Mill" Gambit Inc. 1969

25. A. Lloyd "Winged Disc: The Dark Star Theory" which was available in manuscript form, 2001-4

26. A. Alford "Gods of the New Millennium" Hodder & Stoughton 1997

27. A. Lloyd "Ancient to Modern" p76, UFO Magazine Sept.-Oct. 1999

28. A. Lloyd 'Synopsis of the Dark Star Theory' pp50-5, UFO Magazine August 2001

29. J.J. Matese, P.G. Whitman and D.P. Whitmire, "Cometary Evidence of a Massive Body in the Outer Oort Cloud" Icarus, 141, 354-336 (1999),

30. J.G. Hills "The Passage of a "Nemesis"-like object through the Planetary System" The Astronomical Journal, 90, Number 9, pp1876-1882, September 1985

31. P. Blakemore writing in The Telegraph, 22nd October 2002 http://www.viewzone.com/nemesis.html

32. Kathy A. Svitil "Dogged scientist looks for 'Planet X'" from Discover Magazine 5/12/01

33. Dr. Matese's website: http://www.ucs.louisiana.edu/~jjm9638, citing ("Biases in Cometary Catalogues and Planet X", J. Horner and N. W. Evans, MNRAS (2002)

34. L. Moulton Howe interviewing Dr. John Matese, 2001, http://www.earthfiles.com/earth317.htm

# 4

## Binary Companion

In the last chapter, we looked at some of the history of the hunt for Planet X. This search has been going on for about 100 years, sometimes in vogue, sometimes not. The suffix 'X' denotes either a potential Tenth Planet (in Roman numerals) or simply an Unknown. But, the term "planet" itself covers a wide spectrum of objects in space.

At the small end, we have small rocky worlds that are really just very large asteroids. The point at which an asteroid begins to be labelled a planet is not a clear-cut one, but generally it is the point where a world becomes spherical in shape, rather than being irregularly shaped. Thus, Pluto is generally accepted to be a planet.

However, the reader will no doubt point out that the Moon is spherical, as are many other moons in the solar syst. Are these also planets in their own right? So, the additional factor appears to be whether the body is independently orbiting the sun, as we would normally understand a planet to do. A moon that is spherical may have the appearance of a planet, but because it orbits a parent planet, we generally think of it as a moon.

Examples include our own Moon, the Galilean moons of Jupiter and Titan. The latter is even more like a planet, though, because it has a thick atmosphere and a dynamic weather system, with liquid oceans and land-masses. We are left with the uncomfortable realization that Titan is more like our idea of a planet than, say, Pluto, which is small, barren and orbits the sun in a rather odd way.

It is clear, then, that the label 'planet' is not easily definable even at the lower end of the celestial market. Yet, these difficulties pale into insignificance when faced with defining a planet at the top end. Where once we thought we could easily distinguish between stars and planets, now the black and white labels are becoming increasingly confused.

Our common sense dictates that a planet does not emit its own light, and a star does. However, there is an array of bodies which lie in a grey area between these definitions. There are planets that behave a bit like stars; and some that behave like stars for a short time then die down a bit; and others that are almost stars, but not quite.

In Chapter 5, we shall look at some of the science behind the understanding of these objects, many of which are called brown dwarfs. "brown dwarf" is not a great name for this kind of hybrid planet/star really, but it has stuck because no one's come up with anything better. They're the cosmic equivalent of a difficult teenager; not terribly easy to understand and full of surprises.

There's a lot to think about with these brown dwarfs, but I would first like to first spend a little more time looking at the hunt for Planet X. That hunt has, on occasion, concentrated on the possibility that the tenth planet is a brown dwarf, or perhaps something larger. The speculation has been that we live in a binary star system.

Now, that is not to say that there is a full-blown star near the sun that has somehow evaded everyone's attention for the last 6000 years or so. No, the thinking is that there might be an undetected planet which is so massive that it is warm, and possibly gives out its own light. If it emits a lot of light, then it would have to be very, very far away. If it's essentially dark, then it could be closer and still have evaded detection.

So as a rough guide, we could imagine the following as reasonable possibilities: a terrestrial tenth planet like Mars or Earth might yet be found about 100 times as far away from the sun as the Earth (150 Astronomical Units). A planet heavier than Jupiter, but essentially still 'dark' might yet be discovered further still, perhaps 1000 astronomical units away. This lies somewhere between the Edgeworth-Kuiper Belt and the inner Oort cloud. Lastly, a substantial brown dwarf, which is large enough to emit its own light, might lie undiscovered in the outer Oort cloud, more than 10,000 times the distance from the Earth to the sun.

Any of these possibilities are plausible I would argue, although many astronomers would rather dismiss them all. This is because the theory of planet-building, that is currently accepted, but does not readily allow for the 'construction' of planets so far away from the sun. However, things are not that straightforward anymore, as we shall soon discover, so I suggest we should remain open-minded for the time being.

Large bodies that emit heat, glow in the infra-red part of the spectrum. That includes relatively cold objects as well, because the background temperature of space is itself so low. In 1983, there was an extensive sky survey carried out by a mission called IRAS, and thousands and thousands of 'warm' objects in the heavens were catalogued as a result. One of the hopes of the sky search was that it would turn up a tenth planet. Two decades later, controversy still rages about certain alleged discoveries made by IRAS, which were widely publicized at the time, stoking public interest in the possibility of a new planet.

## The IRAS 'Discovery'

A very famous Planet X 'sighting' was made by IRAS in 1983, and it has become the centre of several conspiracy theories that NASA has attempted to hush-up the discovery of Planet X. The report does appear to be very encouraging for a Dark Star, in that it described the object as being about the right size (like Jupiter, which is similar in size as a heavier brown dwarf), and at the right sort of distance (about 500AU). It might even be moving in the correct direction (towards us), although this was denied fervently by Gerry Neugebauer, the chief IRAS scientist at Cal Tech at the time (1).

Arguably, its location is not without merit either. The controversial 'object' was spotted in Orion, which is a favorite potential location for Nibiru among many alternative researchers. Orion is one of the best known constellations in the sky, despite the fact that it lies south of the ecliptic and is not a zodiacal constellation. But its appearance in the Autumnal months in the Northern hemisphere is dramatic, and it appears clearly as a Hunter wielding his club in his right hand, whilst symbolically holding a lion skin in his left.

Over 100 years ago, Emmeline Plunket considered the idea that the constellation of Orion was known to the ancient people of the Indian subcontinent in a similar form to the later Greeks, who are credited with the name Orion. An etymological argument has been made that the Greek name was originally derived from the Sanskrit names of the Nakshatra, one of which means 'first-going'.

From this, Plunket argues that the characterization of this constellation may have been as early as 4600BC, a quite extraordinary contention (2). Whether this very ancient dating is correct or not, it is evident that Orion was held in high esteem by the ancients. For instance, the Babylonians named the constellation after Tammuz, coincident with their month of the same name, which saw the heliacal rising of its famous belt of three stars.

Adrian Gilbert thinks that Orion was pivotal to our understanding of ancient religions (3), and his colleague Robert Bauval became famous for his influential theory about the juxtaposition of the earthly Pyramids of Giza, with the heavenly belt stars of Orion (4). Even the esteemed archeo-astronomer E.C. Krupp recognizes the significance of the star Sirius and the constellation of Orion to the ancient Egyptians when he describes the account in the ancient Egyptian Pyramid Texts about the ascent of the departed king to Orion (Osiris), with Sirius as his guide (5).

So is it little wonder that the pinpointing of an allegedly new solar system object in Orion by IRAS would ignite tremendous interest? However, I suspect that the Dark Star is to be found currently in the exact opposite part of the sky, in the sky north of Sagittarius. I have some very good reasons for holding this view, which I will explain in due course.

Over the past several years, many have asked me why I seem to have ignored the IRAS finding, given the sensational way it was reported at the time. The answer is that the controversial result was never confirmed by optical means. There have been many contemporary astronomers interested in Planet X, including Brunini, Matese, Whitmire, Anderson and Harrington, to name but a few. If JPL, through the Washington Post, gave these fellows a treasure map back in 1983, one imagines that the buried planet would have been dug up long ago. Instead, it has become the stuff of Internet legend.

At the time, there were various suggestions for the identity of this 'object'. It may have been a Jupiter-sized planet, whose distance from the sun was anything from Pluto's distance, to all the way out to the nearest star. This covers a very significant range of possibilities, indeed. But, other ideas included the possibility that the 'object' was a "dark, young galaxy" that had not been detected before, or even a proto-planetary gas cloud (1).

In contrast to the fuss made about this finding, a second report emerged around the same time about a massive planet discovered by IRAS. The rumors of this next find created waves in the scientific community.

## An IRAS Object Quietly Forgotten

In 1986, a rather diligent researcher named William Corliss published his book "The Sun and Solar System Debris - A Catalog of Astronomical Anomalies". Several observed anomalies are cited which may allude to Planet X, or even a dark companion to the sun. These anomalies remain unconfirmed, of course, but make for interesting reading nonetheless. One of them describes an object captured by the IRAS survey which sounds very much like the 'Orion' sighting, only this time it is located in the zodiacal constellation of Sagittarius, in the opposite half of the sky (6).

This report was written by two British science journalists, Martin Redfern and Nigel Henblest (7). I wrote to Mr. Corliss in the hope of finding out more, but his back catalogue of files was simply too extensive to hunt through in depth. He politely had to decline my request. However, last year my research colleague Greg Jenner kindly sent me a selection of Planet X documents, and among them was the article I had hoped to uncover. It certainly makes for interesting reading.

The article was published in "New Scientist" on 10th November 1983, and discusses the discovery of an object in space whose temperature is 230K, which is too cool for a star, but too warm for a dust cloud. It was spotted by the infra-red space telescope in the constellation of Sagittarius, and fit the bill for an object 'several times heavier than Jupiter'. Remarkably, British scientists at the time accused their American colleagues of keeping the information of this find to themselves. The British scientists publicly questioned why the Americans had "been keeping quiet about it in recent weeks". Speculation was rife, that the discovery was nothing but an intriguing ploy to bolster the chances of further funding from NASA for a new infrared space observatory (7).

Those few weeks of silence which followed the report of a new Jupiter-sized planet in the solar syst, have now extended to 22 years! Part of the problem might have been that funding ran out before all the observed heat sources could be properly analyzed. Observed objects had been properly catalogued, but there remained an estimated 3 years of further scientific analysis undone. Some might be satisfied with this explanation.

If you're not feeling quite as charitable as that, you might wonder why this remarkable data was never properly announced to the world. Somehow, it leaked to the British researchers co-working on the project, who discussed the matter openly in the scientific press. They had their own political agenda, it seems, which probably fuelled this minor trans-Atlantic spat. But the net result is that we are left with a tantalizing report in New Scientist of the discovery of a Dark Star in our solar syst, located in the constellation of Sagittarius.

I suspect this "leak" represented something substantial. Personally, I think they really did find the Dark Star, a planet weighing several Jupiter masses, and that its temperature is indeed 230 Kelvin. Somewhere along the line, its discovery was quietly ditched by the Americans, much to the annoyance of their European counterparts. But given a lack of access to the actual data, the war of words eventually petered out.

Without this article in New Scientist, no one would have known any different. There is usually some fire behind the smoke, after all. But, why would anyone want to shelve such an incredibly important discovery?

## The Case for Sagittarius

In his analysis of ancient texts, Zecharia Sitchin offered a number of constellations as probable points along the path trodden by Nibiru. These include, in order, the Great Bear (Ursa Major); Orion (along with the star Sirius); then, Taurus and Aries; before heading towards Sagittarius (8,9,10). The last of these is not listed as a constellation that Nibiru visits, but rather one that it usually disappears from, in its course away from our solar system.

If Sitchin's textual quotes are to be accepted, then the destination for the fabled planet -- as it disappears once again into the primordial deep -- is Sagittarius. This area just happens to coincide with the location of our reported IRAS object of several Jupiter masses. The Zodiacal constellation of Sagittarius lies on the ecliptic, or the plane of the planets. This would infer, if it truly represents the Dark Star's aphelion location, that the entire orbit of the rogue planet is not particularly inclined to the others. More on this later.

Suffice it to say for now, that I believe that the extent of the Dark Star's deviation from the ecliptic is not as great as proposed by Sitchin. I suggest that at perihelion, or the closest point to the sun, that the sighting of 'Nibiru' is slightly south of the ecliptic, in the vicinity of Sirius and Orion.

This is supported by the listed constellations from the ancient texts. This is the part of the sky that is known as the 'Duat' to the ancient Egyptians. It is a sky location of great importance. But, the Dark Star is not located there at the moment. It is currently very, very far away in the opposite half of the sky, in Sagittarius.

## The Busy Archer

Sagittarius is a large constellation, through which runs the path of the planets, or the ecliptic. Sagittarius is not always easily seen by observers in the northern hemisphere, because it is a summer constellation which sits very low in the Southern portion of the sky. This is a pity, because within this constellation lies the heart of our galaxy, the Milky Way, "...studded with clusters and beautiful nebulae and brilliant with dense star clouds" (11). In the centre of these star fields lies the heart of our galaxy, some 30,000 light years away.

This is very important, because the Milky Way is at its brightest in Aquila and Cygnus in the Northern Hemisphere, and Scorpius and Sagittarius in the southern hemisphere. So our search for this distant 'planet' will be made all the more difficult by the sheer mass of background stars. Not only that, but there is a huge band of solar system objects, particularly asteroids, all of which reside in a belt around the line of the ecliptic. Searching for more distant objects along this ecliptic will often throw up these solar system objects in the field of view, be they asteroids or short period comets.

Trying to find the distant Dark Star among this array of galactic stars, nebulae and clusters, creates the same difficulties already faced by astronomers looking for other, nearer objects. Sagittarius is just not a great place to hunt for new objects and, frankly, most astronomers avoid searching there because of these difficulties. The plane of the sun's planets, the ecliptic, and the Milky Way, are like two great circles crossing the sky at angles to one another.

They cross over twice, in Sagittarius, and on the other side of the sky, between Gemini and Taurus. And so, these locations are awkward places to hunt for a faint, practically stationary source of light against the backdrop of millions of others (12). Not only that, but Sagittarius is difficult to observe from the more northern latitudes, anyway. This is a hunt for a needle in a haystack, with the lights turned off.

Because of these problems astronomers like Dave Jewitt and Jane Luu, famous for their discovery of the first trans-Neptunian object, avoid searching for Edgeworth-Kuiper Objects (EKOs) at these nodal regions. Instead, they turn their attention to the much darker constellations, like Pisces (12). As a result, distant solar system objects are almost certainly going to be discovered in the darker constellations, and if the Dark Star just happens to be located in front of the Milky Way galaxy, well, it will probably remain undiscovered. Furthermore, because its motion across the sky is negligible, it will remain in this part of the sky for several generations to come.

## John Bagby and the Binary in Sagittarius

A gentleman who has long argued for the existence of a substantial tenth planet is the engineer and amateur astronomer, John Bagby. He wrote several papers outlining evidence he had put forward for the existence of a Massive Solar Companion, or 'MSC' (13). Bagby was quite sure that such a body existed, and he claimed to have data to prove it, if only someone would listen. He shared this information with astronomers at the US Naval Observatory, including Drs. Harrington and Van Flandern; Dr. Anderson at JPL and Dr. Marsden, who collates sightings of new solar system bodies. He also publicly presented his work at seminars and scientific meetings back in the 1970's.

Bagby produced papers between 1978 and 1980, which went unpublished, that set out his observational data and theoretical underpinning for either a tenth planet, or a massive solar companion. He claimed that the discovery of Pluto in Gemini was located 180 degrees opposite to the massive undiscovered planet, and that the pre-discovery prediction work of Lowell and

Pickering could be put down to a classical "direction finding and distance ambiguity" (13). In other words, Lowell had been right, but had looked in the wrong direction. Planet X lay in Sagittarius, Bagby claimed.

This proposal from the late 1970s finds itself in accordance with my own analysis of the location of the Dark Star. Was John Bagby onto something?

Problems emerge for Bagby, when we come to look at his proposals about the size and distance of the binary companion. Basically, Bagby was proposing a full-blown brown dwarf in the Edgeworth-Kuiper Belt (14). We'd be able to see it with a regular telescope. How had he arrived at this fantastic, utterly impossible, conclusion?

It turns out that Bagby was interested in the work of one E.R. Harrison who, in 1977, postulated the existence of a massive nearby body, lying in Sagittarius, required to explain observational anomalies regarding a "pulsar period time derivative" (15). This sounds like a bit of a mouthful, doesn't it? Simply put, pulsars are highly regular emitters of strong radiation. If a gravitational field comes between a pulsar and us, as observers on Earth, then the highly specific data from them pulsar will be altered slightly. This will allow us to imply the existence of a dark gravity field, which is what Harrison proposed in Sagittarius. His finding may thus imply the location of the Dark Star.

Other interesting ideas emerged from the pen of John Bagby. He wondered whether these Massive Solar Companions might have a distributed mass of some description; that a reasonable proportion of the mass of the companion could be found at the LaGrange points of its orbit, presumably in the form of lesser bodies orbiting in a similar pattern to his main candidate object (14). Such an idea might help to explain anomalies encountered by various space-probes that are on their way out of the solar system, namely the two Pioneer spacecraft, which appear to have changed their trajectories over time without a clear causal explanation (16). They seem to be getting dragged back towards the sun. Could this be something to do with an extra quantity of distributed mass in the solar system?

## Murray and Sagittarius

So, the location of Sagittarius becomes a more exciting possibility when we look at the evidence of pulsar period time derivatives. The Dark Star may lie within this constellation, at a great distance from the sun, causing the gravitational effects that we have on record as "unexplained anomalies". Is there other evidence pointing towards this constellation as the keeper of our most wonderful secret?

In 1999, a tentative position for a Dark Star was proposed by Dr. John Murray, an academic with the Open University in England with an interest in astronomy. As we noted in the last chapter, his published scientific paper towards the end of 1999 (17) coincided with a similar paper by a group led by Professor John Matese in Louisiana (18). But where John Matese was careful not to indicate where he thought his version of the Dark Star might be located, Dr. Murray opted for a tiny constellation called Delphinus, next to Aquila (17).

This location lies in the skies to the north of Sagittarius, within the vast star fields of the Milky Way. John Murray came to his conclusion based upon his treatment of comet trajectory data, assuming that a perturbing influence within the distant outer Oort Cloud of comets was causing them to enter the solar system in a more orderly manner than predicted. He worked backwards from the trail of historical comet passages to pin-point the location of this Perturber, or Dark Star, which he considered to be several times the mass of Jupiter.

Dr. Murray's planet lies too far away for my liking, and we should be aware that his work has received some criticism among his own peers (19). Nevertheless, there are some interesting aspects to his conclusions; the Perturber's size, its inclination to the ecliptic and its position, all find parallels with my own conclusions for the Dark Star, but are based upon very different sets of evidence.

But there is a fundamental difference in agreement about the distance of this object. Murray's Perturber more closely resembled the proposed 'Nemesis' object at the very edge of the sun's influence, tens of thousands of astronomical units away. Nemesis was the name given to a proto-star thought to be circling the sun some 90,000 AU away, a remarkable distance indeed. It was thought that such an object circled the sun every 27 million years or so, showering our planetary zone with a deadly hail of comets during that interval. This proposal was then neatly presented as an explanation for extinction cycles found on Earth over similar periods of time. Thus, the name 'Nemesis'.

Compare this to my version of the Dark Star orbiting the sun at 500 astronomical units or more at aphelion, very significantly closer, and smaller! The sub-brown dwarf proposed by Matese and Murray respectively, lies somewhere in the middle of these two more extreme possibilities, at about 20-50,000 AU.

There is no known mechanism to help us understand how a planet could form so far away from a star in the latter case, and many think it unlikely that a 'free-floating' planet might be captured into such an extended orbit. However, if firm data pointed to the existence of such an orbit, the scientific community would quickly figure out a plausible mechanism to explain its presence, I'm sure.

In support of the potential for a small Nemesis-type object, a recent precedent has been discovered by astronomers. In 2002, scientists imaged a young, bright planet in a star-forming region whose distance from the nearest star is over 100,000 astronomical units Called SOri70. The object's distance from what is possibly its parent star is immense. It should not be so far away, and it is a mystery as to how it got there (20).

Is this Jupiter-sized planet orbiting the star, or simply free-floating through the region? It's hard to say right now, but imagine this star was the sun, and the bright planet SOri70 a similar Dark star forming as a distant binary with this sun. This finding sets a precedent for quite an extraordinary orbit, in keeping with Murray's hypothesis.

## An Interactive Binary

So, a Dark Star located more than 20,000 times as far away from the sun than the Earth is by no means impossible. It may form in that region in its own right, as part of a dense star-forming cluster inclusive of the sun's proto-planetary Disk, or it may have been captured later on (though this seems less likely).

There may be a dynamic principle in place as well, whereby such an object is itself perturbed into a close approach to the sun, rather like a comet. There are many gravitational influences outside the solar system which could create such an event, and this scenario would allow us to overlap the existence of a very distant binary object with an observed phenomenon many, many thousands of years ago (21).

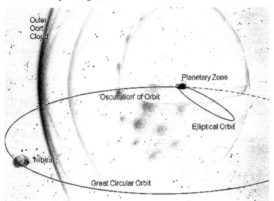

According to the independent researcher John Lee, a brown dwarf lying in the Oort Cloud at tens of thousands of Astronomical Units could have swept past the solar system after interactions with various external gravitational influences (22). I think this is a viable proposition. The problem with talking about such an idea is that it is a complex scenario, and this puts a lot of people off. But it definitely has its merits, satisfying both the Nemesis and Tenth Planet scenarios simultaneously.

Let me briefly spell out the basics of such an idea: The Dark Star would be in an unstable orbital configuration, easily disturbed by outside influences. Millions of years ago, it was moving along the kind of path advocated by Drs. Murray and Matese. That is, a roughly circular orbit over 20,000 AU away. This caused the initiation of movement of long-period comets to drift down towards the sun. Scientists observe those comets today, recording their movements. Some have wondered whether there are patterns to be found, establishing the existence of a distant planet in the outer Oort Cloud.

There is a cause-and-effect taking place over millions of years; the cause being the disturbance of comets in the outer Oort cloud at the Dawn of Humanity, and the effect being the observation of those same comets by modern-day astronomers.

However, in the meantime, the Dark Star itself is jolted from its orbit towards the sun. It also acts like a comet, and takes on a new, elliptical orbit. This then changes the energy configurations of the planets in the solar system, which we will ponder upon later.

Scientists may then detect the presence of the Dark Star by looking at the affect it has had more recently on the Edgeworth-Kuiper Belt.

In other words, the Dark Star causes two sets of data to emerge, but over different time frames. Its dynamic orbit creates a complex picture which seems to indicate two bodies, when there is in reality just one. The constellation Sagittarius thus becomes the location of the 'jolt' that sent the Dark Star into its new orbit, and probably shifted a significant set of comets from that part of the sky in so doing. So, it is simultaneously the location of Murray's sub-brown dwarf, and my Dark Star at aphelion, or the most distant point of its present elliptical orbit.

If the Dark Star had been perturbed into a 'close' approach past the solar system millions of years ago - therefore creating the kind of effects recently discovered in the outer solar system - it may yet be awaiting discovery within the boundaries of the inner Oort Cloud.

The reader will now appreciate the sheer variety of science-based possibilities, to which may be added one or two more.


## The Latest Binary Theorists


In the autumn of 2003, an organization called the Binary Research Institute produced a well-written, scientific-style paper that appeared on the Internet. It was accompanied by a professionally produced web-site complete with eye-catching graphics and charts, and more recently a promotional video. The authors of this well-financed work also favour a Binary System solution, and used it to argue a radical new explanation for the observed Precession of the Equinoxes.

They also speculated about a Dark Companion to the sun located over 1000 AU away, but this time large enough to create a measurable effect upon the sun's own movement. This is a radical suggestion (23).

The problem for Walter Cruttenden and Vince Dayes, who wrote the article, is that their calculated size for the companion body is huge; either a full-blown massive brown or red dwarf, or a normal star. In order to provide the appropriately stretched centre of mass for the solar syst, their companion body quickly becomes far too large to have evaded detection. Although, they add in that the highly elliptical nature of the companion's orbit may mean that it currently resides up to 20 times further away than these average figures suggest (23).

Cruttenden and Dayes advocate an orbital period of about 24,000 years, close to the known precessional cycle. They would presumably argue that for the body to have evaded discovery it must be near to aphelion, and so many thousands of astronomical units away, which is on the order of John Matese's brown dwarf. Except that Matese's small brown dwarf took a few million years to orbit the sun at that distance (18).

To be able to cover that amount of ground in a mere 12,000 years, seems nothing short of miraculous. Unfortunately, such a break-neck trajectory would send their binary star into a hyperbolic orbit, and thus fling it out of the entire solar syst. Which presents a bit of a problem.

A massive object large enough to affect the sun's own movement cannot lie close by at the present time, and must be located in the outer Oort cloud, in order to have evaded detection. But, such a distance implies an orbit substantially greater than 24,000 years, or else the object is lost through achieving an escape velocity from the sun. I faced this same dilemma. The only answer is to have a smaller body or a recent change in its orbit. Neither of these would be consistent with the proposed explanation for the Precession of the Equinoxes put forward by the Binary Research Institute.

Nevertheless, the authors do have some very interesting things to say about the angular momentum of the solar system (24), and describe the importance of the "sheer edge" within the Edgeworth-Kuiper Belt. But, like John Bagby before them, their final proposal seems too ambitious to be viable. So, like Bagby, I would recommend their work for its originality and thought-provoking material, but I would be wary about their implied conclusions.

Another previous advocate of the Binary Theory is the author Joseph H. Cater. He argues in his book "The Ultimate Reality," that Mars is partially warmed by the rays of a binary star (25). This is quite impossible, of course; at least insofar as no solar binary is sufficiently close or bright enough to affect the climate of one of the sun's inner planets. At least, according to the physical laws of the Universe as we currently understand them.

These latter examples are simply two of the myriad sets of theories offered concerning Planet X and binary star companions. The apparent lack of interest in this subject displayed by actual astronomers doesn't seem to be because they don't think about these ideas; it's just that they don't particularly want to be seen thinking about them. A vacuum has emerged within this particular niche of science, which allows independent thinkers to propose sometimes radical ideas.

I am one of those independent-minded researchers as well, of course. I am acutely aware of how many others are rolling similar ideas around in their minds. The result has been an explosion of speculation about Planet X over the Internet, and a confusing, often mystifying set of theories. One of the aims of this book is to bring some greater focus upon the subject.

## The Binary Theory

It is as clear as there is day and night that we are not living in a 'real' binary star system. If we talk in terms of a 'binary' companion to the sun, then we are at best discussing a dwarf star at a very considerable distance; or a 'failed' star; or small brown dwarf, residing among the comets. As we have seen, many people have advocated such a view over the last few decades, from esteemed university professors, to those often labelled as 'crank' alternative theorists.

As far as I can see, there is a wide spectrum of possibilities, and some of those possibilities are quite plausible. Given the results of various deep-space analytical data, I don't think anyone should entirely dismiss the possibility of a substantial Planet X object awaiting discovery.

Over the next few chapters, we will explore various pieces of scientific evidence which have emerged in the last few years that considerably strengthen the case for the existence of a binary companion of some description, awaiting actual discovery. Some of that evidence is actually compelling, taking the form of anomalous data which flies in the face of our orthodox understanding of the solar system. Other pieces of evidence are from other star systems, where precedents exist for the kind of models that I am proposing.

For example, the Epsilon Indi B object is a clear example of a reasonably large brown dwarf orbiting its parent star at the kind of distance which I would advocate for our Dark Star around the sun. This testifies to the potential for such an object to be found at about 1500 AU, because whatever arguments may be put forward theoretically for questioning how that could have come about, it clearly already has; elsewhere.

"The failed star and its companion form a wide binary system, separated by more than 1,500 times the distance between the sun and the Earth...Astronomers estimate that Epsilon Indi B has a mass just 45 times that of Jupiter, the largest planet in our solar syst, and a surface temperature of only 1,000 Celsius" (26).

Other star systems also provide some wonderful precedents, and many of the new discoveries of extra-solar planets are wonderful and diverse, challenging astronomers to think again about accepted dogma. They require us to remain open-minded, and to remember that the unexpected is no stranger to scientific progress. There are no stranger planetary objects than brown dwarfs, of course, and their existence is no longer simply speculation, but hard scientific fact. In the next chapter we will explore the realm of these strange celestial characters.

# Chapter 4 References

1. J. d'Arc "Space Travellers and the Genesis of the Human Form" pp43-4, The Book Tree 2000

2. E. Plunket "Calendars and Constellations of the Ancient World" (1903) pp227-8, Random House 1997

3. A. Gilbert "Signs in the Sky" Corgi 2000

4. R. Bauval & A. Gilbert "The Orion Mystery" Mandarin 1995

5. E. C. Krupp "In Search of Ancient Astronomies" p218, Penguin 1984

6. W. Corliss "The Sun and Solar System Debris - A Catalog of Astronomical Anomalies" p172, 1986. With thanks to Greg Jenner

7. "Redfern, Martin, and Henbest, Nigel; "Has IRAS Found a Tenth Planet?" New Scientist, 10/11/1983

8. Z. Sitchin "Genesis Revisited" p326-8 Avon 1990

9. Enuma Elish Tablet VII, 125-133

10. Enuma Elish Tablet V, 1-10

11. R. Kerrod "The Illustrated Guide to the Night Sky" p88, Quarto 1993

12. J. Davis "Beyond Pluto" p63, Cambridge University Press 2001

13. J. Bagby "Evidence for a Tenth Planet or Massive Solar Companion beyond Uranus" 1982

14. Editorial Post-script, (F.B.J.), 'Kronos' Journal, Vol. IX, No 3, Summer 1984

15. J. Bagby "Further Speculations on Planet "X"", correspondence sent to the 'Kronos' Journal, Vol. IX, No 3, Summer 1984

16. B. Akins "Pioneer Home: Mission Status" http://spaceprojects.arc.nasa.gov/Space_Projects/pioneer/PNStat.html Updated 22nd February 2001

17. J.B.Murray Mon. Not. R. Astron. Soc., 309, 31-34 (1999)

18. J.J. Matese, P.G. Whitman and D.P. Whitmire, Icarus, 141, 354-336 (1999)

19. Correspondence from John Lee re: academic criticism, 17th March 2004

20. R. Britt "Mysterious Object Might be First Extrasolar Planet Photographed" http://www.space.com/scienceastronomy/astronomy/brown_dwarfs_020522.html 22 May 2002 Thanks to Theo

21. A. Lloyd "Winged Disc: The Dark Star Theory" 2001, Available from the author

22. Correspondence from John Lee, aka Maurice Devon, 'The Real Deal', 22nd March 2004

23. W. Cruttenden and V. Dayes "Understanding Precession of the Equinox: Evidence our Sun may be part of a Long Cycle

Binary System" Fall 2003 http://newfrontiersinscience.com/
Members/v02n01/a/NFS0201a.shtml

24. Binary Research Institute "Evidence: Angular Momentum"
http://www.binaryresearchinstitute.org/evidence/angular.shtml

25. J. Cater "The Ultimate Reality", with thanks to Dean from
the 'Cosmic Conspiracies' post-board.

26. D. Whitehouse "'Failed star' found nearby" 15th January
2003 http://news.bbc.co.uk/2/hi/science/nature/2660953.stm

# Brown Dwarfs

In the last chapter, we looked at various types of binary bodies that have been proposed over the years. Some of these are dwarf stars, the 'black' and 'red' versions of which are quite large, and generate light independently. To be circling around the sun and yet to have evaded detection, these types of dwarf stars would have to be located practically halfway to the nearest star - light years away.

So, we looked at arguments for a smaller body, and I advocated a smaller, darker body which is several times the mass of Jupiter and orbits the sun in an eccentric manner. This body is similar to the type of planet proposed by John Matese and John Murray. Currently, this massive planet is remarkably faint, and has probably not been detected directly (although there is always the possibility that it has been spotted, but misunderstood to be a more distant star). The tenth planet is a dark, distant body which reflects very little light back to us from the sun at the sorts of distance we are talking, despite its size.

## Is This Dark Star, As I Call It, A 'Brown Dwarf'?

Brown dwarfs are neither stars nor planets, but something in between. For a long time, their existence was just theoretical. This was because they don't shine with the intensity of stars and are, for the most part, 'dark' objects in the sky. Stars and planets form through the accretion, or clumping together of matter. Stars form in stellar nurseries, alongside other sibling stars, often in quite close proximity.

This is why there are so many binary star systems. They then spread out, like young birds leaving the nest. They carry with them immense discs of material which swirl around the star, gradually clumping into planets and other bodies. These planets can be very diverse, in terms of both size and properties.

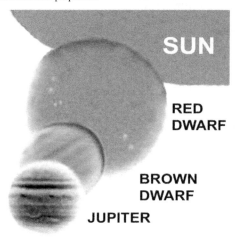

It makes sense that there should exist a huge range of different shaped objects in the galaxy, from the smallest comets, through the range of planets, through a range of these 'brown dwarfs' and on through an equally large range of different sized stars. In the galaxy, variety is the spice of life.

Until fairly recently, our knowledge of stars and planets was pretty straightforward. Stars shone, emitting light by hydrogen fusion processes, and planets were dark objects orbiting them. This was simply common sense. No one spent too many sleepless nights worrying about what would happen when an object, undergoing the process of gas accretion to form a star or planet, would end up with mass somewhere in between.

Brown dwarfs are those bodies which have insufficient mass to begin the internal nuclear processes that fire stars. The smallest are about 12 times the size of Jupiter, the largest about 80 times, which is still less than a tenth of the mass of our sun. The more massive the dwarf, the brighter it will appear.

They are capable of emitting their own light and heat, even though via by a different set of processes as compared to the sun's nuclear fission. Also, their ability to create light and heat depends very much on their age. Even very small brown dwarfs are quite bright to begin with, but their luminosity quickly drops away with advancing age. One could say that they age quickly; the flower of their youth is dissipated through intense activity early on.

It is thought that there is a "50:50" chance that a brown dwarf might exist between us and our nearest star (1). Brown dwarfs tend to be about the same size as Jupiter, despite being many times heavier. They are denser, and also hotter and more active. They have hydrogen cores, like the gas giants, and can spin as

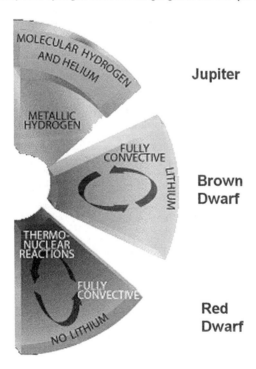

**Jupiter**

**Brown Dwarf**

**Red Dwarf**

quickly as once per hour. They radiate most of their energy in infra-red light.

There are still many gaps in our knowledge about these objects, because their inherent dark properties make them difficult to observe directly, particularly the older ones that have used up their light-emitting fuels. There is some debate as to whether brown dwarfs form more or less like stars, or whether they are more characteristic of planets ejected from emerging star systems in dense stellar nurseries. The current thinking is that they form like stars do, but tend to get pushed about before they accrete enough matter to become proper stars.

There is a critical size of about 80 Jupiter masses, where such a body can sustain hydrogen fusion by the action of temperatures and pressures generated by its own gravity (1). Then a star is born. The formation of planets is less well understood, and the emerging discoveries of extra-solar planets are challenging astro-physicists to revise their theories. Nevertheless, when a planet is forming, up to several Jupiter masses in size, then it remains simply that: a planet. As the object's mass increases further, things start to get more complicated.

## The History of Brown Dwarfs

The concept of brown dwarfs has been bandied about for some time, although no reliable astronomical data has been available until quite recently. Carl Sagan once wrote about Harlow Shapley, an astronomer working in the 1950s. Shapley had suggested that brown dwarfs (or 'Lilliputian stars, as he called them) would have warm surfaces upon which astronauts could survive and explore (2). We now know this to be quite untrue: Brown dwarfs are warm versions of Jupiter. This massive planet has no surface, only an immense gaseous atmosphere, full of clouds and storms. I discussed this with an expert on brown dwarfs some years ago, who stated in passing that "while brown dwarfs are not inhabitable, they might have moons that might be habitable." (3) These mini failed stars might harbour life on their own systems of planets.

The term "brown dwarf" was first used by Jill Tarter of the SETI institute, in her 1975 PhD thesis. She used it in order to correct the use of the previous term "black dwarf" which was deemed inappropriate because it had already been used to describe the end phase of a fully evolved star as it cooled from the white dwarf stage (1).

Brown dwarfs are very difficult to find. They glow only faintly, emitting most of their radiation in the infra-red bands. This is because they are below the 0.08 solar-mass stellar limit, and fail to ignite as stars in their own right. Instead, they emit radiation from energy left over from their formation.

During the life-span of a brown dwarf, the younger they are, the brighter they appear. So, we have a better chance of discovering brown dwarfs that have just formed. As they get older, they start to appear more like Jupiter, only much more massive. In general, a brown dwarf's luminosity is expected to be about a hundred thousandth of the sun's (4). Its spectral characteristics are different than those of very cool stars, unusually showing an absorption line of the short-lived element lithium.

Contrary to the description implied by its name, brown dwarfs appear red, actually very red. A brown dwarf was discovered in the Solar vicinity by Maria Theresa Ruiz of the European Southern Observatory in 1997, a discovery which offered the potential for much better study of these elusive objects. She called it KELU-1, the term for 'red' in the language of the indigenous population of central Chile.

Although it is located at a distance of 33 light-years, its visual magnitude is 22.3, which is the sort of brightness projected for Murray's proposed brown dwarf in the Oort cloud. This sets a precedent for discovery of an Oort cloud planet/brown dwarf (5). If my thesis is correct, however, and Murray's planet is now more closely bound to the sun, then it should be significantly brighter than this object.

## Gliese 229B

The best known brown dwarf, and one which we can actually look at through an Earth-bound 60-inch telescope, is Gliese 229B, discovered in 1995. This one is in a binary system along with the low-mass red dwarf Gliese 229A, at a distance of just 19 light-years from the sun. The separation between the brown dwarf and its companion star is about the same as that between the sun and Pluto. Its luminosity is about one-tenth of the faintest star. Its spectrum has large amounts of methane and water vapor.

Methane could not exist if the surface temperature were above 1500K.

| TYPE OF OBJECT | Gas-Giant Planet | Brown Dwarf | Brown Dwarf | Red Dwarf Star | Yellow Dwarf Star |
|---|---|---|---|---|---|
| MASS (Jupiter-masses) | 1 | 30–40 | 55 | 300 | 1,000 |
| RADIUS (kilometers) | 71,500 | 65,000 | 150,000 | 250,000 | 696,000 |
| TEMPERATURE (kelvins) | 100 | 1,000 | 2,600 | 3,400 | 5,800 |
| AGE (years) | 4.5 billion | 2–4 billion | 120 million | 2–4 billion | 4.5 billion |
| HYDROGEN FUSION | No | No | No | Yes | Yes |
| DEUTERIUM FUSION | No | Yes | Yes | Yes | Yes |

Astronomers consider its temperature to be about 900K (compared to Jupiter's 130K), its mass to be between 20 and 55 Jupiters, and the age of the binary system to be between 1 and 5 billion years old. It has a smoggy haze layer deep within its atmosphere, essentially making it "much fainter in visible light than it would otherwise be". It is possible that the ultra-violet light from its companion star changes its atmospheric properties from those of an isolated brown dwarf, such as KELU-1 (1).

## Our Closest Known Brown Dwarf

In November 2000, a team of scientists analyzed a dim object of 60-90 Jupiter masses, which has been found at just 13 light years distance from the sun (6). Depending on its actual mass, it might be a high-mass brown dwarf or a low-mass star. The lack of a lithium signature indicates the latter.

This star/brown dwarf lies alone in space, and is the nearest such object spotted so far. Scientists have speculated that more such objects probably await discovery, perhaps even closer to us than this one. Our knowledge of our own backyard with respect to its resident stars is still very much incomplete.

So brown dwarfs emit visible light, albeit faintly, but are cool enough to retain a planet like atmosphere! Stars and planets no longer appear to be entirely different entities. Imagine living on a moon of a brown dwarf: the 'dark star' which your moon is orbiting around would be emitting red light and heat, yet it would appear like Jupiter as far as its size and atmospheric consistency went. Rather like Jupiter on fire, perhaps!

Your moon would not only be warmed by the intense infra-red emitted from the brown dwarf, but also by its tidal effects (like Io and Europa are warmed by the otherwise cool Jupiter), and by its ambient red light. If your moon was terrestrial, in other words had aqueous oceans and a nitrogen-rich atmosphere, might the emergence of life there be entirely possible? Without the dangerous ultra-violet radiation and cosmic rays emitted by the sun, one could argue that this sort of environment is actually preferable to the environment on Earth!

## Brown Dwarf Flares

Brown dwarfs also display unpredictable behavior. They are capable of emitting intense flares detectable in the X-Ray range. This is similar to those flares emitted by stars. Because Brown dwarfs are thought to behave more like gas giants, this was an unexpected discovery (7). The intense activity appears to be the result of turbulent magnetized material below the surface of the brown dwarf, heating the atmosphere and giving rise to intense X-ray flares, rather like storms on Earth create lightning (8,9).

In Chapter 2, we looked at some of the ancient descriptions of the Dark Star, known in the creation myths as Marduk. These flare-like properties are clearly in keeping with the Babylonian god's ability to breathe fire! Brown dwarfs, although dim, are clearly emitting light to some degree. At times, they seem to emit a great deal of light.

Brown dwarfs are at their brightest when young, particularly under 1 million years. In 2000, the Hubble Space Telescope focused its attention on 2 sets of these young brown dwarfs, as they emerged from their respective birth-places some 1,500 light years away. The images show piercing red stars, as predicted by the various models describing very young brown dwarfs (10). As brown dwarfs get older, their ability to radiate light diminishes rapidly, explaining the apparent ease with which these much younger clusters of brown dwarfs were photographed at a distance of 1,500 light years. Other, older brown dwarfs in our vicinity continue to prove difficult to image despite being significantly closer. The Dark Star is as old as the sun, so its light emission will be substantially dimmer than these objects: in fact, many orders of magnitude less.

But the fact that older brown dwarfs emit strong flares indicates that a Dark Star is anything but 'dead'. Privately, experts on brown dwarfs consider it likely that the smaller, older variety might yet hold some surprises of its own. Despite the age of our Dark Star, the density of these objects creates intense surface gravity which consequently affects their magnetic activity, thereby leading to flares and intense storms.

## Weather Patterns of Brown Dwarfs

Astronomers specializing in the study of brown dwarfs have been trying to explain why many of these objects are brighter than expected to be according to theory. Common sense would dictate that as brown dwarfs cool over time, their relative brightness should also diminish. Apparently, this is not necessarily the case.

Using weather models derived from Jupiter's own atmospheric system, and applying them to brown dwarfs, a model has emerged which may explain the anomaly. Brown dwarfs emit a faint glow, like an ember from a fire that gives off both heat and light energy as it dims (11). This glow can be monitored by scientists using infra-ed detection equipment.

The reduction in this glow as the brown dwarf ages is not as linear as it was once believed. For a while, at least, brown dwarfs appear to get brighter as they cool. This may be due to fluctuations in upper atmospheric conditions. The higher cloud layer may part, exposing the inner regions of the brown dwarf, and allowing significant sources of heat to be recorded. In other words, the weather systems of a brown dwarf produce fluctuations in the heat and light they emit, making them less predictable objects to study.

## Light-emitting Planets

The term 'light-emitting planet' has been used to describe free-floating planets which are so young that they emit light, and can be imaged (12). Such discoveries overturn our entire understanding of the difference between stars and planets.

Of particular interest is the fact that these 'planets' are free-floating, as Nibiru was before crashing through the planetary zone 4 billion years ago. These wandering light emitting planets may provide us with a model of what happened to our own star system shortly after its birth; nomadic giant planet-sized entities ejected from their parent stars to wander within stellar nurseries.

Was the Dark Star such an entity, propelled from another star's proto-planetary disc to find itself crashing into our sun's own young planetary system?

We now know that many of the newly discovered 'extra-solar planets' have eccentric orbits, indicating that non-circular orbital arrangements in star systems might be fairly normal (13). In at least one case, a brown dwarf has been found embedded within a 'normal' extra-solar planetary system, without its presence seeming to create chaos among the other planets (14,15). The birth of planetary systems appears to be anything but simple.

In relation to the Dark Star Theory, the modern understanding of these failed stars appears to offer an ideal platform to explore the concept of an inhabitable world in our comet-cloud, as described by the Sumerians. A world orbiting a dark star that is essentially invisible to us, but that emits massive amount of heat and enough low-frequency light to support life, whilst not subjecting the denizens of that world to the sort of harmful radiation we are subject to from our sun.

Could this also explain the almost immortal life-spans that Sitchin claims for the Anunnaki? One might speculate that our woefully short life-spans are due to our constant exposure to high energy particles radiated from the sun. Astronaut 'Gods' coming to our world might find their life-spans significantly shortened, as well as the subsequent life expectancies of their children. Life on Earth is necessarily mortal. Perhaps the less hostile environment of a habitable moon orbiting a brown dwarf would help to extend the human life cycle.

## Brown Dwarfs Have Planets Too!

When we talk about brown dwarfs, we are walking the line between stars and planets. Their properties fall into one camp or another, and one of the more important distinctions to be made is when the brown dwarf is forming. Does it form like a star does, in a stellar nursery, or is the brown dwarf simply an over-sized planet? Research by Ray Jayawardhana of the University of Michigan would tend to suggest that they follow the star route (16).

Dr. Jayawardhana also indicates that young brown dwarfs have dust discs, in a similar way to the proto-planetary discs of stars, and that these may allow the formation of planets around brown dwarfs as well. Indeed, it seems quite possible that brown dwarfs could have an entire retinue of asteroids, comets and planets which formed in these discs during the early period of the life of the parent brown dwarf (16).

Let us say, then, that the sun was born in a stellar nursery, whose environment was fairly dense with other simultaneous star formations. Let us say that a brown dwarf was born in the sun's vicinity, and gravitationally held to it as a distant binary. If that binary failed star, or small brown dwarf, followed Dr. Jayawardhana's logic, then it would have its own dust disc and the potential for the creation of its own system of planets/moons, comets and asteroids. These would then form separately from the sun, excluding us from having to account for their formation from the accretion models of the sun's own proto-planetary disc. In one fell swoop, we can avoid a whole raft of objections to the potential existence of a massive solar companion.

## The Chaos of Star Birth

The stellar nurseries containing new born stars are sometimes densely packed. Astronomers analyzing the chaotic conditions of star-birth have noticed that stars can form so close together that they interact during the formation process, competing for the remaining material in the stellar environment (17). This leads to chaotic, dynamic conditions, during which proto-planets are tugged from their initial circular orbits in the accretion discs. Similarly, brown dwarfs might be ejected proto-stars that never really got the chance to accrete enough mass to become proper stars. This mechanism may explain why there appear to be as many brown dwarfs in the Milky Way galaxy as there are actual stars.

When brown dwarfs are ejected from young star systems, they take with them the material from their immediate environment. This essentially strips the young star system of some of its outer proto-planetary disc. It is thought that this mechanism explains why some proto-planetary discs are seen to be curtailed, what astronomers refer to as 'truncation' (17). If brown dwarfs are as common as thought, then examples of this kind of truncated disc should be common, and there should be a measurably shortened 'edge' to the planetary zone of a given star, stripped of a brown dwarf companion.

Our own solar system appears to have a healthy series of planets, implying that it did not itself lose a brown dwarf during its early development. However, it also has a measurable 'gap' in its outer regions, known as the Kuiper Gap. This implies some kind of dynamic process having occurred there, which is at the moment unexplained.

But, losing brown dwarfs from star systems is not the only new mechanism being considered by astronomers. A brown dwarf has also been imaged orbiting its parent star at a distance of 14 AU, equivalent to a position between Saturn and Uranus in our system (18). This was not thought to be possible, given our present understanding of planet formation in the outer regions of planetary zones. Some other process appears to be taking place. Again, this opens the door for new science, and increases the likelihood that we may yet find a Dark Star orbiting our own sun.

## The Age of the Companion

When we consider the possibility that our sun might harbour a binary companion, or may have had one in the distant past, we are dealing with two possibilities: it formed alongside the sun as a classic Binary star system, or it was captured after the sun was born.

If it was born into the solar system, then it is the same age as the sun i.e. 4.6 billion years old. An established companion brown dwarf is likely to have been born in the same cluster as the sun, complete with its own proto-planetary disc.

If the companion is a captured object, then it probably became so 3.9 billion years ago during the "late, great bombardment". But, the chances that a brown dwarf from interstellar space moved so close to the sun that it became captured is remote. Of course, nothing is impossible, but statistically it is unlikely, even taking into account the probability that there are a similar number of brown dwarfs in the galaxy as stars.

However, when the solar system first formed, the density of stars and brown dwarfs in the immediate neighborhood was much greater, and so such a capture was more likely. In that case, a captured object is also likely to be of a similar age as the sun, having been born into the same stellar nursery.

So, the likely age for a binary brown dwarf companion is that of the sun, except in the extreme example of a more recently captured inter-stellar object. This means that a proposed binary companion will be old, small and thus very dim in terms of its luminosity. This, of course, is why none has been discovered orbiting the sun so far, given the kinds of orbital distances we are talking about. Just because we have not yet found a companion, does not rule out the possibility that one exists.

Even the infra-red sky-search IRAS left room for doubt, as we have seen. Some sources detected by IRAS are still to be examined, meaning that some data from the 20-year old sky-search is still left untouched by scientists.

Perhaps aware of this short-coming, there are a large number of new sky-searches due to begin work in the next few years. Our updated abilities to detect increasingly cold and dim objects in the solar neighborhood are orders of magnitude better than IRAS was, allowing scientists to probe the skies for a greater range of cool and dark objects in the sun's vicinity. This also means that within the next decade, scientists should be able to state with greater authority whether the sun is truly alone with its present cohort of planets, or whether new additions to its flock must be added on.

## The Dark Star

When I first started writing and researching this subject in the late 1990's, I was working on the basis that every celestial object bigger than Jupiter but smaller than the sun, could be categorized as a brown dwarf. So, when I talked about Sitchin's mythological planet being a brown dwarf, I was allowing for a huge range of possibilities...after all, the sun is about 1000 times as massive as Jupiter.

But for my theory to hold ground, it became increasingly evident that my Dark Star must be much closer to Jupiter's mass than the sun's. In fact, it was likely to be smaller than the minimum requirement for its inclusion in the brown dwarf set. It was a 'sub-brown dwarf', whose mass was less than 12 Jupiters. The reason I came to this conclusion was that a more classic brown dwarf-sized object would produce enough light to have been detected, even given the great distances involved, along with the extended age of the Dark Star.

It is a fact that 'planets' a few times larger than Jupiter are denser than it is, and hence actually smaller. It is also true that they would be warmer, yet less reflective of the sun's light: as its upper cloud-layers would be darker, hence more absorbent of light. So, for example, a sub-brown dwarf of several Jupiter masses that was located next to Jupiter, would actually be smaller and also less luminous than its bright brother. It would simply be warmer, like the embers of an extinguished fire.

But the Dark Star isn't located near Jupiter; it is likely to be at least 100 times further away. It can thus defy detection, at least for the time being. Within the next few years, that situation could easily change as the new detection systems come into line.

The best chance lies with a system now called WISE (previously NGSS) (19). This project actually has as part of its scientific remit, the task of discovering brown dwarfs in the solar neighborhood. Another system, called SIRTF, will hunt down infra-red sources to a much better accuracy than IRAS, to the extent that any 'Dark Stars' within about 30 light-years should be discovered (20).

Readers new to this subject might find this all rather far-fetched. How could we not have discovered such massive bodies so close to us, when we have the capability to see the most remote galaxies in the Universe? Yet, this is not that unlikely.

Charles J. Lada, of the Smithsonian Astrophysical Observatory, has spoken publicly about the possibility of discovering planets orbiting around a nearby free-floating brown dwarf. He expects that this brown dwarf would be discovered outside the solar system, at a minimum distance of 1 light year (21), a quarter of the distance of the nearest star. This kind of thinking is clearly not science fiction.

## A New Breed of Brown Dwarfs

Although hard facts about brown dwarfs are still fairly hard to come by, particularly for the smaller ones, they have already been split into sub-species. Between them, they cover quite a range of masses, starting from 12 times the mass of Jupiter. These cooler brown dwarfs, at the lower end of the scale, are known as T-dwarfs. These bodies are thought to be dimly magenta after the initial flourish of their youth is over (22), which gives us a possible color for our Dark Star.

But it is also possible that the Dark Star lies on the edge of the brown dwarf spectrum. It is too large to be simply a massive gas giant, but its stellar properties may be too minimal to allow it to be classed as a brown dwarf. It would fit into a class of objects that have yet to be properly defined or studied. However, astronomers are contemplating what these sub-brown dwarfs might be like, with accompanying speculation that there might be at least one more stellar class beyond the T-dwarfs (23).

If the Dark Star was to be discovered here in our solar system, this would clearly be the opportunity that astronomers have been waiting for. At the present time, the knowledge of these small sub-brown dwarfs is limited, even at a theoretical level. We do not know the extent of their stellar characteristics; how warm they are, how active their atmospheres are, and how much light they emit, if any.

Their extensive magnetic fields are a mystery, and they may or may not form like regular stars. With so many unknowns, we cannot predict what scientists will discover next about these objects, and what this will tell us about a possible Dark Star orbiting our own sun. But what we can comfortably predict is that new discoveries will be forthcoming in the near future, and that, based on the history of brown dwarf studies so far, those findings will contain the unexpected.

## Small Brown Dwarfs Have Their Own Planets

The discovery of a binary brown dwarf Companion in the solar system could come at any time. If it did, then scientific speculation about the existence of a planetary system orbiting even the smallest type of brown dwarf would be rife. This is because an example of just such a planetary system has been found, leading to speculation that similar examples may be observed in the future, in the case of tiny brown dwarfs.

This ground-breaking direct observation was made possible because the glare of the young brown dwarf was so much smaller than that of 'regular' stars, so astronomers were able to directly image material in a disc around it. Some of this material was clumping, indicative of planet formation. It is thought that the total mass of the proto-planetary system orbiting a brown dwarf would be equivalent to about 10% of the Dwarf's own mass. That provides enough material to form a Saturn-like planet, as well as a number of terrestrial worlds.

The brown dwarf in question lies about 500 light years away, in the sky region known to astronomers as Chamaeleon I, which is a known stellar nursery. The disc was observed by the Spitzer telescope, appearing relatively bright in the infra-red part of the spectrum. The finding has fuelled speculation in the scientific community, that life-supporting planets might be discovered around brown dwarfs. The observed disc itself covered the brown dwarfbrown dwarf's habitable zone; which was between 1.5- 7 million kilometers away. Given that the parent dwarf is about 2000 degrees Celsius, liquid water may eventually be found at this distance among the orbiting planets (24).

Jupiter          OGLE-TR-122b          Sun

Finding habitable worlds in these kinds of systems might actually be easier than looking for planets in more classical star systems, where the glare of the stars makes it very difficult to image much of anything in its immediate vicinity.

The scientific team, led by Kevin Luhman of the Harvard-Smithsonian Center for Astrophysics in Cambridge, Massachusetts, US, hopes to extend its search to even smaller brown dwarfs to see how small they can get, while still allowing planetary formation. They have been studying this particular region of the sky for a while, hunting for small brown dwarfs. In 2004, they discovered a binary brown dwarf system that was separated by a distance of 240 AU. This is quite a wide separation, similar to the kind of distances envisioned for our own binary companion, thus creating an interesting precedent. The difference is that the Dark Star is likely to be in a highly elliptical orbit, creating a much greater distance at its furthest point from the sun.

Astronomers are generally sceptical about finding planets at this distance, because they believe that the orbits would be easily subject to perturbation, causing the binaries to break down. This discovery brings this long-held belief into question. It implies that the brown dwarfs did not form in a larger star system, as per the ejection scenario already discussed. Instead, they must have slowly formed in the vicinity of each other, which leads us to suspect that at least some brown dwarfs form independently from parent star systems (25).

Not only does this research raise questions about how star and their planetary systems develop, but it also opens the door to more urgent speculation about the nature of a binary brown dwarf Companion in our own solar system, should such an object be discovered in the future. The potential for life to have developed in such a system is increasing; at least, that is the verdict of science!

## A Brown Dwarf 'Sun'

We have seen that brown dwarfs are sub-stellar objects that are many times more massive than Jupiter. Yet they remain approximately the same size. As a result their mass is confined to an area roughly the size of Jupiter, and this makes them extremely dense. This, in turn, makes their atmospheric activity levels so much greater than mere gas giants as their surface gravity becomes proportionate to their density. This is what gives these planet-sized objects the ability to create significant flares of high-energy radiation, as well as emit light, particularly in their early years.

This idea is generally accepted on a theoretical level, but there have until recently been few small brown dwarfs observed to test the theory. It was thought that the brown dwarfs would gradually increase in size as they moved towards a more typical dwarf star, like a red dwarf. In the absence of evidence to the contrary, it is natural to assume some kind of smooth linearity to this trend.

However, scientists on the 'OGLE' program have analyzed one particular binary brown dwarf, which is closely orbiting a sun-like star towards the centre of the Milky Way, and which has a density that is way off the charts. They have discovered - to their surprise - that this binary companion shines like the sun, yet is only 16% larger than Jupiter (26). This is amazing, because the binary companion is 50 times as massive as Jupiter, which makes it very dense indeed (27). Previously, brown dwarfs of this magnitude were imagined to be much larger objects.

This 'sub-stellar object' has broken the trend set out by theory because it is simultaneously in the mass range of the brown dwarfs, shines like the sun but is the size of a regular planet! This creates diversity among these objects in practice which has surprised experts on brown dwarfs. As far as the Dark Star studies are concerned, the finding enables us to be versatile when discussing the properties of the smallest of these objects. Even though our brown dwarf companion may be only the size of a gas giant like Jupiter, it may still be very massive, and so active. That's not to say that our binary solar companion shines as brightly as the sun, of course, because if it did we would clearly have detected it by now. But we are left with a spectrum of possibilities that defies previous attempts to discredit my general thesis regarding how a binary solar companion might actually behave.

In the near future the Wide-field Infrared Survey Explorer mission will undoubtedly reveal more of the mysteries surrounding these strange objects called brown dwarfs. The launch date for this NASA mission is set for 2008. The space-based telescope will carry sky-survey instruments that are half a million times more sensitive than the previous IRAS mission in the 1980s (28). This mission will be the best chance for discovering the Dark Star, an incredible object which lies at some considerable distance within our own solar system.

## Chapter 5 References

1. R. Naeye 'Astronomy' Aug. 1999, p36-42

2. C. Sagan "Pale Blue Dot" p392 Headline Book Publishing

3. Correspondence from M. Marley, 28/1/00

4. David Griffin "How can we detect brown dwarfs?" 1998

5. ESO press release 7/97 <http://www.eso.org/outreach/press-rel/pr-1997/pr-07-97.html> "A Faint and Lonely Brown Dwarf in the Solar Vicinity".

6. R. Britt "New Neighbor may be Closest Known Brown Dwarf" http://www.space.com/scienceastronomy/astronomy/brown_dwarf_001122.html Space.com 27/11/2000

7. Reuters, 11 July 2000, By Deborah Zabarenko, Washington

8. K. Leutwyler "Bright X-rays, Dim Dwarfs" 17/7/2000 http://www.sciam.com/exhibit/2000/071700dwarf/

9. "TWA 5B: X-Rays Found From a Lightweight Brown dwarf" http://chandra.harvard.edu/photo/2003/twa5b/    With thanks to James Monds

10. Unopened Files "Hubble Focuses on Rare 'Brown Dwarfs'" p82, Oct./Nov. 2000

11. Astronomers Find Jupiter-Like Weather On Brown Dwarfs" http://www.spacedaily.com/news/extrasolar-02l.html or http://www.ucla.edu/Templates/NewsItem1.html 23rd May 2002 Thanks to Brant

12. http://news.bbc.co.uk/hi/english/sci/tech/newsid_957000/957518.stm 5/10/2000 "Mystery of free-floating 'planets'"

13. G. Marcy & P. Butler 'Astronomy' March 2000 , p42-47

14. J. Foust "Bizarre new planets puzzle astronomers" Spaceflight Now, 10th January 2000

15. Associated Press "We Prefer Not to Call It a Failed Star. We Call It a Specially Challenged Brown Dwarf" http://www.aci.net/kalliste/ 9th January 2001

16. Peter Bond "Brown dwarfs form in the same way as stars" Astronomy Now, p13, Mar 2004

17. Young Stars in Chaos", Press Release 12th April 2002, http://www.astro.ex.ac.uk/people/mbate/Research/pr.html, based on M. Bate, I. Bonnell & V. Bromm "The Formation Of Stars And Brown Dwarfs And The Truncation Of Protoplanetary Discs In A Star Cluster", With thanks to Rob Astor

18. R. Stenger "In a first, object near a star caught on camera" 7 January 2002, with thanks to Allene Keller and Theo http://www.cnn.com/2002/TECH/space/01/07/brown.dwarf/index.html

19. Kirkpatrick, J.D., 2003, "The Next Generation Sky Survey and the Quest for Cooler Brown Dwarfs", in Proc. of Brown Dwarfs, Ed. Martin, E. L., IAU Symposium, Vol. 211, p. 497-504

20. Burrows, A., Sudarsky, D., & Lunine, J. I., "Beyond the T Dwarfs: Theoretical Spectra, Colors, and Detectability of the Coolest Brown Dwarfs" to appear ApJ, in press, astro-ph/0304226

21. R. Britt "Dark Planets May Orbit Strange Nearby Objects"
7th June 2001 http://www.space.com/scienceastronomy/
astronomy/aas_browndwarfs_010607.html

22. An Artist's View of Brown Dwarf Types" Dr. Robert Hurt of
the Infrared Processing and Analysis Center  http://
spider.ipac.caltech.edu/staff/davy/2mass/science/
comparison.html

23. A. Burrows et al "Beyond the T Dwarfs: Theoretical Spectra,
Colors, and Detectability of the Coolest Brown Dwarfs" astro-ph/
0304226 April 2003, with thanks to J.D. Kirkpatrick and John
Lee

24. Hazel Muir, "Brown Dwarf may Someday Harbour Habitable
Planets" 8th February 2005, http://www.newscientist.com/
article.ns?id=dn6977 with thanks to Peter Gersten, et al

25. Amitabh Avasthi "Brown Dwarfs win Star Status" 9th July
2004, with thanks to David Pearson
http://www.newscientist.com/news/news.jsp?id=ns99996133

26. The Guardian "Hot Star Shines in Tiny Role" p11, 5th March
2005

27. Robert Roy Britt "Newfound star smaller than some planets"
3rd March 2005  http://msnbc.msn.com/id/7081156/

28. W. Clavin "NASA Approves Mission To Seek Nearest Stars,
Brightest Galaxies" JPL News Release, 6th October 2004 http://
www.jpl.nasa.gov

# Anomalies in the Solar System

There are a number of anomalies in the planetary science of the solar system that have not been satisfactorily explained by science. There are compelling reasons to suspect that there is a missing piece to the planetary jigsaw. I think that there is a companion brown dwarf awaiting discovery somewhere beyond the Edgeworth-Kuiper Belt.

The evidence suggests that any catastrophic movement of this sub-brown dwarf through the planetary solar system would have taken place during the early period of our sun's life. Things have settled down a lot since then, it seems. Still, there are anomalies that need to be addressed, which we will look at in some detail over the next few chapters. These are important considerations, because the anomalies themselves suggest that our understanding of the nature of our solar system is not quite as good as we generally think.

When we take a look at our solar system, we have an ingrained understanding that what we are now seeing is how it has always been. The regularity of the planets denotes how they came to be, even though it is understood that the early solar system was in a state of chaos. One assumes that a 'normal' planetary system would be comprised of a series of planets in spaced-out, circular orbits.

Bode's Law allows astronomers to predict the stable placement of planets within harmonic distances of the sun. But, the new picture emerging from giant extra-solar planets causes certain problems for this model. Their eccentricity and remarkable proximity to their stars belie the acid test of common sense that our system seems to provide.

We tend to think that the solar system presents a fairly stable scenario whereby the planets sweep around in a common direction, enjoying roughly circular orbits, with each spinning uniformly with respect to each other. Well, that's not quite how it is.

## Pluto

Pluto and Charon, the planetary binary that generally marks the limit of the planetary solar system, share an elliptical orbit that is inclined to the ecliptic by 17 degrees. Pluto is a small, rocky planet about two thirds the size of our Moon. It's moon, Charon, is very large in relation to the parent planet, in a similar way to our Moon in relation to the Earth. Astronomers consider it likely that Pluto was once a moon of Neptune that escaped long ago (1).

No mechanism is offered for how the moon may have escaped. Compare this to Sitchin's description given in the Enuma Elish, about Pluto having originally been a moon of Saturn, that was ripped away by the first passage of Marduk into the solar system. Pluto was then named 'Gaga' by the Babylonians (2).

In a sense, then, Sitchin's planetary interpretation of the Mesopotamian myth is consistent with the modern scientific idea that Pluto is a rogue satellite. They simply disagree about which planet was the 'parent'. It is possible that future space probes to Pluto and Charon might help to answer this question, particularly if we could analyses the rocky materials found on these worlds and compare them to similar satellites of the outer planets.

Astronomers still argue as to whether Pluto should be classified as a planet at all, although those that advocate that it should, maintain the upper hand in the debate. Regardless, Pluto's elliptical orbit, inclined to the ecliptic, breaks the flat, circular mould. It raises questions at to why this world behaves in the way that it does, questions not readily answered by a stable, circular model for the entire solar system.

## Titan

The effect of Nibiru/Marduk's primordial passage past Saturn, as described by Sitchin, can also be recognized in a little known anomaly regarding its largest moon, Titan. This moon has a dense, cold atmosphere of hydrocarbons, mostly consisting of methane. It is now known that Titan also has oceans of liquid methane, and that it probably rains methane too.

Titan exhibits a non-circular orbit around Saturn, a property that implies a smooth surface. This is anomalous, because Saturn, the giant parent planet, should raise substantial tides on the surface of Titan. The resulting tidal friction should have made the moon's orbit around Saturn circular over a period less than the age of the solar system.

Carl Sagan and Stanley Dermot argued in 1982 that Titan's elliptical orbit implied either an all-ocean planet, or else a planet with no substantial bodies of water at all. They showed that "the tidal friction in places where the ocean is shallow would have taken its toll" resulting in a different orbit from the one observed (3).

Sagan cites radar measurements of the surface of Titan that indicate its surface to have both oceans of hydrocarbons, and continental land-masses, exactly what should not happen. It is generally accepted now that Titan's surface is varied, and the Cassini spacecraft, with its Huygens probe has proved this. But, these contradictory findings created an uncomfortable difficulty for the late Dr. Sagan, who set about a bit of soul-searching. He provided some complex arguments which could reconcile the eccentric orbit with the Titan surface features, but does not seem convinced himself that this line of reasoning is likely. There is an anomaly here.

Perhaps the Dark Star can provide the answer, both to the fact that Titan's lunar orbit is eccentric to begin with, and to why it has not become circular since the Celestial Battle 4 billion years ago. It may continue to influence worlds in the outer solar system with heterogeneous surface features, explaining this anomaly. Worlds with more homogenous surfaces, whether dry like Pluto, or oceanic like Europa, are not affected in the same way. The question is: how does the Dark Star tug Titan into a more eccentric orbit than the one implied by its surface features? Also, was the migration of Pluto to an orbit essentially beyond distant Neptune somehow part of this puzzle too?

## Cyclostratigraphy

So, does this mean that Earth's orbit is similarly prone to variation by the maverick passages of an unknown body?

Evidence from the study of Earth rock strata could indicate so. Earth exhibits a number of rotational and spin effects that cause minor variations in the way it lies in relation to the heavens.

These effects can only be seen over long periods of time, and the best known of these is the Precession of the Equinoxes. This effect is due to a small wobble as Earth spins on its axis, which causes the heavens to move ever so slightly around each year. The heavens appear to rotate over exactly one year by one degree every 72 years.

The ancients were aware of this precessional effect, which causes the rising of the sun on the spring equinox to gradually move backwards through a zodiacal house year-to-year. The ground-breaking book "Hamlet's Mill" by Santillana and Von Deschend, originally advocated the link between ancient myth, ancient architecture and the precession of the equinoxes (4). Their theory was later picked up by Robert Bauval as he applied the astronomical principle of precession to the layout of the Pyramids at Giza, and to the leonine Sphinx.

The sun enters a new constellation every 2160 years, marking the change of the Age. Bauval's dating of the Pyramid field using precession, when comparing it to Orion's belt, produced the figure of 10,450 BC, in the Age of Leo. The leonine Sphinx faces due East, seeming to indicate the importance of the spring equinox, sacred to the Egyptians, and supports the dating symbolically to this Age (5). This has been supported by geological surveys of the Sphinx that have indicated weathering by rain. This data quixotically sets its age back far further than the 'Pyramid Age' of the Fourth Dynasty (6). As a result, such archeo-astronomical studies have become highly controversial.

Precession, itself, provides astronomers with a bit of a dilemma. It cannot be readily accounted for by the interactions of the Earth with the sun, Moon and other planets. The scientific study of cyclostratigraphy provides evidence for a precessional fingerprint in rock layers.

Roger Cunningham argues that Earth's precession, and other unusual minor obliquities in Earth's orbit, show an historical record in the rocks that contains a harmonic period. He also claims that the period of that harmonic, in other words the time difference between each effect being regenerated, is approximately 3600 years. This then coincides with the Sitchin's claim for the periodicity of Nibiru (7). It should also be mentioned that other researchers have claimed that the Precession of the Equinoxes is directly attributable to a hidden binary companion in the solar system, as we noted previously in Chapter 4.

## The Nineveh Constant

Cunningham's research into cyclostratigraphy has certain parallels with similar work carried out by the NASA scientist, Maurice Chatelain, into the "Nineveh constant". The Nineveh constant takes the form of a sexigesimal-equivalent 15 digit number that was found on a clay tablet. This tablet was found within the Library of the learned Assyrian King Assurbanipal, who reigned in Nineveh from 669 to 626 BC. It translated to 195,955,200,000,000, a remarkable number to have been written at all in ancient times, irrespective of any meaningful significance we may attach to it.

Chatelain's research showed that this figure represented an all-inclusive multiple of all the orbital periods and cycles of the planets in the solar system, including Earth's precession of the equinoxes, when the cycles were expressed in seconds. Each cycle period he tried to divide into this figure fit to within 4 decimal places, including sidereal cycles of Uranus, Neptune and Pluto. Chatelain claimed that this showed that the Sumerians, and later Assyrians, had astronomical and mathematical knowledge of these planets (8). This implied that the ancient Mesopotamians had somehow acquired 'impossible' data about the solar system.

Chatelain claimed that the "Nineveh constant" represented a much sought after magical formula known as the "Great Constant of the solar system" (8). If true, this would imply a kind of cosmic resonance throughout the solar system. Now, it is known that neighboring planets do tend to find agreeable orbits between them, which become harmonic. In ancient modes of thinking, we might consider this to be the 'Music of the Spheres' or some such. Is it possible that the ancients could have been aware of these kinds of detailed mathematical relationships?

There is a physical relationship between the energies of the planetary orbits. They are mutually inter-dependent, and a change in circumstance for one planet leads to an alteration in the orbital parameters of the others (one wonders whether this relationship between the planetary 'binding energies' is the Sumerian 'bond Heaven-Earth', or DUR.AN.KI?). Perhaps this is what the Nineveh Constant alludes to. The importance attached to this inter-dependence is now lost. That may be because we do not really fully understand our own solar system.

The planetary orbits all have their own angular momentums, which are in turn related to the binding energies. A distant Dark Star companion would bring with it an additional and considerable quantity of angular momentum to the overall solar system. If its orbit is somehow variable, then its 'binding energies' are subject to change.

Yet, there has to be a conservation of overall energy within the system. As such, a sudden change in the variable orbit of a rogue companion, would upset the order of the entire solar system. Knowledge of this would bring the importance of the relationships between the planetary bodies into sharp focus.

This is because any such change to that relationship could spell disaster for this planet.

## The Solar Pole Shift

The researcher Maurice Cotterell has investigated the cyclical nature of sunspot activity, and how it might relate to other orbital parameters in the solar system, in particular the Earth's orbit and the sun's rotational movement. It is not immediately obvious how this might be so, but a 'great solar cycle' does seem to emerge from his findings, which, remarkably, correlates well with the orbit of the Dark Star. Cotterell took raw data from solar satellite experiments, and ran it through a super computer at the University where he worked. The solar data used in his calculations was tied to the sun's rotational cycle.

Because the sun is a fluid body, it rotates faster at the equator than at the poles, and the common denominator of these two periods was chosen. Bringing in the Earth's orbital period, Cotterell was able to amass a data-base and study the cyclic periods that might come out of it. He was not to be disappointed.

He was able to establish a relationship between these rotational periods and the sunspot activity cycle of about 11.5 years, although the observable cycle is 11.1 years. But his graph also threw out other patterns, and the most significant of these was a period of 3,740 years, which saw the complete reversal of the solar system's "neutral sheet" (9,10). This appeared to be related to an external phenomenon that was affecting the entire solar system. I would suggest that external phenomenon would be the Dark Star, whose perihelion passage may well cause this kind of effect upon the sun and known planets.

As we saw last chapter, the magnetic fields of brown dwarfs are very substantial indeed, creating observed effects in the X-Ray region of the electro-magnetic spectrum, far greater than the size of the bodies would otherwise have suggested. Like bringing two large magnets into close proximity, the motion of the Dark Star around the sun may create a reaction in the overall magnetic field of the sun, and the solar system as a whole.

If Maurice Cotterell's work is correct, then it might well be direct evidence of the presence of a failed star orbiting the sun, with a periodicity of approximately 3,740 years. But this novel idea has not been scientifically proven, and remains on the fringes of scientific thinking. As such, this can only stand as a potentially useful piece of corroborating evidence for an orbital cycle of this length. Indeed, it is by no means certain that things are quite as simple as this, as we shall see later.

## Uranus

Uranus potentially offers further evidence of the primordial presence of Nibiru. Uranus is tilted onto its side with respect to its orbit around the sun. Its moon circulates in this tilted plane, giving the appearance of a dart-board facing the sun.   All of the other planets orbit with their equatorial regions facing the sun. Astronomers have long speculated that Uranus was knocked onto its side by another planetary body (1).

The Enuma Elish describes a close encounter between the Dark Star Marduk and Uranus, which the Sumerians called Anu. The text describes how Anu and Marduk seemed to both obtain moons as a result of that encounter (11). The Uranus system is full of unpredictable anomalies; carbon-rich deposits on Uranus's moons, and swiftly circling elliptical rings around the planet itself.

In August 2000, the General Assembly of the International Astronomical Union gave formal numbers and names to an additional 3 moonlets around Uranus;  Prospero, Setebos and Stephano, all of which were derived from Shakespeare's "The Tempest".  These tiny moons were discovered telescopically in 1999, and added to the new satellites which had been found orbiting Uranus in 1997, called Caliban and Sycorax.  Sky and Telescope Magazine reported their eccentric orbital properties:

"Unlike the planet's inner moons, these new finds are considered "irregular" because they occupy distant, eccentric, highly-inclined orbits and travel in directions generally opposite that of Uranus's rotation." (12)

Again, the inference of these findings is that the Uranus system is anomalous, and seems to have been affected by another large body.

On the face of it, then, the data about Uranus and its moons supports the idea that the planet was struck 3.9 billion years ago by a terrestrial-sized body, causing an expulsion of energetic debris, and resulting in the bizarre tilting of Uranus itself.  But that is not the only possibility.

Let us say that Marduk is a failed star, not a planet. It is then several times as massive as the biggest planet in the solar system, Jupiter. Surely, a close encounter between this colossal 'planet' and Uranus could have been enough to spin Uranus on its axis, without any catastrophic collision. This would be in keeping with the Enuma Elish, where a description of an actual battle between Anu and Marduk is conspicuous by its absence. One can speculate that Uranus was tilted onto its side because it had a cosmic 'near-miss' with a failed star, not because anything collided with it. During this encounter, it happened to pick up some of the cometary debris accompanying the Dark Star: "Anu brought forth and begot the four winds".

## The Moon

The Moon's gravity is one sixth that of the Earth's, but its presence in orbit around our planet remains a puzzle. The other terrestrial-sized worlds in the solar system either have no moons, or they have only asteroid-sized satellites, like Phobos and Deimos around Mars, or Charon around Pluto. There are many possible explanations for the presence of our Moon in Earth's orbit, but none of them appear completely convincing, suffering as they do with contradictory evidence. It appears that the jury is still out in scientific circles. The main problem is that the Moon is remarkably large in proportion to the Earth.

It seems unlikely that a planet the size of Earth could have captured such a body, simply because it is too small to attract such a large satellite. Others consider it likely that the Earth and Moon initially formed as a binary system. Personally, I am persuaded by those who argue that the Moon was once a chunk of the Earth, and became a satellite following a very early primordial collision. Again, this implies primordial chaos in the solar system as proto-planets were battered by each other.

Zecharia Sitchin is a solid proponent of the idea that there were catastrophic events in the early solar system which played a dominating part in the formation of many of the planets, and the order of their orbits, including the Earth and Moon (13). Most scientists would agree with the assumption that underlies this approach, but would argue that the sudden presence of a rogue planet is not necessary to explain the devastation that may have seen moons evicted from their orbits around planets, with Uranus literally knocked onto its side.

They admit to still being stumped by the problem of how massive planets the size of Uranus and Neptune were able to form in the outer zone of the planetary system, when their computer models indicate that there doesn't appear to have been enough time for all the material to accrete. They wonder about migration of planetary orbits to explain such difficulties, but stop short of considering the possibility that the inner planets themselves may also have migrated. It is a wild thought.

The idea put forward by Sitchin that our Earth and Moon were somehow initially sharing a different destiny in the solar system, is judged to be derisory. After all, on the face of it, the Earth's orbit appears perfectly normal. It occupies one of the positions predicted by Bode's Law.

Yet, so does a missing 'fifth' planet between Mars and Jupiter, an area currently occupied by a belt of planetary rubble. Is it possible that the Earth migrated inwards from this zone, leaving behind it the scattered debris of a devastating collision between it and another, smaller planet? Is the Moon itself a highly visible reminder in our skies of such a catastrophe, early in the life of the solar system?

Recent astronomical research has supported the case that the Moon was formed in the same location relative to the sun as the Earth. It might prove to have been an off-shoot of the Earth itself. In March 1999, NASA scientists issued a press release about findings presented at the 30th Lunar and Planetary Science Conference in Houston, which said the following:

"Analysis of data from NASA's Lunar Prospector spacecraft has confirmed that the Moon has a small core, supporting the idea that the bulk of the Moon was ripped away from the early Earth when an object the size of Mars collided with the Earth" (14).

Scientists put the date of this impact to a time 4.45 billion years ago, only 100 million years after the initial formation of the Earth. However, recently discovered traces of liquid water in zircon crystal, dating to 4.404 billion years, has brought this dating into question, suggesting that liquid oceans were existent upon the Earth a relatively short time after this collision (15). It seems to me that the Earth must have been a bigger planet prior to this supposed collision, and that it would have lost large amounts of its primordial oceans as a result.

I, like Sitchin before me, wonder whether such a massive collision could have propelled the Earth into a new orbit, closer to the sun. Eventually, such an unstable orbit would have settled down into a more or less circular one, shepherded as it is by Jupiter. Similarly, take the asteroid belt; it clearly formed from some early destructive event. Yet, the motion of its asteroids is relatively well-behaved, resulting in their skating around the sun in an eternal circle. No one wonders why they aren't far more erratic.

The similarity between the Earth and the Moon's rocky constituents answers those who have hypothesized that the Moon is a relatively recent companion of the Earth. The writer Immanuel Velikovsky tried to explain various ancient myths that hinted at a previous absence of the Moon and infamously promoted the idea that the Moon had been recently captured by the Earth following a catastrophe, and that the time scale for this event was relatively recent (16). If we can take the evidence presented by NASA scientists at face value, then it seems that Velikovsky was wrong. Yet this evidence is in accordance with Sitchin's version of events in that the Moon was formed by a cosmic collision very early on in the history of the Earth. The researcher and author Joan d'Arc has highlighted the importance of other findings presented by NASA at the same 1999 conference:

"Papers presented at this conference also indicated that "similarities in the mineral composition of the Earth and Moon indicate that they share a common origin". However, it was noted that, if they had simply formed from the same cloud of rocks and dust, the Moon would have a core similar in proportion to that of the Earth's. Based on information obtained during the Apollo era, the press release stated, it was suggested that a "Mars-sized body" hit the Earth in its earliest history after its iron core had formed. The impact ejected rocky, "iron-poor material" from the outer shell into orbit, which collected to form the Moon, and was then caught in orbit around the Earth" (14).

Was this Mars-sized body one of the early moons of the Dark Star? There appears to be two distinct options for such a catastrophic event. The scientific evidence from the Moon suggests that such an impact occurred very early in the history of the solar system, only 150 million years after the formation of the sun and its proto-planetary disc. If this immense impact was with a moon of the Dark Star, then it would indicate that the rogue planet's entry into the solar system was very early indeed.

This might be in keeping with the idea that the Dark Star itself formed as a binary companion in the first place, and was jolted closer to the Earth by the gravitational action of a passing star in the relatively densely-packed stellar nursery. It is a tantalizing possibility. The Moon itself could have resulted from such an impact. However, Sitchin relates that the Moon was already in orbit around the primordial Earth before the appearance of Nibiru/Marduk. So, we might conclude from this that the Moon was formed by a collision with a small planet within the chaos of the early solar system.

There still remains some doubt about the origin of the Moon. Studies of terrestrial rock crystals have shown that liquid water was present on the Earth at a very early stage in its primordial development, seemingly precluding a collision that was big enough to re-melt the Earth, as a direct collision with a Mars-sized body surely would have done.

Recent research highlights a means by which the Earth/Moon system's original distance from the sun could be ascertained. We know from radiological studies that the Earth and the Moon are roughly the same age. It seems that they share common stable isotopes of oxygen, which is a strong indicator that they formed at a similar distance from the sun (17). This isotopic analysis supports the idea that the Earth and Moon were derived from one source.

If the Earth and Moon had always enjoyed the same orbit around the sun, then the isotopic constitution of their rocks would indeed be a unique cosmic fingerprint. The question in my mind is whether this fingerprint is common to other debris in the solar system, like the asteroids. If the Earth was once orbiting the sun at a greater distance from where it is now, then it would surely share this isotopic fingerprint with the asteroids. This would be a simple test of this idea.

## The Late Heavy Bombardment

As I mentioned, there are two possibilities for the timing of an interaction with the Dark Star and its retinue. Planetary scientists have puzzled over the catastrophic damage that both the Earth and Moon suffered 3.9 billion years ago. This does not appear to be the tail-end of the primordial chaos of the solar system, but rather a later, sudden onslaught of cosmic debris lasting about 100 million years. Because at least one of the rocks studied turns out to be iron-rich, it is thought likely that the impactors were asteroids, not comets (18).

At that time, there was a devastating attack by comets, many of them sizeable. The Earth lay in ruins as a result, and the Moon still bears the scars of that widespread destruction. It was like receiving a rapid series of extinction level impacts.

The timing of this momentous bombardment was not during the formation of the Moon. It is a quite separate, later event not directly linked to the chaos of the early solar system. We know this because of the age of Moon rocks, which turned out to be mostly 3.9 billion years old, 600 million years later than expected. This correlates with the age of ancient rocks on the Earth and on Mars, as well as cratering features of the asteroids (18). The implication of this is that the entire solar system was

subject to a series of massive bombardments around that time, and that 3.9 billion year old rocks will one day also be discovered on the surfaces of Venus and Mercury. Scientists who have studied this pattern of cratering have speculated that the bombardment occurred at intervals of about 10,000 years during this catastrophic period (19).

This implies that an initial catastrophic event disrupted the asteroid belt and then was followed over a period of 100 million years by cyclical after-shocks. Perhaps this temporary cycle of bombardment was connected to the movement through the inner solar system of a massive planet on a 10,000 year orbit that then migrated out, restoring calm thereafter.

Some Moon rocks were indeed 4.5 billion years old, though, implying two separate catastrophic events leading to the formation of the Moon's surface (18). Other ancient surfaces throughout the solar system tell a similar story; massive impacts 3.9 billion years ago. The source of the cataclysm appears to be from within the solar system. This is most likely to be the asteroid belt itself, which turns out to have a smaller than expected population.

There are two possible explanations for the depleted population of the asteroid belt. Either the asteroids were once part of a planet that existed at that location which was destroyed in some way, or a planet was never able to properly form there in the first place because of the proximity of Jupiter's intense gravity field, which destabilized the region. Both mechanisms are able to show how asteroids were lost in large numbers. Scientists tend to favour the latter suggestion, whilst catastrophists favour the former. The population of asteroids in the belt is also diverse in terms of their chemical constituency, suggesting differing origins (20). Personally, I think this implies catastrophism, linked to the impacts of the late, great bombardment. I'm quite certain that the Dark Star is implicated in all of this.

Scientists are now grappling with the problem of how the very primitive life on Earth which preceded the collisions 3.9 billion years ago might have survived the onslaught. Life is tenacious, that's for sure. The timing of this bombardment would seem to be in keeping with Sitchin's analysis that the rogue planet Nibiru/ Marduk crashed into the solar system at that time, and that its devastating "attack" left the Moon battered and the Earth scourged of much of its oceanic water (21). It is also possible that the nearby transit of the Dark Star, which I consider to be Marduk, had the gravitational effect of causing the Earth to migrate into the inner solar system.

There are two possibilities for a possible migration, then. The first is that the Earth was propelled inwards by the same impact that caused the formation of the Moon. The second is that the Earth and Moon were later pummelled by debris accompanying the Dark Star, and that the action of this brown dwarf itself was enough to cause the migration. The presence of the asteroid belt tends to suggest the former.

At this point, you might be wondering why I am so convinced that the Earth once orbited near to the present location of the asteroid belt. Why not simply accept that the Earth and Moon have always been found the same distance from the sun? Everyone else does...The answer is that most simple of molecules; water.

## Water in the Desert

As our knowledge of the solar system has improved, it has become increasingly clear that water is a more significant component of the planetary bodies than previously thought. The gas-giants Jupiter and Saturn, as well as their more distant cousins Uranus and Neptune, have all been found to contain significant quantities of water in their atmospheres, a finding that has surprised astronomers (22).

When the fragmented comet Shoemaker-Levy 9 collided with Jupiter in 1994 (23), it allowed astronomers to analyses atmospheric gases deep in the planet's cloud structure, giving them an unprecedented amount of atmospheric data regarding the hidden layers. There they found water, in quantities that they had not expected. This would not have been possible without the comet causing catastrophic damage to Jupiter.

This was a once-in-a-lifetime opportunity for us to see the forces of nature at work in the heavens. Comets really do hit planets, and the effects are truly catastrophic, even for a planet as massive as Jupiter. If that's what a fragmented comet could do, what were early collisions between actual planets like in comparison?

It was not just the collision with Shoemaker-Levy 9 that allowed astronomers to access Jupiter's atmospheric secrets. By a stroke of fate, the Galileo spacecraft was en-route to Jupiter in 1994, and captured the collisions on camera from a different angle than that from Earth. But Galileo also carried an atmospheric entry probe that dropped into Jupiter's clouds on 7th December 1995.

The probe survived just an hour, but sent back invaluable data, as it floated though the upper levels of Jupiter's cloud cover. Then it succumbed to the immense pressures and rising temperatures of this colossal planet (24). Again, the atmospheric entry probe confirmed higher than expected levels of water.

Galileo has also given us unprecedented access to the Jovian system of moons, including the remarkable world Europa. It is now generally accepted that Europa has a liquid, aqueous ocean under the surface ice-sheet. In fact, the two larger Galilean moons, Callisto and Ganymede, might also harbour hidden oceans.

This finding is entirely due to the detailed imagery afforded by Galileo's fly-bys. Its images showed giant chunks of once-moving ice covering certain areas of the moon. Some of the chunks resemble ice-floes on Earth, and astronomers suspect that the kilometers-thick ice that covers Europa's surface may move in response to a heated ocean-like interior, made watery by the tidal pull of the parent planet (25).

Jupiter's great mass acts as a magnet for comets and asteroids. Its entourage of 16 moons stand in the way of this incoming barrage, so starkly demonstrated by Shoemaker-Levy 9, and most of them exhibit the scars in their rock and ice surfaces, in the form of a myriad of craters. Europa, by contrast, is as smooth as a billiard ball. Yet, it must have received its fair share of impacts. So, it is evident that its surface is being constantly reworked.

A similar re-working is occurring on the Galilean moon closest to Jupiter, Io, whose volcanic activity is the most violent in the solar system's, driven by the tidal forces of Jupiter's immense gravity. It is these tidal forces that warm Europa's kilometers-deep ocean, an ocean that wraps around the planet, capped by a healthily thick ice sheet. Many now speculate about the possibility of extra-terrestrial life thriving in the oceanic depths of Europa. Ganymede and Callisto, slightly more distant moons of Jupiter, may, likewise, play host to life (26).

A pattern is emerging. Water is common-place in the solar system. It is central to life on Earth. It is a major component of the comets. It exists in abundance in the Jovian system, whose rocky satellites have hidden oceans. Water is also a major component of many of the surfaces of the moons of the outer planets (25).

Thanks to the NASA/Department of Defense lunar satellite Clementine, we are now aware of a lake of frozen water ice on the Moon, surviving deep within a crater near the Moon's pole, where the rays of the sun could not penetrate to sublimate the ice. Water may once have existed on the Moon in greater quantities, most of which would have been driven off by direct exposure to the sun's relentless radiation bombardment. The ancient age of the Lunar surface indicates that water has not played a part in this satellite's geography for many billions of years. But still, water has been found there.

## Water on Mars

Mars is the latest world to give up its aqueous secrets. Scientists have long suspected that Mars once had water in abundance, based on the ancient river beds etched into its surface. They suspected that vast quantities of water might lurk below the Martian surface. However, they did not expect to find that water was playing an active role in the planet's current surface geography. Detailed images from the Mars Global Surveyor have produced hundreds of cases of gullies, apparently recently formed by flash-flooding of some kind (27).

The Martian atmospheric pressure is about 100 times less than that of the Earth's at sea-level, and this means that water should boil into the Martian atmosphere when exposed to it. Yet, it appears to have been flowing along the surface under these conditions, leading scientists to speculate that the flows are sudden and violent - although what causes the sudden watery eruptions from these underwater aquifers remains a mystery. What is clear is that water is a commodity on Mars, despite the adverse atmospheric conditions.

Recent findings have confirmed that liquid water has existed on the surface of Mars in relatively recent times. Images taken by ESA's Mars Express spacecraft, which is orbiting the red planet, have highlighted what appear to be ice floes across the region known as Elysium. A press release by University College London (UCL) confirmed the existence of a sea frozen just 5 million years ago, which is now covered in volcanic dust, preventing the sublimation of the ice by Mars' frigid and thin atmosphere.

This discovery tied in with a previous detection of methane gas over the same general area. The combination of a deep body of water and methane gas is strongly suggestive of life existing at the current time under the Martian surface (28,29). So water is prevalent throughout the solar system, not just on Earth.

If water exists in a liquid form, as on Europa, possibly Ganymede and Callisto, and now Mars, then the chances of life being found in these locations is greatly enhanced. Where did it all come from? There are a number of possibilities, but the significant quantities of water in the solar system are consistent with the Sitchin's radical account of the solar system.

When the primordial Earth, a world with an abundance of oceanic water, was cleaved apart by both a Mars-sized planet and the later bombardment of comets, water and terrestrial debris were widely dispersed throughout the planetary solar system. The planets and moons around the sun would have been inundated with water and ice, and this is evident today with these ongoing discoveries.

The Earth managed to hold onto a great deal of its precious commodity, which is actually a mystery too, as we shall see in the next chapter. A problem with Earth's own water, is the reason why I think that it was once located farther from the sun.

# Chapter 6 References

1. W. Lee "To Rise from Earth" p239-242 Cassell & Co 2000

2. Z. Sitchin "The 12th Planet" p221-222 Avon 1976

3. C. Sagan "Pale Blue Dot" p111-117 Headline Book Publishing 1995

4. G. Santillana & H. Von Deschend "Hamlet's Mill" Gambit International 1969

5. R. Bauval & A Gilbert "The Orion Mystery" Mandarin 1994

6. R. Bauval & G. Hancock "Keeper of Genesis" p16-23 Mandarin 1996

7. L. Pye "Cyclostratigraphy" <http://www.coastvillage.com/origins/articles/pye/cyclostratigraphy.htm> 2000

8. M. Chatelain "Our Ancestors Came From Outer Space" Ch1 Pan 1979

9. D. Wilcock "Convergence" http://www.dprins.demon.nl/convergence/9903.html "Maurice Cotterell and the Great Sunspot Cycle"

10. Gilbert & M. Cotterell "The Mayan Prophecies" App. 4, Element 1995

11. Z. Sitchin "Genesis Revisited" Ch 2 Avon 1990

12. Sky & Telescope "New Names for Uranian Moonlets" p32 November 2000

13. Z. Sitchin "Genesis Revisited" p126-129 Avon 1990

14. d'Arc "Space Travellers and the Genesis of the Human Form" p29 The Book Tree 2000, Reproduced with kind permission.

15. Hecht "Old Timer: The Oldest Mineral on Earth is Found, Challenging Ideas about the Birth of the Moon" 10th January 2001,http://www.newscientist.com./news.jsp?id=ns9999315

16. Velikovsky "In The Beginning" <www.velikovsky.collision.org>

17. P. Tyson "Origins" http://www.pbs.org/wgbh/nova/ tothemoon/origins.html.

18. D. Kring & B. Cohen "Cataclysmic bombardment throughout the inner solar system 3.9-4.0 Ga", J. Geophys. Res., 107(E2), 5009, 2002

19. J. TenBruggencate "Asteroid theory explores impact on Earth life" 24th March 2002 Honolulu Advertiser, with thanks to Lee Covino

20. E. Chaisson & S. McMillan, "Astronomy Today", 1st Ed., Prentice-Hall, Upper Saddle River 1993

21. Z. Sitchin "Genesis Revisited" Ch 1 Avon 1990

22. I. Semeniuk "Neptune Attacks!" New Scientist p27-9 7th April 2001

23. D. Levy "Comets" p208 Touchstone 1998

24. P. Weissman & M Segura  "Astronomy", p36-45 "Galileo Arrives at Jupiter" Jan. 1996

25. P. Barnes-Svarney "Astronomy" p46-47 "Frozen Assets" Oct. 1997

26. M. Milstein "Astronomy" p38-43 "Diving into Europa's Ocean" Oct. 1997

27. M. Hardin  "New Images Suggest Present-day Sources of Liquid Water on Mars" 22nd June 2000

28. Philip Ball "Mars may have a frozen sea" 22nd February 2005 http://www.nature.com/news/2005/050221/full/050221-7.html

29. Bloomberg News "Mars Has Frozen Sea; Raises Chance of Life on Planet" 22nd February 2005 http://www.bloomberg.com/apps/news?pid=10000103&sid=adraOqIQmDEo&refer=us.

CHAPTER

7

# The Great Water Conundrum

My colleague, Lee Covino recently sent me an article from "Science News" (Vol. 161, no 12) about the source of Earth's oceanic water (1). Written by Ben Harder, the article outlined the latest scientific thinking about where all the water on Earth came from. This is a particular problem for planetary scientists, because the Earth simply should not have the amount of water that it does.

The Earth is relatively close to the sun, and water, a volatile, should have been expelled from the early inner solar system before the Earth formed. As such, the Earth should really be a much drier planet. So where did all the water, that is so crucial to the biosphere of this planet, originate?

Ben Harder describes various theories that are currently doing the rounds in scientific circles. Up until recently, the leading theory was the notion that the oceans were deposited by comets impacting the newly formed Earth (the 'late-veneer' hypothesis) (2). This bombardment occurred over a billion year period (and might also explain how life appeared on Earth so early in its geo-history). But according to Ben Harder's article, recent data from comets has overturned this possibility. The problem is that the isotopic ratios of terrestrial water and cometary ice are quite different, dependent upon where the comets initially formed.

The comets analyzed thus far contain relatively large quantities of deuterium, yet this isotopic form of water is rare on Earth. If this composition of known comet ice is representative of solar system comets in general, then very little of the Earth's water can be attributed to cometary impact following the Earth's formation. Taking this into account, it appears that only half of the Earth's oceans could have been deposited by impacting comets.

Puzzled scientists have tried to patch the flagging 'late-veneer' theory up, topping up the comet contribution with that of water-rich asteroids, but that doesn't explain other problems to do with the Earth's chemical composition. The Earth is rich in many other volatiles, and these elements (mostly noble gases) are not found on meteorites. Topping up comet water deposition with that of water-rich asteroids would not explain the relative abundance of these other volatile chemicals. For example, recent studies by scientists at the University of Arizona regarding the relative isotopic ratios of osmium in carbonaceous chondrites sink the late-veneer theory still further; the upper limit for deposition of volatiles from space after the Earth's formation is a meagre 15% (3). These new findings are causing planetary scientists a big headache. The natural implication is that the Earth formed with its volatiles in place right from the start. Yet, current models of the primordial solar system rule this out. Various new ideas are being floated, in varying degrees of complexity, to explain this contradiction.

Perhaps the primordial inner solar system was a cooler place than originally thought? Perhaps the Earth was formed from a multiplicity of planetary 'embryos', some of which originated nearer Jupiter than the Earth, thus allowing a build-up of indigenous volatiles? Perhaps the rocks that formed the early Earth trapped massive quantities of water within them, preventing the volatiles from being routinely expunged from the inner accretion disc?

But these ideas appear to be the scientific equivalent of clutching at straws. This particular anomaly is a real problem, yet there seems to be no satisfactory answer. The Earth simply shouldn't be so well endowed with life-giving water.

## The Earth Migrated

The solution is staring all of these planetary scientists in the face. It is so obvious that its absence within Ben Harder's otherwise excellent article speaks volumes in itself. The Earth has a rich mixture of volatiles, including water, because our planet must have originally formed much further away from the sun!

It's the only simple solution to this problem. If the Earth began life at the position of the asteroid belt, then the problem is solved.

I can claim this because other scientific work also points in this direction.

Clues as to Earth's early distance from the sun can be gleaned from the "embryo" theory of the Frenchman Allessandro Morbidelli (4,5). He proposed that the Earth formed from the coalescence of Moon-sized embryos, derived from various chaotic orbits in the primordial solar system. The "volatile carriers" would have formed at about 4 Astronomical Units; four times further away from the sun than the Earth, but still within the orbit of giant Jupiter.

Morbidello notes that the water-bearing carrier from 4 AU would have been geo-chemically unique in the solar system. This reminds us of the similar isotopic signature of oxygen on Earth and the Moon, which we encountered in the last chapter. This is why it's so important to gain a statistical understanding of the isotopic balance of water throughout the solar system.

The data about water isotope composition in the inner solar system enigmatically suggests that the Earth formed about 4 astronomical units away from the sun. This, of course, does not 'fit' the standard model for the evolution of the solar system. Yet, the evidence points in this direction, so one would expect that scientists should be reviewing the standard model. Further evidence has emerged to underline this issue.

When the Comet LINEAR was studied by NASA, it was found to have an isotopic composition similar to that of the water on Earth. One might assume that this meant it formed in the same place as the Earth, that is, at 1 Astronomical Unit. But in fact, the isotopic ratio implies that it formed near to Jupiter! Incredible, isn't it? NASA also makes it clear that the water from Earth's oceans have a similar isotopic balance as LINEAR; they established this by looking at the amount of volatile organic compounds, which turned out to be low (6).

On the one hand, it means that the Earth could have received some water from known comets. On the other, it implies that ALL of those comets must have come from one specific location: i.e. around Jupiter. Does this really seem likely to you?

Unfortunately, LINEAR broke up before all the necessary science could be completed. Perhaps this proved fortunate for scientists who might have been keen to explain away such anomalous findings. Was LINEAR a comet from Earth's oceans, ejected into the solar system due to some mighty impact? Does its isotopic ratio of oxygen imply that the Earth formed nearer to Jupiter than to our present location?

I think the answer to both of these questions is 'yes'.

Somehow, the Earth migrated inwards, despite its strong bond to the sun. If the Earth was once four times further away from the sun than it is now, then we must explain how it managed to find itself in its current close proximity to the sun. The inner solar system planets are quite tightly bound to the sun, and do not flippantly change their orbits at the drop of the hat. Something happened, something that the scientists don't really want to think about.

A model for this action already exists in the form of Zecharia Sitchin's "12th Planet" hypothesis. Interpreting the myths in an astronomical context suggested to Sitchin that an undiscovered planet exists among the comets, one that was not an original member of the solar system, but an interloper wandering in inter-stellar space that blundered into the planetary zone.

There it encountered a watery world at about 4 Astronomical Units, and a great 'celestial battle' took place between these planetary 'gods'. The result was the shunting of this Water World into the inner solar system, where it became the Earth. The intruder spun off into an eccentric orbit beyond the known planets, where it remains to be re-discovered to this day (7).

This is controversial material, of course. Not the kind of speculative reasoning that readily appeals to the rational mindset of our academic brethren. But, the Water Conundrum we have just considered is remarkably consistent with this hypothesis. Not wishing to rely too heavily upon that old die-hard 'Occam's Razor', we seem to have a simple solution to a difficult problem.


## The Origin of Earth


Current theories of the formation of the Moon are centred upon a massive collision between the early Earth and a Mars-sized body, scattering debris into orbit around the Earth, which eventually coalesced to form Luna (8). The lack of a significant iron core within the Moon suggests that this impact took place after the Earth's own iron core had already gravitated to the centre of our planet (9). It's conceivable that the remainder of the early Earth's scattered debris formed the asteroid belt, given

Sitchin's proposal, and this possibility is readily testable by further scientific study of the composition of asteroids within the belt between Mars and Jupiter. This might have occurred when the Moon formed, or as a result of later impacts upon the recovering Earth.

If correct, then the primordial Earth must have been a very significant planet indeed, such that major impacts upon it created the asteroid belt, the Moon and possibly some of the comets. Furthermore, such a wide scattering of water into the solar system may explain the relative high content of water on other planets, which we discussed in the last chapter. The implication would be, then, that the Earth was once a much larger world, the excess made up to a great degree by water.

Such a massive terrestrial planet could have readily held onto a vast amount of volatiles at the original distance of 4 astronomical units; its greater gravity alone could have meant a greater retention of water and other volatiles. It also would not be so incongruous that the larger primordial Earth would have brought into being and then successfully held onto such a massive satellite as our Moon. In other words, our Moon is colossal because at one point the Earth was much bigger relative to how it is now.

The migration of the Earth into the inner solar system would then have driven off much of that water, as predicted by theory. Also, the scientific discovery of the 'late, great bombardment' upon the Earth/Moon system 3.9 billion years ago brings a further insight into how successive massive bombardments of the Earth might have caused more oceanic water to be suddenly lost (10). Even so, because we started from a much higher threshold of domestic water, we now enjoy oceans and seas and lakes.

Our aqueous environment is due to our planetary origins lying near to Jupiter, not to cometary bombardment. This migration might make the Earth a rather special place. After all, without it a reasonably sized planet would not enjoy such abundant water so close to the sun. Earth might just have a unique signature; a planet in the habitable zone that somehow managed to retain its early water resources.

However, before we become too wrapped up in this idea, we must look at a vital point about the heat output of the sun over time.

## The Cold Sun

When discussing the conditions that existed on the primitive Earth, it is important to note that different conditions existed in the solar system at the time. The sun was probably one of many thousands of stars in a cluster or star nursery. It's possible that the Dark Star was a wide binary companion to the sun, and that the system was disrupted early on, causing dramatic changes.

Examples of other young star systems present us with evidence of such binaries, where spiral structure has appeared in the proto-planetary discs, implying either massive distant stellar companions, or close stellar encounters (11,12,13). These findings imply that the stellar environment surrounding the early solar system was certainly busier than was previously thought. We should not infer from the stable, rustic charm of the present formation of planets that things were always this way.

The other thing to bear in mind is that the early sun emitted less light than it does now, and this may have contributed to a cooler primitive Earth. The sun's nuclear fires were concentrated in a relatively small sphere near its centre early on. This means that the Earth received about 70% of the sunlight it enjoys today (14). However, such considerations should already have been taken into account by scientists looking at the isotopic balance of oxygen in terrestrial and extra-terrestrial water. Nevertheless, it's worth bearing in mind that the sun's own activity levels may have played a part.

## Earth's Special Character

So, was the formation of the Earth a rather special, possibly unique phenomenon? If the Earth should not be nearly as wet as it is, being so close to the sun, then it is perfectly possible that the Earth is actually a rather special place. Without the action of a passing intruder planet of vast proportions, or the shunting effect of a significant impact, the Earth would be a much colder place than it is now. It would be more like the so-called "Snowball Earth", a condition that applied to our world some 600 million years ago (15).

Life relies upon liquid water…would the current bio-diversity on this planet have arisen if Earth was still residing in the Asteroid Belt?

If a newly forming planet is close to a star - like Earth is to the sun - and thus warmed by it sufficiently to maintain liquid water later in its history, then these exact same conditions should preclude the inclusion of water on that world in the first place. The presence of abundant liquid water on the cooled planet becomes a paradox, because heat and water do not appear to mix when terrestrial planets form. So, this paradoxical situation we currently find on Earth is solved either by considering the possibility that the Earth has moved significantly closer to the sun since its formation, or by rethinking how planets form.

Whatever caused our world to have so much water so close to the sun, it may be unusual, possibly even unique. The Earth's abundance of liquid water may be very rare, if the action of an intruder planet is required to explain its shunting into a closer inner orbit. Saying that, some of the extra-solar planets found so far have distinctly odd orbits; particularly gas giants that swing wildly around the parent stars at very close proximity (16).

Why were the constituent volatile gases of these planets not blown away by the star before the planet got a chance to form? Does this imply that planetary orbits can change radically, possibly as a result of outside interference?

The sheer variety of the extra-solar planets seems to mitigate against our conclusion of uniqueness for the planet Earth. If this 'Great Water Conundrum' helps us to understand anything it is that planets can migrate around - and end up enjoying orbits that seem, on the face of it, to be docile and placid. This overturns our previous assumptions that the observed planets in their nice quiet circular orbits must have always been that way. It opens the door for other possibilities further out into the colder regions of the solar system as well. Because if planets can migrate inwards, they can also migrate out.

## Life Around Cool Stars

We always assume that our average boring old sun is the blue-print for other star systems that might harbour the conditions for life. Perhaps this assumption is correct, and the search for Extra-

Terrestrial Intelligence should remain targeted at similar stars to our own sun. But, if Earth's acquisition of abundant water is truly an anomaly given the local heat generated by our sun upon its formation, then perhaps we should be looking for life on star systems whose primordial fires aren't so hot. After all, the spectrum of stellar characteristics does not begin with our own sun.

Red, or dare I say, even brown dwarfs would have formed without the same water-purging enthusiasm as our own yellow star. In fact, brown dwarfs themselves contain large quantities of water within their fiery atmospheres. They also have been seen to have their own planetary systems, even the smallest of the brown dwarfs (17).

Perhaps that means that we should direct our attention to the less bright members of the celestial family; even those who remain hidden entirely. These relatively cool stars might have allowed watery worlds to form more readily around them, but bombard them with less harmful radiation than our own overenthusiastic sun.

Ironically, SETI may have been searching in the wrong place all this time.

## Water Worlds

The concept of 'migration' of planets has becoming increasingly acceptable of late. It was not so long ago that Tom van Flandern heavily criticized Zecharia Sitchin's "12th Planet Theory" on the basis that Earth could not have migrated into the inner solar system from the asteroid belt. Van Flandern argued that Earth's orbit should still be highly elliptical if that was the case, and that the orbit should still cross through the asteroid belt. These arguments were partly sufficient to swing the author Alan Alford away from the idea of the existence of a substantial Planet X body (18).

But science has moved on in recent years, and is now generally more open to new possibilities about undiscovered planets in our solar system (19). This is not only partly due to discoveries about our own outer solar system, but also because of the data which has accumulated about extra-solar planets.

Many of these "exoplanets" have anomalous orbits. Some of them are orbiting their stars at very small distances, and are known as "Hot Jupiters". These bizarre giant planets are too close to their stars to have formed where they currently lie (according to existing theoretical models of planet formation), so the concept of 'migration' is increasingly mooted to help planetary scientists sleep at night. If such a model can be widely applied elsewhere, then surely it could have happened in our solar system too?

The science writer Andrew Pike once described a possible new class of planets that sound remarkably similar to the large, watery primordial Earth we have been thinking about here. This class of planets, called the "Water Worlds", is still theoretical. The idea was suggested by Alain Leger of the Institut d'Astrophysique Spatiale, France.

He wondered whether worlds twice as large as the Earth might exist with a super-abundance of water. This aqueous environment would take the form of a planet-wide ocean many kilometers deep, along with a gaseous atmosphere. He envisioned them beginning life as the extra-solar equivalents of Uranus or Neptune, but then migrating inwards (20).

Again, the notion of planetary migration is being used to explain distant anomalies. Other examples of proposed migratory patterns of planets have also been seen in the scientific press lately (21,22). It does not take much imagination to apply the same principles here in our own solar system.

There is so much that we don't understand about the formation of planetary systems. This can be only one of a myriad of possibilities, but its early introduction to scientific speculation would indicate its potential. If such Water Worlds are found to exist, then they would provide a huge lift for the ideas presented here. Our own planet may once have been like this.

## Electron Glow

Scientists are now actively discussing how life might emerge on planets orbiting brown dwarfs, or Dark Stars, I have described how an ecosystem might have arisen on a moon orbiting a small brown dwarf, whose light emission is minimal. It can be easily argued that the conditions on that moon would be warm enough for liquid water. But, some commentators have offered a counter-argument that there still would be insufficient light for photosynthesis to take place in the outer solar system. After all, it takes more than just liquid water to create life; light itself is often a useful ally.

Such light as there is would have to come from the Dark Star, a rather old sub-brown dwarf, which belongs to a new class of failed stars about which we have little actual knowledge.

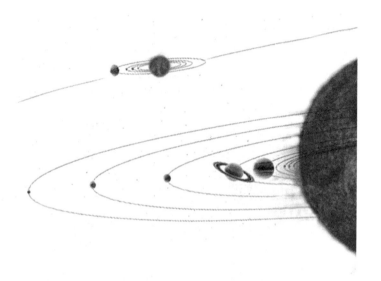

Astronomers argue about whether such bodies can even emit light, but there does seem to be a good possibility that they do - through chemical reactions in the outer layers of atmosphere, driven by extreme magnetic fields and surface gravity. These effects result in 'flaring', but is this enough of a light source to allow photosynthesis to take place on nearby terrestrial worlds?

Uranus exhibits an inexplicable internal lighting effect known as "electron glow". This effect is in addition to Uranus' magnetic aurora. It is thought that the luminous effect, seen on such a 'dead' world, is due to electrons exciting hydrogen in the upper atmosphere, although it is not at all clear where those electrons originate from (23). Perhaps such an effect is possible on a sub-brown dwarf, to a greater extent, supplementing the other light-sources from this failed star that we have already discussed.

So, there are several means by which the Dark Star could be classified as a "light-emitting" planet. Indeed, it could be a highly excitable combination of them all. This is rather like arguing for light-emitting fish in the Deep Sea oceans.

Before their discovery, no one would have expected 'Angler Fish' at the bottom of our oceans. Is the Dark Star the planetary equivalent of a neon red Angler Fish? Is its moon system lit by this little oasis of red light in the deep abyss of the outer solar system? I suspect so.

So, would this be sufficient for photosynthesis to take place out there? We can look to events on our own planet to answer that question, particularly under the Antarctic ice. The scientist Chris McKay has studied eco-systems that depend upon the dimmest of light emerging through the ice to trigger photosynthesis, and has concluded that photosynthesis can be easily supported by just 2 percent of the sun's available light. He argues that there are plants here on Earth that are able to photosynthesize in luminous environments equivalent to 100 Astronomical Units from the sun, which is twice as far as the most distant body in the Edgeworth-Kuiper Belt yet discovered (14).

Arguments about photosynthesis are thus rather redundant. I would argue that a Dark Star can supply not just direct and indirect warmth, through gravitational tidal action - but sufficient light as well, to allow photosynthesis to take place on one of its moons.

## Life Among The Comets?

Even so, to establish whether life could exist among the comets around an object as exotic as a sub-brown dwarf, we must first establish its presence there. In the next chapter or so, we shall look at recent scientific studies that imply the previous presence of a substantial planet. These anomalous findings in the outer solar system have become central to our hunt for the Dark Star, because they offer indirect evidence for its existence.

Currently, astronomers are considering things they once would never have countenanced. The reason is their new appreciation for how strange the Edgeworth-Kuiper Belt is.

Beyond the orbit of Neptune is a swarm of bodies orbiting the sun, whose individual sizes, and great distances, have prevented their detection until relatively recently. The first Edgeworth-Kuiper Belt Object (EKBO) was discovered in 1992, and since then there have been many more, some of which exhibit very strange orbital properties. One such object, known as 2000 CR105, has an orbit of 3300 years, and behaves in a very odd way, leading some astronomers to suggest that its orbit is being affected by an external influence, such as another planet beyond Pluto (24).

This piece of evidence is of some importance to us. The astrophysicists studying the Kuiper Belt Object 2000 CR105 have speculated quite openly about how it could have come to have such a large orbit, one that seems to have developed beyond the scope of Neptune's influence. A massive Perturber causing anomalies in the Kuiper Belt is now considered a very real possibility by many astronomers. Other minor planets, also showing unexpectedly eccentric orbits, are being discovered, including one known to be greater in size than the planet Pluto.

In the next chapter we will begin our crucial exploration of the Edgeworth-Kuiper Belt.

## Deep Impact

As this book goes to press, findings are emerging about comets which may vindicate some of the ideas we have discussed in this chapter. NASA created the biggest Independence Day firework in the history of, well, America, on 4th July 2005. This awesome display was the result of the careful steering of a washing machine-sized projectile into the path of the comet Tempel 1. At the time, concerned citizens of the Earth wondered whether this 'Deep Impact', as NASA called it, might cause the comet to fracture, sending fragments hurtling towards our unprotected world. Scientists reassured us that the experiment posed no more danger to the comet's integrity than a gnat would to the windscreen of a car.

The impact was sensational. Though not, perhaps, as sensational as the scientific analysis of the impact might turn out to be. That's because there was more to this colossal firework than just American patriotism. The Deep Impact spacecraft was joined by several other telescopes, each carefully studying the materials that were forcefully expelled from the interior of the Tempel 1 comet. Such studies should give scientists the first real idea of what comets comprise of.

Such information could establish an intrinsic link between the composition of comets and the Earth.

The results of the studies have not been released to the public yet. This is frustrating, but somewhat understandable. It takes time to calibrate the spectra, work through all of the data and write up the scientific papers. However, one of the scientists involved has given some good insights into what we might expect when the complete picture of the composition of Tempel 1 is eventually released (25).

The comet is composed mostly of ice: the Deep Impact event releasing large quantities of hot water into space. This much was expected. However, the geology of the comet is complex, with a cratered landscape suggesting a multi-faceted life. What's more unusual is the composition of the rocks in the comet, which include limestone. This material can form in the presence of water, but it seems unlikely that such a mechanism could take place in the frigidly cold conditions of the outer solar system. It doesn't seem possible that limestone rock ended up as part of a comet. Yet the tell-tale sign of carbonates clearly show up on the spectra.

The comet seems to have all the elements associated with Earth rocks present, but lacks iron. This is also providing scientists with a headache. Iron tends to concentrate in the cores of planets, but in smaller bodies with lesser internal forces at work, iron should be present throughout the comet. So where is it?

These provisional findings suggest to me that the comet is a chunk of watery rock knocked off the surface of a planet whose iron had already sunk into the planetary core. I think that the comet didn't form independently way out in the outer solar system, but was once part of a watery planet. Such a scenario is consistent with the presence of limestone.

Yet Tempel 1 seems to be a regular short range comet. It is not an unusual body. All of this suggests that short range comets may be connected with previous catastrophic events in the solar system. It is very tempting at this early stage to wonder whether Zecharia Sitchin is correct; that the collision between Nibiru and Tiamat not only left a battered Earth spinning into a new orbit closer to the sun, but also spawned a celestial ocean of comets.

Those comets should then have a composition broadly in line with that of the Earth.

It's a pity that more detailed data is unavailable at this time, particularly regarding the isotopic ratios of the water of Tempel 1. Rational reasons for delay aside, one might be forgiven for wondering whether the scientists charged with probing the secrets of Tempel 1 are struggling to come up with an explanation as to why this comet seems to be a piece of a familiar world. Namely, the Earth! Such a link would be an extraordinary revelation, and would have far-reaching repercussions. We can only wait and see what news the coming months bring.

# Chapter 7 References

1. B. Harder "Water for the Rock: Did Earth's Oceans come from the Heavens?" Science News 23 March 2002; Vol. 161, No. 12 Thanks to Lee Covino

2. A. Delsemme "An Argument for the cometary origin of the biosphere" American Scientist 89 (Sept.-Oct.) 2001; pp432-442 [cited in (1)]

3. M. Drake & K. Righter "Determining the composition of the Earth" Nature 416 (7th March) 2002; pp39-44 [cited in (1)]

4. A. Morbidelli, et al. "Source regions and timescales for the delivery of water to the Earth" Meteoritics and Planetary Science 35 2000; pp1309-1320 [cited in (1)]

5. L. Mullen "Borne Bone Dry" 17th February 2004, with thanks to Shad Bolling, http://www.astrobio.net/news/article833.html

6. Astrobiology News "A Taste for Comet Water" 25th May 2001 http://nai.arc.nasa.gov/news_stories/news_detail.cfm?ID=154

7. Z. Sitchin "The Twelfth Planet" Avon 1976

8. L. David "Long-Destroyed Fifth Planet May Have Caused Lunar Cataclysm, Researchers Say" http://www.space.com/scienceastronomy/solarsystem/fifth_planet_020318.html 18th March 2002

9. J. d'Arc "Space Travellers and the Genesis of the Human Form" p29 The Book Tree 2000

10. I. Semeniuk "Neptune Attacks!" pp26-9 New Scientist 7th April 2001

11. J. Augereau & J. Papaloizou, A&A, astro-ph/0310732, 2003

12. A. Quillen, P. Varniere, I. Minchev & A. Frank, AJ, 2004

13. C. Grady et al, AJ, 122, p3396, 2001

14. D. Koerner & S. LeVay "Here be Dragons: The Scientific Quest for Extraterrestrial Life" pp20-1, 43, Oxford University Press 2000

15. Horizon' BBC2, "Snowball Earth" Shown on 22nd February 2001

16. G. Marcy & P. Butler "Hunting Planets Beyond" pp43-7 Astronomy March 2000

17. Hazel Muir, "Brown Dwarf may Someday Harbour Habitable Planets" 8th February 2005, http://www.newscientist.com/article.ns?id=dn6977

18. A. Alford "The Phoenix Solution" pp171-4, Hodder & Stoughton 1998

19. A. Lloyd "Planet X: Past and Present", pp32-7, UFO Magazine January 2004

20. A. Pike "Exoplanets: What's New?" , p72-3, UFO Magazine, February 2004

21. J. Foust "Bizarre new planets puzzle astronomers" Spaceflight Now 10th January 2000

22. Planetary Correctness' Associated Press, 9th January 2001
http://www.aci.net/kalliste/


23. The Similarities of the Planets (and Other Celestial Objects)"
http://www.livingcosmos.com/celestial.htm, With thanks to
Lloyd Pye


24. J. Kelly Beatty  "Big-orbit Object Confounds Dynamicists",
5th April 2001, with thanks to Frank Cordell and Theo
Kermandis  <http://www.skypub.com/news/
news.shtml#bigorbit>


25. L. Moulton Howe "Deep Impact Spectra: Carbonate, PAHs
and Some Amino Precursors in Comet Tempel I"  Interview with
Dr. C. Lisse, Professor of Physics, 12/8/05  http://
www.earthfiles.com/news/news.cfm?ID=960&category=Science
With thanks to Lee Covino

# The Edgeworth-Kuiper Belt

Scientific evidence for the existence of Planet X is growing. That is not just my opinion, it is a fact. More and more astronomers appear to be incorporating into their thinking the possibility that something big is playing around with the cometary bodies that make up the Edgeworth-Kuiper Belt (sometimes more simply known as the 'Kuiper Belt').

This large belt of planetesimals was first proposed by a British researcher called Kenneth Edgeworth. His idea was first published in 1943, but there was a more significant paper published in the Monthly Notices of the Royal Astronomical Society in 1949 outlining his ideas. Two years later, the same proposal was made by the American astronomer Gerard

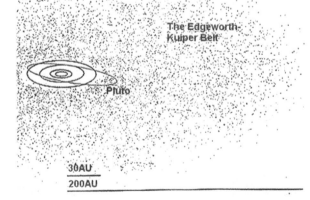

Kuiper, "in a chapter which he had contributed to a book edited by J. Allen Hynek" (1).

The now prevalent term 'Kuiper Belt' seems to have been first coined by Scott Tremaine in 1988, and was consequently used in the first paper describing the historic discovery of a solar system object beyond Pluto. This discovery was made by Dave Jewitt and Jane Luu, who entitled their paper "Discovery of the candidate Kuiper Belt Object 1992 QB1". The name quickly caught on (1).

As a result of the confusion caused by the controversial naming of this belt beyond Neptune, different researchers call it different things. Because I have a misplaced sense of patriotic duty towards all things British, I will call it the Edgeworth-Kuiper Belt, and objects within it Edgeworth-Kuiper Belt Objects (EKBOs).

The Edgeworth-Kuiper Belt is a sizeable body of planetesimals and comets, many of which have been herded into stable resonant orbits with Neptune over time, and lie within poorly-defined bands just beyond this outer gas giant. Pluto, the outermost planet, could itself be said to be a large EKBO. It has a resonant orbit with Neptune such that it avoids the larger planet, even though it periodically crosses its orbital path. In theory, all of the objects in the Edgeworth-Kuiper Belt should have orbits that are in some way related to the known outer planets.

But, as it turns out, they don't.

## 'Ten in a Bed...'

Although the sheer scale of the belt is immense, there is a problem of missing mass. The Belt shows a surprisingly large deficiency of predicted objects out to about 50 Astronomical Units, a fact that puzzles astronomers. Even though there will be times when some of these objects interact with Neptune in such a way that they are eventually ejected from the solar system, there still seems to be too few of them. The astronomers Petit, Morbidelli and Valsecchi theorized that primordial planetary embryos up to the mass of Earth could have spent time in the Edgeworth-Kuiper Belt, flinging the normal EKBOs around, and thus leading to a massive loss of comets (2).

So where are those planets now? If they were still orbiting just beyond Neptune they surely would have been found by Clyde Tombaugh over 60 years ago, as he thoroughly searched the sky for similar planets to Pluto. If they are still out there, then they are further away than this, having migrated out. It is thought that there might be Mars-sized bodies embedded in the Edgeworth-Kuiper Belt that have so far evaded detection.

Edgeworth-Kuiper Objects exhibit different orbital properties, falling naturally into sub-categories of 'classical belt' objects and 'scattered disc' objects, with further sub-divisions looming as the data-base of objects increases (3). This is a complex set of solar system objects whose system of classification is far from straightforward. The more extreme examples of these objects may be indicative of an unknown influence affecting the belt, as we shall see.

The Belt itself lies predominantly in the plane of the ecliptic, along with most of the rest of the solar system. But some of the EKBOs are inclined to the ecliptic, as is Pluto, and thus create a diffuse band in the sky. This is quite different from the more distant Oort Cloud of comets, which covers the sky in a spherical way: long-period comets arriving from the Oort Cloud do so from all regions in the heavens. Although, as we have seen, there are those who argue that the 'random' positioning of these comets around the solar system is nothing of the sort!

Between the Edgeworth-Kuiper Belt (which is more like an asteroid belt of comets) and the Oort Cloud, there is an immense gap of essentially nothing. This, I would suggest, is significant in itself. It implies the presence of something undiscovered.

Our present technological capability has allowed astronomers to detect some of the Edgeworth-Kuiper Objects that lie nearest to the orbits of Pluto and Neptune. Trying to pinpoint these hidden objects in the sky is difficult work, to the extent that objects that are discovered during a particular sky search are even difficult to confirm during later observation attempts, despite knowledge of their whereabouts. This is important, because it can require several observations over time to work out a given object's exact trajectory, which then allows astronomers to pinpoint the objects position at a later date.

Only the 'inner' part of the belt is currently within the limits of our observational capacity. But even so, astronomers are seeing examples of the more distant 'scattered disc' populations, as they are sighted during their perihelion passages just beyond Neptune. These distant objects are only observable at their closest approaches to the sun, implying that there are a great many more so-called 'scattered disc objects' beyond (3).

A system of classification for newly-discovered solar system objects is widely in use, and the registering of such objects is managed by the International Astronomical Union's (IAU) "Central Bureau," based at the Smithsonian Astrophysical Observatory in Cambridge, Massachusetts. The label attached to any given object begins simply with the year it was discovered. Then, a letter is applied for each half-monthly interval in that year, ignoring I and Z. Then, a second letter is applied denoting the order in which reports are officially received (1).

As the number of new solar system objects discovered each month steadily grew, the need arose to supplement that system with a suffix number. That is how we have arrived at a name like 2000 CR105. It was discovered in February 2000, and was one of several hundred similar official reports of Edgeworth-Kuiper Belt Objects.

## Anomalies Emerge

The Edgeworth-Kuiper Objects 2000 CR105 and 1995TL8 are 'scattered-disc objects', and exhibit orbits that are difficult to explain dynamically. They are potentially highly significant, because their orbits seem to be 'de-coupled' from the influence of the giant planets in the solar system. The implications seem to the astronomers, including Brett Gladman, to be significant (3).

His team have speculated that the anomalous scattered disc objects of the Edgeworth-Kuiper Belt have been subject to gravitational forces 'out there', expanding their perihelia distances beyond that allowed by normal interactions with the classical EKBO 'shepherd', Neptune. The researchers offer a number of possibilities to explain this, all involving large objects passing through, or even currently resident in the Edgeworth-Kuiper Belt. These include perturbations caused by passing stars (see also (4), now-absent primordial embryos passing through the belt as they were ejected from the solar system (as detailed above), and, of course, Planet X (and even Planet XI, Planet XII, etc.) lying undiscovered within the EKB (3).

One of the team, Matthew Holman, of the Harvard-Smithsonian Centre for Astrophysics, made no bones of the fact that he thought it entirely possible that a Mars-sized body might lie within the extended Edgeworth-Kuiper Belt, and that such a body could easily have escaped detection thus far, despite the infra-red sky searches carried out to date (5). This contrasted sharply with the previous scientific attitude towards the case for a substantial Planet X.

## 2004 DW

Dr. Holman's optimism is not without foundation. The luminosity of objects in the solar system drops off dramatically with distance from the sun. Large bodies, only slightly further away than those already discovered in the vicinity of Neptune and Pluto, remain to be discovered. Examples of recent massive EKBOs include Quaoar in 2002, a spherical object the size of a small moon, and Sedna, a more substantial body still, which brought with it a whole raft of problems. The floodgates of discovery appeared to be opening.

In 2004, a substantial planetoid was detected 4.4 billion miles (48AU) from the sun. Currently known as 2004DW, it may be 1400 kilometers across, and orbits the sun every 300 years. It has a high eccentricity, a remarkable 20 degrees from the plane of the ecliptic, which brings forward questions about its origins. One of the scientists who discovered this object, Mike Brown, an associate professor of planetary astronomy at Caltech, had this to say about the discovery's possible implications:

"It's now only a matter of time before something is going to be discovered out there that will change our entire view of the outer solar system (6).

This was an ambitious statement that was partly due to the discovery of 2004 DW, but may also have be driven by all the new evidence coming in about the Edgeworth-Kuiper Belt. Mike Brown's team went on to discover Sedna, the most dramatic discovery so far. But it is not just the objects that are being found that are amazing scientists, it is also a certain lack of objects...

## Standing at the Edge

In the last year or two, the astronomical community has been shocked by another finding about the Edgeworth-Kuiper Belt. According to the consensus of scientific opinion, it was expected that the Belt would extend beyond the current ability to observe objects, and that as the technical proficiency to capture dimmer objects grew, our knowledge of deeper objects in the Belt would expand. However, workers on the cutting-edge of this field soon discovered something that was not expected, and not readily explainable. The Disc stopped.

The EKB has an empty band in it known as the "Kuiper Cliff" or "Gap" where the predicted distribution of planetesimals simply is not observed. The problem is a significant one, because the population of 'EKBOs' beyond this point should actually be greater than those within it. This is because they are too distant to have been disrupted by Neptune and the other planets.

The acquired observational knowledge of this area is currently limited, but it appears from work carried out by Allen, et al. that the populations of EKBOs here drops off unexpectedly, and somewhat mysteriously (7,8). It either marks the end of the Belt, or a sizeable gap. In the terminology of the astrophysicists, the Edgeworth-Kuiper Belt is "truncated".

This has profound implications for our understanding of the formation of the solar system. In fact, such a predicament has allowed the idea of an undiscovered distant planet to creep back into the thoughts of astronomers. A lack of objects beyond this 'cliff' would imply that the original proto-planetary disc of the sun was curtailed at this point; an unexpected and unlikely discovery.

Various ideas have been proposed to explain the Gap. We have already noted the possibility that giant planetesimals may have been prevalent in the early EKB, causing chaos. Then there's the Planet X debate. Another possibility is that a passing star may have torn part of the outer belt away (9).

This finding presents a major problem that several research groups have been urgently attempting to address, and, as we shall see, some tentative conclusions appear to be pointing in the direction of the Dark Star Theory.

## Perihelion Beyond Neptune

I had been corresponding with an independent researcher named John Lee (aka 'Rajasun') who, like me, was not a professional astronomer, but had learned a great deal of technical information by immersing himself in papers and books about the outer solar system. He was of the opinion that the brown dwarf could not travel too far into the planetary zone during perihelion. In fact, he felt that it would remain beyond the orbit of Neptune for the entirety of its perihelion passage. I could see that his technical arguments were good ones, although they were in direct contrast to the case put forward by Sitchin, that 'Nibiru' was capable of reaching as close as the asteroid belt during perihelion.

John Lee's work seemed to mesh well with this new material about how objects in the Edgeworth-Kuiper Belt were behaving, and I began to wonder whether he might be onto something. Perhaps this more distant belt of comets and planetesimals was actually the 'hammered bracelet' that Sitchin wrote about, not the Asteroid Belt. After all, there were now two 'asteroid belts' in the solar system to choose from, a situation that was not well known when Sitchin had written most of his books.

I began to wonder whether the Dark Star's perihelion passage occurred beyond Neptune. Neptune is not visible from Earth at all, of course, and it was quite late on in the history of astronomy before it was first observed. How could a Dark Star have been recorded in classical times, then?

Nibiru was once a luminous, glowing planet, as described in the ancient texts. I wondered whether an approach to the planetary zone would reveal these characteristics, as the old brown dwarf crossed through the Heliopause and encountered the solar wind. After all, we know that these brown dwarfs are highly active magnetically, and the influence of the Solar Wind within the confines of the Heliopause might have been sufficient to 're-ignite' the old flame.

John needed convincing though, because he was quite sure that a brown dwarf as old as the solar system would not be capable of emitting any light, no matter what the circumstances. And since we are unable to see either Uranus of Neptune at these distances (and they are sizeable planets in their own right), then the brown dwarf beyond Neptune would also be too faint to see without a good telescope. His viewpoint was characteristically persuasive, based as it was on the conventional scientific wisdom. This led to some soul searching on my part.

We had an on-going debate about this issue for some time. At the crux of the problem, was whether the rogue brown dwarf could ever become visible from Earth. If it did appear as a flaring red star, rather like a comet on fire, then this could have created a series of mythological descriptions, which formed the basis of much of my earlier work. If it was invisible throughout its orbit around the sun then I had a big problem on my hands.

To try and solve this problem, we sought various scientific opinions. This in itself was a tricky business: most scientists were making a point of avoiding the subject. Fortunately, John was sufficiently versed in the technicalities of astrophysics to engage professional astronomers in debate, and even to precipitate new research on his behalf!

Eventually, I came to realize that the visible aspect of 'Nibiru', as described by Sitchin, might not actually be the Dark Star itself. Perhaps 'Planet X' was a planet orbiting the Dark Star that somehow got significantly closer to us as the distant Dark Star moved through the Edgeworth-Kuiper Belt. As John and I contemplated these ideas, new calculations were being made by members of the scientific community which provided more grist for the Planet X mill.

## The Gap in the EKB

Matthew Holman's considered opinion about the possibility of an unknown perturber affecting EKBOs was strengthened in 2002, by work published by Adrian Brunini and Mario Melita (10). Dr. Brunini has been a long-standing Planet X hunter within the professional astronomical community, and works at the observatory at the La Plata National University in Argentina. He had teamed up with Dr. Melita, an astronomer and mathematician at Queen Mary College in London, to model the effect that an embedded planet-sized body might have on the Edgeworth-Kuiper Belt.

Their mathematical modelling aimed at gauging the effect of a Mars-sized body orbiting at only 60AU from the sun, about twice the distance of Neptune. This seemed to me to be a remarkable leap of faith to be even contemplating such a body, given the usual vitriol about Planet X. Just a couple of months before, an astronomer from California was publicly discrediting any form of Planet X research, saying that it was strictly for the loony fringe and, I quote, "chicken-little" writers. While it may be true that the term 'Planet X' has become synonymous with speculative pseudo-science - particularly in the United States - the paper published by Brunini and Melita stands as a testament to the actual scientific potential of this exciting idea.

Of course, the wording used in scientific papers covering this subject is carefully chosen to be adequately removed from the Planet X fever more commonly found on the Internet. Many astronomers prefer to use different terminology, mainly because the term 'Planet X' itself can mean a variety of things (11). Also, astronomers, like all academics and professionals, are well-versed in the use of jargon.

They have at their disposal a wider selection of words to describe the various Planet X possibilities, and can elucidate their meaning in a more clear and technical way. In a way, they can protect themselves from association with the fringe by their use of this jargon. Even so, the name 'Planet X' has a lot of popular appeal, and the term is a generally accepted one among science writers in the media (12). Succinctly put, the potential for the discovery of Planet X sells science magazines and newspapers.

Anyway, Brunini and Melita have tried to address the problem posed by the gaping hole, or empty band, in the EKB, which begins at 48 AU and is thought to extend to 76AU (13). Although, it's quite possible that it never resumes, and that a complete gaping hole extends right out to the inner Oort cloud. Even given the emerging distinction between various divisions of the Edgeworth-Kuiper Belt, such a hole was a surprising discovery. It requires an urgent explanation.

The answer proposed lies with an undiscovered planetary object that has been sweeping that part of the EKB clean over billions of years. Planet X appears to have been ploughing through the Edgeworth-Kuiper Belt, propelling cometary bodies out of the solar system. This sweeping action is considered to be roughly similar to the formation of gaps in the rings of Saturn, which have been carved out by the larger bodies orbiting the gas giant. Over the course of many millions of years, the statistical distribution of EKBOs in the massive belt beyond Neptune has been altered to such an extent, that perhaps only the presence of the perturbing body can explain how the observed data seems to vary with the theoretical expectation of population densities.

Brunini and Melita tested their hypothesis by mathematically modelling the Edgeworth-Kuiper Belt, and this time including an additional planet in its midst. They assumed the object circles the sun at a similar sort of distance as the Kuiper Gap, and they tested for various angles of inclination, planetary mass and orbital eccentricity. They then produced a set of parameters which could best define the orbit of the alleged planet.

They theorized that the planet would move neatly within the boundaries already proposed for the Kuiper Gap, and that it would be somewhat inclined to the ecliptic. This would then help to explain why it had not yet been discovered. These parameters seemed to produce sets of data that agreed relatively well with observations of the EKB:

"The size of the gap cleared by such an object depends on the eccentricity of the planetoid... According to Trujillo and Brown (13), the cut-off in the EKB would begin at ~48AU and the distribution could resume at 76AU. Thus, a consistent value for the perihelion of the planetoid would be ~49AU and its aphelion ~78AU: then the corresponding semi-major axis would be ~62AU and the eccentricity ~0.21. As mentioned above a large inclination would ensure that it remains undetected at present. The effect of such an object...would be roughly consistent with current observation" (10).

Based on these findings, Brunini and Melita encouraged the search for Mars-sized bodies embedded in the EKB, citing the research efforts of Gladman, et al. (13) and Collander-Brown, et al. (14) on scattered disc objects as corroborating evidence, to support the now-familiar call for the hunt for Planet X.


## Planet X in the Media


Their paper created a stir in Britain, hitting the news-stands through the Independent (15) and the popular science magazine New Scientist (12). I also placed this new information in the alternative community's domain, which at the time was rather taken with the idea that Planet X was about to bring about the end of the world, as had been comprehensively recorded by Mark Hazelwood (16), amongst others. For some reason, Planet X had become synonymous with an imminent End of the World.

It is true that a planet-sized comet moving through the solar system would not be without its risks to Earth, but the idea has gotten rather tied up with Millennium Fever of late. More level-headed academics have pointed out that the Sumerians didn't even have a word for the equivalent of Apocalypse (17). Which is a moot point.

Anyway, I naively thought that this exciting new scientific research would temper the debate with some rationalism. Instead, the finding appeared to be simply ignored by the Planet X 'community'. Without the accompanying threat of world-wide apocalypse, the scientific progress towards a real tenth planet, no matter how grounded in good science it might be, was not enough to stem the tide of Cataclysm fever.

Perhaps that was because an object embedded within the Edgeworth-Kuiper Belt seemed, on the face of it, to be no more of a threat to us than distant Pluto. How could such a body equate with a mighty mythical body that I had likened to a brown dwarf? If this body was a 'weapon of mass destruction', then the dossier outlining the threat it posed needed 'sexing up'! Well, jokes aside, I could see plenty of potential within the Brunini and Melita paper for a larger, more distant body causing the effect they were studying. I could also see related mechanisms to account for catastrophism on Earth, and other solar system planets. Just not in 2003.

## British Eccentricity?

There are a number of reasons to believe that their findings are simply the cautious side of a larger spectrum of possibilities for a Planet X roaming the Edgeworth-Kuiper belt. As noted above, the greater body of scattered EKBOs lie beyond the assumed 'outer' cliff-face of the gap, and are beyond our current detection ability. The assumed outer limit of the gap is not fixed in stone. It may extend further out, which would allow for a more eccentric orbit for the Perturber, and this will be looked at in more detail in the next chapter. In other words, a relatively circular orbit for Planet X cannot be confirmed at this time, and was simply a premise built into Brunini and Melita's calculations.

Their work assumes that the Kuiper Gap is an empty band within a larger extended disc; it assumes that the disc restarts at 76AU. I rather suspect that it does not. Instead, I consider it likely that the Kuiper 'Cliff' is exactly that; a cut-off point that extends 2000AU, all the way to the inner Oort Cloud. I suggest that this massive gap has been almost completely swept out by the Dark Star!

I corresponded with Mario Melita after he published his paper, and suggested to him that a more massive Planet X might be following a more eccentric orbit. I wondered how a planetary body could have escaped detection if it was currently as close as they had speculated in their 2002 paper, even if it was currently located away from the ecliptic (where most of the searches for outer solar system bodies take place).

Somewhat surprisingly, he agreed with me and explained that he was currently running calculations to test how a more elliptical orbit for the undiscovered planet would fit the data. As he noted in his previous paper quoted above, the effect of the object is 'roughly consistent' with current observations. Dr. Melita indicated that his results so far were encouraging, and that a more elliptical orbit for a bigger planet may create a better fit with the observed data:

"I agree that the scenario of a more distant, more massive planet is possible. I am presently studying that possibility. In fact it seems that the agreement with the observed EKBO distribution is slightly better." (18)

The importance of this research by Drs. Brunini and Melita led New Scientist to include the findings as one of its 13 unsolved mysteries of science. Aptly numbered 10 in the series, the author of the article, Michael Brooks, explained that the Kuiper Cliff is where the density of space rocks in the Edgeworth-Kuiper Belt drops off dramatically. There seems to be no viable explanation except for the presence of a hidden terrestrial-sized planet exerting its influence by sweeping this area clean.

The article then quotes Alan Stern, an astronomer at the Southwest Research Institute in Boulder, Colorado, who remarks that the evidence for the existence of 'Planet X' is "compelling"[1] (19).

## Reconsidering the Perihelion Distance

It seems that observed data regarding EKBOs can be arrived at by increasing the orbital eccentricity of the proposed planet as it becomes more massive. So, a smallish terrestrial planet, perhaps a few times the mass of Mars, would create the observed effect when orbiting the sun in a roughly circular orbit, while embedded in the Edgeworth-Kuiper Belt. If we want to consider a bigger planet, then its orbit must become more elliptical.

Given that my interest lies in the potential for Planet X to be a small brown dwarf, the eccentricity would have to be fairly high. Which, of course, is what is anticipated for the 'planet' Nibiru as described by Zecharia Sitchin. However, this encouraging correlation would encounter severe difficulties when considering Sitchin's perihelion distance of about 4AU, i.e. the asteroid belt between Mars and Jupiter. Could Planet X cause both the observed 'sweeping out' of the Edgeworth-Kuiper Belt and still go on to perform a perihelion passage through the Asteroid Belt?

To answer this, we must consider the angle of inclination of Nibiru's orbit with the ecliptic. If the Dark Star's orbit was along the plane of the other planets, then a parabolic perihelion passage might just include both the asteroid belt and parts of the Edgeworth-Kuiper Belt. But the more inclined the orbit, the smaller the interaction between the Edgeworth-Kuiper Objects and the rogue planet. This is because the EKB is, for the most part, a flat disc

As the orbit of a proposed brown dwarf becomes increasingly inclined to the ecliptic, then its destabilizing effect upon solar system objects increases. This is due to the "Kozai effect", and would limit the inclination of a Jupiter-sized Planet X orbit. If the inclination is too high, the solar system would be a more chaotic place than it appears to be. The astronomer Brett Gladman explained to me that a massive undiscovered planet cannot exist with a large inclination with respect to the ecliptic because if it did "the Kozai effect would tend to destabilize the planetary orbits" (20).

It seems as though the Dark Star's orbit cannot be greatly inclined from the ecliptic. This generates a substantial problem for Zecharia Sitchin. He has argued that Nibiru moves through the planetary solar system at an angle of about 30 degrees to the ecliptic. As a result, a number of important ancient texts set out this mathematical relationship as being vital to the understanding of our Cosmos. But the Kozai effect means that such a highly inclined passage would cause chaos in the solar system if Nibiru turned out to be a very massive planet.

So, either Nibiru is a relatively small planet, like Mars, or it behaves itself and moves along the ecliptic like the majority of the known planets. If Planet X moves along the plane of the ecliptic as it approaches the planetary zone, then it would brush past not just the EKB, but also the orbits of the outer planets. Would this not destabilize these planets in this case too?

In 1985, Jack Hills modelled the passage of a Nemesis-type object through the planetary zone, producing a set of data analogous to the debate we're considering here. In that study, it was found that the rogue body would have to be at least 10 Jupiter masses to cause any havoc (21). So, there is clearly room for quite extreme scenarios, which will surprise many.

But this would be applicable to a single passage of a sub-brown dwarf. If such an object moved through the planetary zone repeatedly every 3600 years, then statistically there is bound to be an observable effect generated in the orbits of the planets. Given the relatively concentric nature of the current orbits of the planets, it seems more likely that a body as sizeable as a small brown dwarf has not moved through the planetary zone for some time.

Perhaps a smaller, terrestrial-sized Planet X could move through the planetary zone unhindered, then, as long as it wasn't unduly inclined to the ecliptic. This would be a reasonable compromise, and would work well. But it means that the Dark Star does not move closer to the sun than the Kuiper Cliff at 48AU. That marks the smallest perihelion distance possible. In fact, it may be even greater than this.


## A Further Problem for Nibiru


The scenario outlined by Sitchin has an additional problem to face. It is clear that a planet moving through a cloud or belt of objects will substantially disrupt that body of comets. That is what is observed for long-period comets, for grooves in the rings of Saturn, and probably explains the Kuiper Gap in the EKB. So the same principle must surely apply to the Asteroid Belt.

If Nibiru really did achieve its perihelion transit through the asteroid belt every 3600 years, this body of asteroids would have been broken up completely long ago! Its very presence suggests that Sitchin's claims must be incorrect regarding this point. The perihelion transit must occur further out.

In that sense, my own previous speculations require more careful consideration, built as they have been upon Sitchin's original premises. Yes, a small brown dwarf need not have a large effect on the other planets during a fly-by (20), but repeated passages through the planetary zone would presumably build up the probability that the eccentricity of the planetary orbits would eventually be affected. That they are observed to be relatively stable reflects the likelihood that Planet X's transgressions are experienced beyond the outer planets. And the more massive Planet X is said to be, the more likely this argument holds.

Yet, there is a tremendous body of evidence to suggest that an anomalous planet has been observed by humans in the past, and that it is somehow connected with the enigmatic concept of Nibiru. A brown dwarf in the EKB is too distant to be observed. This means that there is still a piece of the jigsaw missing. Something penetrates into the planetary zone and becomes visible to the unaided eye. The question is; what? We will ponder this problem in the next chapter.

## Predictions

Given the good data set astronomers have collated about the Kuiper Cliff cut-off at 48AU, the likelihood is that this feature in the EKB does indeed mark the edge of the effect caused by Nibiru's perihelion 'sweep'. Its actual perihelion distance would be further out still. Also, its eccentricity would be substantially greater than that envisioned by Brunini and Melita in their 2002 paper. The scope for improvement in their model rests with the semi-major axis and eccentricity, allowing for an object that achieves aphelion much further from the sun than 78AU.

Our current knowledge of objects orbiting the sun beyond 76AU is very patchy at best. The resumption of scattered disc objects beyond this distance is an expectation according to theoretical models, rather than a fact based upon empirical data. If the scattered disc objects beyond 76AU actually aren't there in any great numbers, then a more eccentric, and probably mildly inclined orbit would be the conclusion drawn. Because something would have to be removing the comets from the Edgeworth-Kuiper Belt at these distances. And I suspect this will prove to be the case.

So instead of Planet X being embedded in the EKB at the relative close proximity of ~60AU, its aphelion distance could prove to be much, much further out. The Kuiper Cliff phenomenon could

have been created by Planet X repeatedly cutting through the disc
as it approaches its perihelion passage.    This scenario seems
consistent with the work of the astronomer Jack Hills, who
considered the effect of a passage of a small dwarf 'star' through
the solar system, and the orbital configuration for that body if it
were to become captured by the sun (21). As I've discussed
before (22), his mathematical modelling allowed him to conclude
that such a massive body could even be captured by the sun into a
weakly bound orbit which was both highly eccentric and prone to
dissociation.

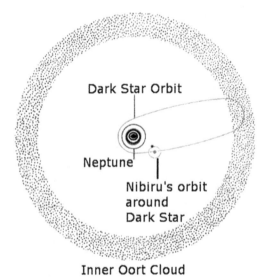

**Dark Star Orbit**

**Neptune**

**Nibiru's orbit
around
Dark Star**

**Inner Oort Cloud**

I believe that the Dark Star did once upon a time move among the
planets, causing disruption at that time.   Long since then, the
planets have migrated back into stable orbits, and the Dark Star
has been exiled to a place beyond the Edgeworth-Kuiper Belt,
where it continues to roam in an eccentric fashion.

## Chapter 8 References

1. J. Davies "Beyond Pluto" Cambridge University Press 2001

2. J-M. Petit, A. Morbidelli & G. Valsecchi "Large Scattered Planetesimals and the Excitation of the Small Body Belts" Icarus, 141, 367-387 (1999)

3. B. Gladman, M. Holman, T. Grav, J. Kavelaars, P. Nicholson, K. Aksnes & J-M. Petit "Evidence for an Extended Disk" Icarus, 157, pp269-79 (2002)

4. S. Ida, J. Larwood & A. Burkett "Evidence for Early Stellar Encounters in the Orbital Distribution of Edgeworth-Kuiper Belt Objects" The Astrophysical Journal, 528: pp351-6, (2000)

5. J. Kelly Beatty "Big-orbit Object Confounds Dynamicists" http://www.skypub.com/news/news.shtml#bigorbit 5th April 2001

6. C.I.T. News Release "Planetoid found in Kuiper Belt, maybe the biggest yet" 20th February 2004, http://spaceflightnow.com/news/n0402/20kuiper/

7. R. Allen, G. Bernstein & R. Malhotra "The Edge of the Solar System", The Astrophysical Journal, 549, 241-4, 2001

8. R. Allen, G. Bernstein & R. Malhotra "Observational Limits on a Distant Cold Kuiper Belt" AJ, astro-ph/0209421v1, 2002

9. R.L. Allen "Current Research:Observational Limits on the Distant Kuiper Belt" http://www.astro.ubc.ca/~lallen/kbo/thesis.html

10. Brunini & M. Melita "The Existence of a Planet beyond 50AU and the Orbital Distribution of the Classical Edgeworth-Kuiper Belt Objects" Icarus, 160, pp32-43 (2002), extract reproduced with kind permission of Dr. Mario Melita

11. Correspondence from Dr. Brett Gladman, 24th January 2003

12. H. Couper & N. Henbest "The Hunt for Planet X" New Scientist, pp30-4, 14th December 2002

13. C. Trujillo & M. Brown "A correlation between inclination and color in the classical Kuiper Belt" The Astrophysics Journal 566, pp125-128 (2002)

14. S. Collander-Brown, A. Fitzsimmons, E. Fletcher, M. Irwin and I. Williams "The Scattered Trans-Neptunian Object 1998 XY95" Mon. Not. R. Astron. Soc 325, pp972-78 (2001)

15. C. Arthur "More signs that solar system has tenth planet" http://news.independent.co.uk/world/science_medical/ story.jsp?story=360803  12 December 2002

16. M. Hazlewood "Delicate Earth History Science Planet X" 2003

17. Dr Irving Finkel (Assistant Keeper, Cuneiform Collections) in 'Waiting for the Apocalypse' Video, by 'The Clockwork Team', (consisting of Parameshwaran Ravindranathan, Samit Basu and Jaideep Undurti) © University of Westminster 2003

18. Correspondence from Mario Melita, 15th January 2003, reproduced with kind permission

19. M. Brooks "13 things that do not make sense" New Scientist, p30, 19th March 2005, with thanks to Peter Gersten

20. Correspondence from Brett Gladman, 30th January 2003

21. J.G. Hills "The Passage of a 'Nemesis'-like object through the Planetary System" Astron. J. 90, Number 9, 1876-1882 (1985)

22. A. Lloyd "Winged Disc: The Dark Star Theory" MSS 2001

# CHAPTER 9

# Planet of Crossing

We established in the last chapter that the Dark Star no longer moves through the planetary zone. Scientific evidence points to its existence beyond the recorded limits of the Edgeworth-Kuiper Belt. It presence there is felt by the objects that move through that belt; some of them show signs of being acutely affected by an external influence such as the Dark Star. We will go on later to look at these examples.

But the last chapter also brought up the problem of the visible appearance of Nibiru. If Nibiru is the Dark Star and it lies more than 50AU away, then it is invisible to us for the entire term of its orbit. It could never have been seen from Earth. Yet Sitchin's account of Nibiru describes a highly observable phenomenon, one held in high esteem by the ancient Mesopotamians.

As we saw in Chapter 2, the account of Nibiru is based upon Sitchin's reading of the *Enuma Elish*, the Babylonian creation myth. This apparently outlines the creation of the asteroid belt from the partial destruction of the watery 'planet' Tiamat by the planet/star Marduk, whose 49th name is Nibiru. Marduk itself appears to be the Dark Star. So what is this visible phenomenon called Nibiru?

## Ancient References

According to Zecharia Sitchin, Nibiru meant "Planet of Crossing" in the sense of crossing over a boundary or barrier. It is a metaphoric cosmic "ferry". He also pointed to the following quotes from the Babylonian version of the *Enuma Elish* to further clarify its character:

*"NIBIRU: The Crossroads of Heaven and Earth he shall occupy. Above and below, they shall not go across; They must await him.*

*NIBIRU: Planet which is brilliant in the heavens. He holds the central position; to him they must play homage.*

*NIBIRU: It is he who without tiring, the midst of Tiamat keeps crossing, let 'CROSSING' be his name - the one who occupies the midst"* (1).

For Zecharia Sitchin, these excerpts from the Enuma Elish provide the additional and conclusive information that allows him to arrive at the claim that Nibiru crossed the asteroid belt during its perihelion passage. However, although it is abundantly clear to any reader of the Enuma Elish that Nibiru is an astronomical phenomenon of some sort, the evidence as to what it might be is ambiguous at best.

Previous work by the scholar and Jesuit priest Franz X. Kugler, entitled "Sternkunde und Sterndienst in Babel" appears to have influenced Sitchin. It was here that the idea was first proposed that the central figure in the epic, Marduk, might be likened to a "fast-moving celestial body, orbiting in a great elliptical path just like a comet" (1). The argument is compelling, given the various clues in the Enuma Elish.

The path travelled by Marduk is 'loftier' and 'grander' than the rest of the 'gods'. It implies that Marduk lies beyond them, as we have described for the Dark Star. Yet, still, the direct quotes about the associated phenomenon 'Nibiru' describe something observable.

Kugler's argument seems to have been the intellectual seed that sparked off Sitchin's wide-ranging theory about the planet Nibiru, and the pantheon of gods associated with it. Since 'regular' comets sweep through the planetary zone during their perihelion passages, it must have seemed reasonable to Sitchin that Nibiru/Marduk would behave in the same way, particularly as its point of origin as a member of the solar family began with its catastrophic encounter with the celestial Tiamat at a location between Mars and Jupiter.

The fact that this solution for the meaning of "Nibiru" was considered by scholars before Sitchin is lost on many of his critics, particularly those in the academic community.

# Waiting for the Apocalypse

In 2003, I was interviewed on film by three post-graduate journalism students, who were completing their studies at the University of Westminster, London. They were making a documentary called "Waiting for the Apocalypse", which featured several prominent astronomers, including the celebrated Astronomer Royal, Sir Martin Rees (2).

The video outlined three possible threats from space: impact events from asteroids and comets, the infiltration of cosmic viruses into the atmosphere, and the coming of Nibiru. Unfortunately, this fascinating video is not available commercially, but I have published some details about it onto the Internet (3). I felt compelled to do this because the video contained some controversial criticisms levelled against Zecharia Sitchin by two Sumerologists, who are curators at the British Museum.

They contended that Nibiru is actually the planet Jupiter and that the original Sumerian word simply "means a pass, means a passing over from one place to another" (3). They questioned Zecharia Sitchin's scholarship, even wondering whether he had ever worked with the cuneiform texts themselves. I wrote to him about this, and he responded with the following thoughts, emphasizing the long history of this debate:

"The notion that Nibiru is just another name for Jupiter goes back to the debate a century or so ago between Kugler and Winkler and their writings on 'Chaldean' astronomy, when Pluto had not yet been discovered. They assumed that the ancients, without telescopes, could not be aware of planets beyond Saturn, so when they encountered in astronomical texts more planetary names they assumed it just (was) one more name for Jupiter or Mars etc.

"(At least we have an acknowledgement that NIBIRU is (a) named in Mesopotamian astronomical texts, (b) is a planet -- i.e. Sitchin did not invent Nibiru as a figment of imagination. I deal with that at length in "The 12th Planet".)

"Establishment thinking has been thus: Someone (say Sitchin) saying this or that means 'B' must be wrong, because everyone knows that it means 'A' (4).

This seems to answer the criticisms levelled by Christopher Walker and Dr. Irving Finkel of the British Museum. Zecharia

Sitchin's work is controversial in many ways, but, regarding the specific meaning of "Nibiru", his theory was not plucked out of mid-air. There was some scholarly basis under-pinning it in the work of Franz X. Kugler.

However, further questions remain unanswered, as we will now consider.

## The Solution

For years, I have puzzled over the many anomalous and often intractable problems presented by Zecharia Sitchin's Nibiru. A planet that behaves like a comet did not seem to me likely to support life forms similar, if not identical, to us. In 1999, I proposed that the only way that sufficient warmth could be generated among the comets, would be if such life existed on a planet orbiting a Dark Star that was itself orbiting the sun.

For various reasons, I suggested that the Dark Star was itself Nibiru, passing directly through the planetary solar system during perihelion with its own retinue of planets. This was a bold claim, given the size of the brown dwarf required. But I now realize that I was wrong, for some of technical reasons we have already covered.

I remain absolutely convinced that the Dark Star exists, and that it is a binary 'star' orbiting the sun that approaches the planetary zone every several thousand years. But I now believe that this Dark Star is not itself Nibiru. It is simply Nibiru's own parent 'star'. I think it probable that neither the Dark Star, nor the terrestrial Homeworld of the Anunnaki, are easily seen from Earth. The closest approach of the Dark Star is way beyond Pluto, through the so-called Kuiper Gap at the edge of Edgeworth-Kuiper Belt.

What I am proposing is that the observed planet Nibiru is the outermost planet of the Dark Star system. And apart from it being unable to maintain life, Nibiru is essentially how Sitchin describes it; a reddish terrestrial planet that brightens with a cometary aura when moving amongst our sun's family of familiar planets. Nibiru itself is a massive comet the size of a planet, much as Sitchin initially suggested.

But, there is no one living on this frozen rock. It is a barren outpost of the Dark Star planetary system. It appears in the sky merely as a sign that the Dark Star Marduk has once again arrived at perihelion, and for this reason the word Nibiru became one of Marduk's 50 names.

Nibiru is a celestial 'ferry', moving across the cosmic darkness, to the hidden Dark Star.

## That Strange Orbit

My next suggestion is that Nibiru does not appear to orbit the sun properly when viewed from Earth!

This is a remarkably bizarre claim, I know. But it is part of the problem posed by Sitchin's Nibiru. Indeed, it was the primary objection levelled at me by Dr. John Murray, the English astronomer who wrote a paper providing indirect evidence of a brown dwarf orbiting the sun. (He also appears on the documentary "Waiting for the Apocalypse" (2).

Dr. Murray looked at the set of constellations that Nibiru passed through at perihelion and stated, frankly, that the body was simply not orbiting the sun (5). This seemed to create a gaping hole in Sitchin's theory. At the time, I put this down to possible misinterpretation of ancient texts. Now, I realize that this anomaly was actually part of the puzzle...Sitchin's incomprehensible orbit turned out to be right all along.

## The 3-Body Solution

The solution I am proposing neatly answers a number of other problems. In fact, everything seems to fall in to place quite neatly.

Nibiru is seen to enter the planetary solar system moving backwards through the sky (the so-called 'retrograde motion' of Nibiru). This is one of the puzzling aspects of Sitchin's account. The backwards motion of this body has always implied that it could not have been an original member of the solar system, making its initial capture nothing short of miraculous. Is there a way that a body can appear to move backwards, even though it is actually moving in the 'normal' direction through the sky?

Any student of the stars will recognize this pattern. The outer planets are sometimes seen to undergo retrograde motion, particularly Mars. This was a major puzzle for early astronomers, who charted the movements of the wandering planets across the heavens.

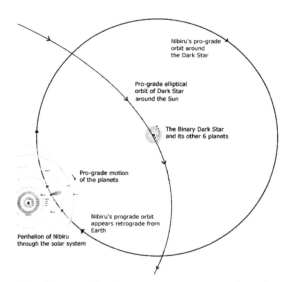

Why did some of the planets seem to stop, and then, for a short while, move backwards? This motion was due to a phenomenon called 'parallax'. As the Earth spun relatively quickly around the sun, an observer looking out into the solar system would see planets overtaken in a relative sense. Their motion was seemingly negated, and from an observational point of view, temporarily reversed by the actual movement of the Earth around the sun.

Before Copernicus released that the sun was the centre of the solar system, this effect was quite inexplicable. It resulted in models of the solar system that allowed for additional movements of the outer planets around their own 'spheres'.

I think that something similar is going on with Nibiru. Let us say that Nibiru is a rocky planet at the edge of the Dark Star system, rather like Pluto is in the sun's. Let us say that Nibiru's orbit is quite extended. It seems quite possible then, that as the two halves of the binary star system move towards each other at perihelion, that the outer rims of each system would overlap. The outermost planet of the Dark Star system might enter the planetary zone of the solar system, becoming a visible comet.

One might also conclude that Pluto, and perhaps other outer Solar planets temporarily enter the Dark Star system, moving within the orbit of Nibiru. Perhaps that is why tiny Pluto's orbit is eccentric and inclined; such a 'crossing' alters its orbit over time. The other planets would be too large to significantly perturb, being significant gas and ice giants bound more heavily to the sun.

Such a scenario affects the way the outer planet of the Dark Star system would be perceived by an observer on Earth. In the same way that the outer planets appeared to pre-Copernican star-gazers to be moving backwards when they weren't, Nibiru also seems to be moving backwards. But this, too, is an illusion.

## The Dark Star System

I now believe that the Dark Star orbits the sun in a similar way to the other planets; pro-grade. This must be the case, because otherwise its capture by our sun would have been a statistical improbability. It seems much more likely that Marduk, the Dark Star, has always orbited the sun, having emerged from the sun's birth cluster as a binary. As such, it must have formed within the proto-planetary disc of the sun, moving uniformly around it, like the other planets.

This removes the difficulty posed by a 'capture' scenario, which is statistically unlikely, although not impossible. The pro-grade orbit is also in keeping with the discovery of Sedna, which also has a pro-grade orbit. I strongly suspect that there is a relationship between the orbits of Sedna and the Dark Star; probably taking the form of a resonant orbit. Indeed, the movement of a brown dwarf through the Edgeworth-Kuiper Belt at perihelion would explain many the apparent anomalies of the bodies found in its scattered disc. It makes sense of the science.

There seem to be seven planets in the binary Dark Star system, according to the myth. I suggest that one of the inner planets is a habitable world similar to Earth. It is warmed by its proximity to the brown dwarf, and is bathed in its very dim, reddish light. I will call this the Homeworld.

All of the planets orbit the Dark Star in a pro-grade movement, in keeping with the initial formation of the binary star system 4.6 billion years ago. They also orbit the Dark Star in much less time than it takes for it to transit perihelion around the sun. Even the outermost planet, which cuts through the outer planetary system of the sun, is moving faster than the Dark Star.

## Relative Velocities

To explain the consequences of this, it might help to create a model in our minds. Let us imagine ourselves to be standing in the centre of a large field. The field is circumnavigated by a curving road, reaching its closest point directly in front of us at the gate. One can readily imagine a car travelling around the field from left to right. We could watch its motion and confirm that it was moving in a clockwise direction from our point of view.

Let us imagine that a fairground is coming to town today, and that various vehicles carrying the fairground rides are travelling along the road, left to right. We might wave at the drivers as they pass the gate. One of the big trucks is carrying one of those spinning rides which people stand in and are held against the sides by centrifugal force. It looks like half a hat box and sits squarely on top of the truck.

This spinning ride is so big that its outer edge hangs over the hedge of our field. The fairground people must have been in a hurry today because they left the brake of the ride off, and as a result it has started spinning in the wind, whilst atop the truck. It is spinning around in a clockwise manner, in the same way as the truck is moving clockwise around the road.

Whenever trucks have oversized loads they place a red piece of cloth, or flag, at the most extreme point, to make sure that other road-users don't accidentally knock into it. Today is no exception. The driver of the truck has attached a red flag to our spinning fairground ride, and so it is also moving around the truck clockwise.

Standing in the centre of our field, we watch the truck slowly drive around us. The fairground ride is turning on top of it, which we can see because the sides of the ride are visibly moving. During every revolution the attached red flag also appears.

We focus our attention on the red flag. We can only see it when it spins around along the nearside of the truck, and this happens to be where the oversized fairground ride overhangs the hedge of our field. For a short while during each revolution of the ride the red flag seems to move into our field, and seems to be moving right to left.

This is how Nibiru appears to us, like the red flag. We only see it when it enters our field; our planetary solar system. Because it is revolving clockwise around a central point on the truck, we see it moving only in reverse, even though the truck, or Dark Star system, is actually moving forward along the road at the same time.

The result is that, although the Dark Star and its outermost planet are actually moving pro-grade, from the point of view of an observer on Earth, the outermost planet is seen to move retrograde across the sky. This explains a long-standing anomaly.

## Nibiru's Apparent Transit

I contend that the outermost planet of the Dark Star system is Nibiru and that it is seen from Earth as a planetary comet, moving backwards through the sky. I don't think it moves into our system anywhere as close as the Asteroid Belt, though. It would be too readily perturbed by the sun's gravity. But I am sure that it would be visible even beyond Jupiter, because of the massive shedding of some of its volatile surface ices; it would act as a massive comet even at a great distance from the sun.

This might be the case under normal conditions in the solar system, but I don't consider the perihelion transit of the Dark Star to be anything like normal. Although the Dark Star remains at a significant distance from the sun, it must still cross the Heliopause, the magnetic boundary of the solar system. I believe that such a transit has an affect on the sun, increasing its activity and leading to a greater intensity of magnetic storms.

These would increase the bombardment of the solar system with charged particles, bringing about a greater visible 'tail' for the cometary Nibiru. This is speculation, of course, because we don't really have any idea what happens when brown dwarfs cross in and out of Solar magnetic fields. But we should remember how active those brown dwarfs can be magnetically, and imagine the consequences.

Its perihelion distance will vary over different passages, as its own orbit around the Dark Star coincides with the perihelion passage of the system as a whole (so my view here is necessarily

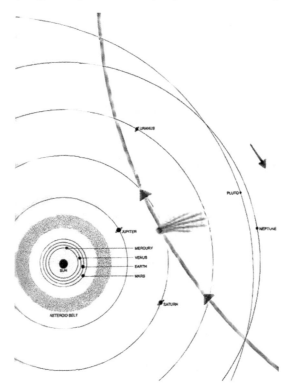

'ball-park'). On occasion, there will be an exact juxtaposition between its own perihelion and that of the Dark Star, along a line of sight from the sun. Other times, it will be on the other side of the Dark Star during the exact moment of binary perihelion. So, the timing of Nibiru will necessarily vary over the ages, as will its sky position and relative brilliance. Perhaps this is why there are so many unknowns about the transitory appearance of this body.

Another important detail is the fact that Nibiru is not seen to swing around the sun. It seems to come towards the sun and then quickly recedes, without traversing a large portion of the sky. This explains the weird set of constellations it moved through (which probably vary between different transits anyway), and also the short period of time that Nibiru can be seen.

Even though the Dark Star may take literally hundreds of years to traverse perihelion, the time that Nibiru is observable from Earth is likely to be short; perhaps a matter of weeks or months. I suppose it's possible that there may even be more than one visible transit during a total binary perihelion. Either way, this scenario opens up a number of new possibilities.

The idea that one of the Dark Star's planets is our 'Planet X' has been suggested to me by a couple of people before, most notably John Lee. At the time, I was mildly sceptical because it seemed unlikely to me that a small brown dwarf would be able to maintain a planetary system at such a distance; I am suggesting here that Nibiru may be orbiting at about 50AU from the Dark Star (and this may vary as well, if its own orbit is elliptical around the binary parent). But a recent precedent was discovered in the form of a large planet imaged at a similar distance from a free-floating brown dwarf known to astronomers as '1207' (6). So it's not difficult to extrapolate a similar situation for our binary Dark Star, with Nibiru as the accompanying planet.

## The '12th' Planet

This finding has turned my thinking around. It presents us with the potential for a 3-body solution to the orbital configuration. Also, instead of one Planet X body, we now essentially have 3 notables; the Dark Star and two major planets orbiting it (the other 5 appear to be minor bodies). Those two notables are Nibiru at ~50AU distance, and the Homeworld much closer to

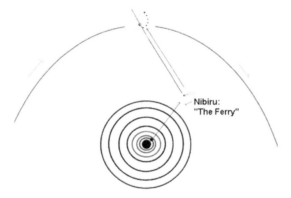

Nibiru:
"The Ferry"

→ Journey to the Homeworld

· Motion of the planets

the Dark Star itself. Add these bodies to the 9 known planets to the solar system brings us to 12 planets, which seems closer to the Sumerian 12th Planet scenario than Sitchin himself!

## The 'Ferry'

Other aspects of the myth surrounding Nibiru become more understandable with this hypothesis. In their classic book "Hamlet's Mill", Giorgio de Santillana and Hertha von Dechend explored the mysterious nature of 'Nibiru' in 1969, and showed that, at that time, no scholarly theory adequately explained its celestial nature. Not much has changed since then, except Sitchin's books of course. Here's what Santillana and von Dechend had to say about what the name Nibiru actually means:

"The plain meaning of 'nibiru' is 'ferry, ferryman, ford' - 'mikis nibiri' is the toll one has to pay for crossing the river - from eberu 'to cross'" (7).

The 'Planet of the Crossing' is thus a ferry of sorts. This has made little sense up until now, because the implication is that

Nibiru takes travellers onto another place. That place was never defined by Sitchin, who insisted that Nibiru was itself the home-world of the Anunnaki; the gods of ancient Mesopotamia. Yet with our new insight, the meaning behind the name 'ferry' becomes crystal clear.

The transit of the Dark Star around the sun at perihelion is still a very remote event. At its closest, the Dark Star is still twice as far away as Pluto. To rendezvous with the Dark Star would take many years of space travel, with the risk of missing an object too remote to observe.

Yet, Nibiru acts as an intermediary. It swoops into the planetary solar system, and then returns to the comet clouds. It would provide space travellers with the ideal stepping stone to the Dark Star. It literally acts as a ferry.

There may be other symbolic overtones to this. If the Anunnaki are physical gods, then their Homeworld is mythological Heaven. It is very similar to Earth ('as in Heaven, so on Earth', 'As Above, so Below', etc.). The myth of the Ferryman coming to collect the dead to take them to the Underworld could have new meaning, in the light of this new hypothesis. This idea works on both a physical and a metaphorical level.

## Angle to the Ecliptic

Another vexing issue with Sitchin's model is the fact that Nibiru is said to move through the heavens at a 30 degree angle to the ecliptic, nearly twice that of Pluto. Yet, a sizeable planet

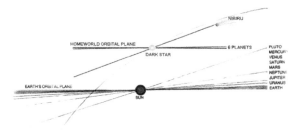

moving through the planetary solar system at such an extreme angle to the plane of the other planets would cause chaos over time to their orbits. This is called the Kozai effect, which has become a huge headache for me in recent years.

Again, this new hypothesis allows us to circumvent this problem, in that the Dark Star does not actually move through the planetary solar system at all. However, Nibiru, its outlying planet, does - and Sitchin seems reasonably clear about its angle of inclination from the texts and scholarly work he has studied. How do we explain this?

It seems likely that the inner planets of each of the binary stars (the sun and Dark Star) should be as they were created; relatively flat to the plane of the initial proto-planetary disc. Billions of years of interaction between the peripheries of these estranged systems, however, will have lead to chaos and perturbation among some of their outer planets. In the sun's case Pluto is clearly perturbed, as are many of the bodies recently discovered beyond it. So it seems likely that Nibiru is similarly affected, along with any of the Dark Star's own retinue of comets in its locale.

In the analogy used in this chapter, we can imagine that our Dark Star fairground ride is experiencing further mechanical difficulties. Not only is the ride spinning around in the wind, but the hydraulic arm has now engaged and has lifted the spinning ride so that it no longer sits on the flat bed of the truck. Instead, it is held at an angle of about 30 degrees, with the ride spinning around the angulated axis. As we look at the red flag (signifying Nibiru) spin around, we see it subtend an angle to the top surface of the hedge at the edge of the field.

To all intents and purposes, an observer watching the movement of the red flag who was unable to see the rest of the Dark Star truck and its spinning ride, could be forgiven for thinking that the flag was moving in such an odd way that it could not be attached to something that was simply travelling down the road. Yet it is.

In astronomical terms, this means that Nibiru's visible arc across the sky could very well be seen to transit at a relatively steep inclination, reflecting this 30 degree angle to the ecliptic. Yet, the binary Dark Star may still move along a path more in keeping with the sun's other planets.

The upshot of this is that we can predict little about the Dark Star's actual location from the reported transit of Nibiru. This has always been my gut-feeling anyway. I tend to think that the Dark Star lies close to the ecliptic, and still favour the area in the vicinity of Sagittarius as its current location (near to its recent aphelion). This is because the actual 'line-of-sight' perihelion is the Duat region, around Sirius and Orion. Sagittarius is opposite this region on the ecliptic.

But this is only my opinion. Others differ. If my hypothesis here is correct, then detailed efforts to deduce the whereabouts of the sun's binary companion and its own system of planets are almost bound to fail. There are simply too many complicating factors at play.

## The Crossing

For a long time, I wondered whether the wording of the 'Crossing' of Nibiru does not apply to a physical location in the solar system - like the asteroid belt - but rather, an observed location in the heavens, as Nibiru brightens towards perihelion. Other researchers have considered similar possibilities, suggesting constellations or imagined lines across the heavens, like the ecliptic.

In a sense, the plane of the ecliptic is synonymous with the asteroid belt, as this orbiting debris field follows the same line as the rest of the visible planets. And this is what distinguishes the 'planet' Nibiru from the others: its path lies at an angle of inclination from the ecliptic. However, this new hypothesis adds further complications to this picture.

It means that we cannot readily predict where Nibiru will appear in the sky, what motion it will perform, or what lines it will cross. It might be spotted in the Northern hemisphere, or even the Southern hemisphere; in other words, it might appear on either side of the ecliptic. However, it is most likely to be located near to the ecliptic, and is most likely to be seen in the vicinity of the zodiacal constellation of Gemini. Previous perihelia may have occurred there, in Cancer, near Sirius, in Orion, or nearer Aries and Taurus. A plethora of possibilities presents itself.

There are multiple meanings for the term 'Crossing'. We have considered that the term refers to the movement across an important 'line' in the sky, like the ecliptic. We have also seen the term refer to the object as a 'ferry', perhaps implying that it acts as an intermediate point between our world and that of the gods. This idea is my preferred option at the moment.

But the first idea attached to this term was that Nibiru physically crossed through the asteroid belt at perihelion, returning to the place of the mighty battle during the early period of our solar system's history. Such a state of affairs implies that Nibiru, a rogue planet that had wreaked havoc with our own world at this location, was in a stable orbit that brought it back to the same spot every 3600 years or so. This has been Sitchin's argument for many years.

## Planetary Migration

One of Alan Alford's main criticisms of Sitchin's theory about Nibiru was that Earth's own orbit should pass through the same crossing point as Nibiru (8). Given that the Earth does not pass through the Asteroid Belt, Alford argues, our planet could not have been involved in the Celestial Battle. This was then cited as a prime reason to doubt the potential of Sitchin's remarkable theory.

But Alford's critique reflects a increasingly conservative view of orbital dynamics. Opinions about migrations of planetary orbits differ, but there appears to be a lot more room for manoeuvre than has been previously thought.

A good instance of this was one of the scenarios explored by Gladman's team, to help explain the anomalous orbital properties of 2000 CR105. They considered a possible mechanism involving the migration of planetary multiple embryos from positions within the orbit of Neptune, to new ones beyond it. They assumed that these embryonic planets would be approximately the size of the Moon or Mars. They argued that the velocities of these objects were sufficient to achieve escape velocities during encounters with each other, propelling some beyond Neptune into new orbits (9).

There has even been some thought given to the idea that Neptune once had a more distant orbit than it does now, which might help to explain various orbital properties of anomalous Trans-Neptunian Objects.

I'm not proposing that these mechanisms might be necessarily correct. But, these ideas were proposed by serious astrophysicists trying to explain observed anomalies. They highlight how planetary migration seems to be on the table to explain the EKBO anomalies.

Brunini and Melita also put forward a similar idea, offering a scenario for the orbital transport mechanism for Planet X to its present location (10). This offers us a prime example of science having to adapt to the new reality. Migration of planets is a very real possibility. It can help is to understand how the Dark Star could have wreaked havoc, and yet now exist in an orbit that does not bring it back to the original point of the ancient conflict.

## Sweeping the Backyard Clean

Criminals often return to the scene of the crime, but it seems that the Dark Star has long ago moved on, keeping its distance from the other planets. This must be the case - because otherwise the solar system would not just contain several chaotic anomalies, it would be completely chaotic. This chaos is not observed, therefore, that we must discount the possibility that the Dark Star regularly sweeps through the Asteroid Belt, nor any other inner solar system location.

If Jupiter can be said to act as a cosmic vacuum cleaner, picking up the rogue comets that get too close to its significant gravitational attraction, then the Dark Star is the equivalent of a cosmic broom, sweeping the solar system's backyard clean of comets.

In 2002, the popular science writers Couper and Henbest, writing in New Scientist, tried to elicit some comment from Mark Buie of the Lowell Observatory in Arizona about the potential for a hidden Planet X. He admitted that he wondered whether there was something strange going on in the outer region of the solar system, acknowledging that there is a possibility that some 'massive object' has swept the zone clean of debris (11). This statement by an esteemed astronomer may not seem particularly adventurous to many, but in the context of the story of the hunt for Planet X, it may represent something of a breakthrough. It reflects the new reality.

# Chapter 9 References

1. Z. Sitchin "The Twelfth Planet" Chapter 8, p188 Avon 1976. These excerpts are reproduced with the kind permission of Zecharia Sitchin.

2. The Clockwork Team (Parameshwaran Ravindranathan, Samit Basu and Jaideep Undurti), "Waiting for the Apocalypse', University of Westminster, 2003

3. See http://www.darkstar1.co.uk/videos.html

4. Correspondence from Zecharia Sitchin, 31st Dec. 2003

5. Correspondence from Dr. J. Murray, 23rd & 25th August 2000

6. M. McKee "First direct sighting of an extrasolar planet" 11th Jan 2005, with thanks to David Pearson http://newscientist.com/article.ns?id=dn6864

7. G. de Santillana & H. von Dechend "Hamlet's Mill" App. 39, pp430-451, http://www.apollonius.net/trees.html

8. A. Alford "The Phoenix Solution" p162 Hodder & Stoughton 1998

9. B. Gladman, M. Holman, T. Grav, J. Kavelaars, P. Nicholson, K. Aksnes & J-M. Petit "Evidence for an Extended Disk" Icarus, 157, pp269-79 (2002)

10. Brunini & M. Melita "The Existence of a Planet beyond 50AU and the Orbital Distribution of the Classical Edgeworth-Kuiper Belt Objects" Icarus, 160, pp32-43 (2002)

11. H. Couper & N. Henbest  "The Hunt for Planet X" New Scientist, pp30-4, 14th December 2002

# The Origin of the Binary Companion

The very idea that we might be living in a binary star system must seem absolutely crazy. We all know that we live in a star system with only one sun. It is common knowledge that most other star systems are binaries, and so we have come to accept that our system is the exception to the rule. But that has never led any serious thinkers to propose that we also may have been living in a binary system without realizing it. The whole idea seems absurd.

But if our orthodox knowledge of the solar system was correct, there wouldn't be an observed edge to the Edgeworth-Kuiper Belt. Something has moved through that distant environment, sculpting the Belt.

We are now able to compare the picture in our outer solar system with distant proto-planetary discs around young star systems. The effect we have noted for our system has been observed around star systems elsewhere. For instance, a much-studied system around a young star poetically called HD141569A brings this comparison into sharp focus. It creates a possible precedent for our own binary solar companion.

Some of the arguments in this chapter are a little technical, reflecting a rather complex set of scientific arguments. The repercussions of these arguments are, fortunately, rather more straightforward in the end.

## An Eccentric Binary

HD141569A has a 500AU-wide proto-planetary disc that shows spiral patterning (1), indicative of a reaction with a external large body (2). The star is only 5 million years old, so it is unlikely that the disruption is caused by its own planets because they should not have formed yet. So astronomers have been left with several other options to explain the effect. The main possibilities are as follows:

**1** The spiral arms were created by the action of a passing star, although the stellar neighborhood is relatively quiet - making this a low probability event

**2** There is a bound companion external to the disk that is affecting it over time with each orbit

**3** The effect is due to embedded Jupiter-sized planets, despite the youthful nature of the system

To figure out what is going on, the astronomers carried out calculations to model the effect. They compared their theoretical results, based upon a set of reasonable starting assumptions, with the observed patterns of the disturbed proto-planetary disc, and looked for a close match.

The results have shown that the spiral pattern is consistent with a highly eccentric binary system (3). This implies the existence of a binary companion which passed within 930AU of HD 141569A. It directly caused the observed effects; the spiral structure in the disk and a wide gap in the disk.

The system is actually more complicated than this, with other effects providing additional headaches at about 150AU. However, it seems clear that the continued action of the binary companion, as its moves through many orbital passages, creates the observed effect, particularly if that orbit is an eccentric one(4). This is very interesting when comparing HD 141569A to our sun with its own proposed Dark Star.

HD 141569A has two neighboring stars, HD 141569B and C, which are each potential candidates as bound companions. So, it may be that one or both of these objects is bound to the main star in eccentric orbits. This scenario seems more likely than the alternative of a single flyby of another star, which would only partially truncate the proto-planetary disc (4). Not only that, but the passing star scenario also has to reckon with the dearth of stars in the immediate neighborhood, making the chances of such a close passage remote. This is a crucial point when we come to consider the observed anomalies of our own solar system.

## Three Options for Our System

While HD 141569A is a very young star system, ours is not.

So the third option listed above becomes possible in our case: that the Kuiper Cliff, or truncation, is the result of an embedded planet in the Edgeworth-Kuiper Disc sweeping it out and creating the edge. This was the scenario explored by Brunini and Melita, as discussed in Chapter 8. Their studies indicated that this was a distinct possibility, and that the body should exhibit a low eccentric orbit.

However, it should also be sufficiently close to have been readily discovered by now, which seemed to be a stumbling block: the semi-major axis of the Mars-sized planet would be only 60AU, bringing it well within detection limits (5). So this third option is not without its problems, even in this older star system of ours.

Some might consider such a scenario to adequately fit the requirements for a 'Planet X' type-body. However, the kind of orbit described by Brunini and Melita would keep the planet within the Edgeworth-Kuiper Belt at all times. This would imply no possibility of prior movement through the planetary zone of the solar system. This might turn out to be the case, of course, but such a body would not be in keeping with that of Zecharia Sitchin's Marduk. Dr. Melita has indicated to me that they would be carrying out calculations for more eccentric bodies in the future (6), which might possibly be more reminiscent of the classic 'Nibiru/Marduk' scenario.

The Dark Star solution may become the middle ground between the 'embedded planet' and the possibility of the passage of a stellar body through the early solar system. The complexity of the Edgeworth-Kuiper Belt may have resulted from a complex interaction early in the life of the solar system, or it may even be on-going. Scientists usually prefer a simple, straightforward solution to any given problem, according to the philosophical mantra of Occam's Razor, but sometimes the complexities of reality get in the way.

Let us look closely at the possibility of a passing star creating the truncated Edgeworth-Kuiper Belt. Perhaps the sun's proto-planetary system was disturbed by the action of a passing star within the sun's primordial star nursery (7). Even though he favours the embedded planet hypothesis, Dr. Melita concedes that a small star 1/10th the size of the sun passing by could have created some of the observed effect in the EKB (5). But, can it explain the truncation completely?

If the sun was born in a 'stellar nursery' surrounded by many thousands of other young stars, such an event increases in likelihood (8). Such young stellar clusters can be 10,000 times more dense than the sun's current location in the Milky Way, increasing the chances of interaction between neighboring stars dramatically. But does such a scenario provide all the answers?

Calculations have been carried out to determine whether a small passing star that approached the planetary zone of the solar system could have sculpted the EKB (8). In the work carried out by Alice Quillen, et al., the disturbing influence could be either a passing star whose own trajectory is influenced temporarily by the sun's gravity, or it is a binary companion, which becomes disrupted by external influences. So, a candidate object need not have been simply a 'field' star or a neighbor in the stellar cluster that the sun was born in, but it could also have been a binary star in a wide orbit around the sun, that could have affected the Edgeworth-Kuiper Belt during a close sweep past it. This is useful, because of the potential for a small binary companion in a generally great circular orbit to periodically pass close to the planetary zone.

Such a scenario was predicted by John Matese, when calculating the orbital properties for his small brown dwarf at 25,000 AU. He called this occasional transient sweep towards the solar system an "oscultation" (9). These are complex matters, but it boils down to this; a star causing a distortion of the sun's proto-planetary disc might be a loosely bound companion in a rather changeable orbit, or it might simply have been a completely independent object, passing close to the sun as it travelled through inter-stellar space.

Bound or unbound, it somehow managed to draw close to the sun's planetary zone. What interests us tremendously, is whether that object is actually part of the solar system or not. This would give us a clue as to the origins of the Dark Star.

In Dr. Quillen's calculations, it is assumed that the object - a dwarf star - moves though the Edgeworth-Kuiper Belt, as it draws close to the sun. The outcome of the calculations is initially encouraging. The simulation creates a complex pattern, including both a set of objects with high inclinations and eccentricities, and also an additional set of objects with low inclinations and eccentricities. This reflects the reality observed in the Edgeworth-Kuiper Belt, as far as the distribution of objects within the observed disc go (8). However, the 'passing star' scenario encounters difficulties when it comes to explaining the Kuiper Cliff itself.

## The Kuiper Cliff

Despite the promising distribution pattern of EKBOs, the 'passing star' solution is unable to tackle the very problem it sets out to solve: it simply fails to create a 'truncation' in the Edgeworth-Kuiper Belt (8). This is a big problem for the 'passing star' scenario, leading us to suspect that the origin of the massive object involved is homegrown.

There is a greater degree of complexity apparent in the observational data that the passage of a passing star struggles to explain in these calculations. Stellar encounters seem to be able to drag out the bodies in the disc to a variable degree, but cannot account for the Kuiper Cliff in its entirety. Dr. Quillen, an Assistant Professor of Physics & Astronomy at the University of Rochester in the USA, concedes this point in her paper, describing another possibility that is of tremendous significance to our investigation: she concludes that if the existence of the Kuiper Cliff is eventually confirmed, then it is much more likely to have formed as a result of "a companion, either stellar or planetary" (9).

I was quite surprised by this conclusion when I read it, because it wasn't the direction the paper initially seemed to head off in. Her calculations not only ruled out a stellar flyby scenario for the solar system, they also pointed in the direction of a massive companion. This was a promising lead which needed following up.

## Game, Set and Match?

I wrote to Professor Alice Quillen and asked her about a few points to do with her paper, and put it to her that a bound companion must have caused the anomalous edge in the Edgeworth-Kuiper Belt, as she had so quietly stated. After urging a little caution about how concrete science's knowledge of the alleged Kuiper Cliff was, she confirmed the point. The edge in the Edgeworth-Kuiper Belt could not be the result of a single stellar fly-by, because this would be incapable of producing a sharp enough edge.

She considers it likely that the effect was produced by a bound companion that is no longer there. That bound companion would have to have been moving around the sun in an eccentric orbit. She argued that it must have been expelled from the solar system some time ago, simply because it must be large, and thus readily detectable even at great distances:

**Alice Quillen:** So suppose we believe that the edge is real and sharp. Then a flyby can't have produced it. Something bound could, because it gets multiple passes. A bound low mass planet could do it, but would have been detected even out at 10000 AU in the Oort cloud. An Earth out there would probably not work, but might not have been detected. You can't have anything further than a few times 10^4 AU, because nearby stars would scatter and remove it. I think that leaves something that was previously bound and is no longer in the solar system. Oort cloud comets are removed from the solar system too. So, it's not inconceivable that there was a planet or nearby star bound to the sun, in an eccentric orbit that is no longer around (10).

**Andy Lloyd:** Did you mean 'low mass star' (rather than "low mass planet")?

**Alice Quillen:** I meant a Jupiter-mass planet. Yes, you have remembered things correctly: Earth-mass type things can evade detection in the Oort cloud, but Jupiter- mass things can't. It's hard to imagine an Earth-mass object being able to truncate the KBO (though maybe this should be checked numerically to make sure). It's easy to imagine a Jupiter-mass planet doing the job (don't need to check, I have done enough simulations with Jupiter-mass objects to be pretty sure about this). A low-mass star can truncate the KBO, too (11).

This statement by a professor of astronomy seems quite remarkable. She considers it probable that the sun once had a bound companion, either a star or a massive planet, which was capable of creating the edge in the Edgeworth-Kuiper Belt over the course of many orbits. Its orbit must also have been eccentric. This conclusion has been reached because nothing else fits the observed facts.

This is the Dark Star Theory, but with the proviso that the Dark Star is no longer there. Not because the observed facts don't imply its existence, but because its existence implies its detection. However, as we have seen, such faith in the assumed ability to observe such a body may be misplaced.

The binary companion existed in the past, though, and either left the solar system at some point, or it is still orbiting the sun and has evaded detection to date. Either way, we seem to have clear scientific evidence that the sun has been, and may still be, part of a binary system.


## The Heretical Planet


I pressed Dr. Quillen a little further about the probable size of this binary companion. She described it as a Jupiter-mass planet, or larger, and that she had run enough simulations with Jupiter-mass planets to be sure that it would truncate the EKB. A low-mass star could also fit the bill.

However, a terrestrial world of the size of Earth probably wouldn't be large enough (11). So, the range of objects that were capable of creating the observed effect is effectively the same as that covered by the brown dwarfs. Her calculations showed that the truncation of the EKB was caused by nothing other than a brown dwarf companion bound to the sun!

It may turn out to be true that a Jupiter-sized object cannot have evaded detection up until now, but this is an arguable point, as discussed already in this book. Certainly, Dr. John Murray thought that such a body could have evaded detection in the Oort

Cloud (12), when he proposed his giant planet solution at the same time as Professor John Matese (9).

This remains a controversial issue, but Dr. Quillen's viewpoint also should be respected. The lack of discovery of a Jupiter-sized planet (which is clearly leaving its footprints in the butter, so to speak) is a puzzle, there's no doubt about that. I personally do not share the opinion that the lack of direct detection to date automatically rules out its existence. I'm not the only one.

Our correspondence confirmed that a body with a mass of Jupiter, or greater, could produce the observed truncation effect in the Edgeworth-Kuiper Belt. I wondered why Dr. Quillen hadn't published those particular calculations as well. After all, she seems very clear about what has created the effect in the EKB. One would have thought this was news-worthy. Bear in mind that I had only asked her about this aspect of her work because I had spotted one or two short lines written into the body of a scientific paper. Because I'm already interested in the potential for a brown dwarf companion, I had pursued the matter.

One can compare this episode directly with how the paper was reported in New Scientist, under the ominous title: "Rogue star smashed up the solar system". The article describes a fly-by of a small star, creating a re-distribution of the objects in the EKB. It doesn't discuss the fact that Dr. Quillen concluded that such an event could not have produced the observed truncation of the Belt. The origin of the "interloper" is described vaguely, but the clear implication is that the object was not bound to the sun, but came from the neighboring star cluster:

"In a paper submitted to Astronomical Journal, the researchers suggest that the interloper probably came from the star cluster in which the sun was formed, and that the close encounter would have occurred within a billion years of the birth of the solar system" (13).

Reading the article in New Scientist, one would be forgiven for thinking that the 'passing star' is the solution concluded by the researchers; the article fails to report that this is only half the story. If the Kuiper Edge is for real, then the 'passing star' scenario simply fails to explain it. Why was this not reported?

I suspect that the writer of the article did not delve too deeply into the paper being reviewed. Perhaps a larger article might have brought up the possibility of a bound Jupiter-sized planet being perfect for the task of explaining the Kuiper Cliff, but somehow I doubt it. Somehow, the idea of a binary companion the size of a brown dwarf creating this observed effect seems too incredible.

Yet, it is eminently plausible.

When confronted by the twin problems of an astronomer burying her real conclusion within her paper, and the scientific news media subsequently reporting only half the story, one could be forgiven for wondering whether the possibility of a rogue brown dwarf companion to the sun is just a little too much for everyone's reputations to withstand. One must wonder whether such a notion is tantamount to a modern scientific heresy.

## Binary Disassociation

It is clear that we cannot rely upon a singular stellar encounter to explain the anomalies observed in the EKB. It seems quite plausible that such an event could have happened during the early days of the solar system, but only if the sun was part of a dense cluster of stars. The potential for such an encounter increases if the intruder is already associated with the sun, as in the case of an early binary companion whose orbit then fluctuates, bringing it closer to the planets and outer proto-planetary disc.

Dr. Quillen was at pains to point out to me that the massive solar companion must have exited solar system some time ago. This is not all that unlikely, it seems. Such a parting of the ways is known as "binary dissociation". It can occur at orbital periods greater than about 3,000 years, corresponding to separations on the order of a few hundred AU (7). This allows astronomers to explain how stars born in dense stellar clusters end up as simple binaries, or on their own. Such dense clusters early in the life of a star system then allow astronomers to argue the case for stellar fly-bys, which might otherwise be rather unlikely.

This is a rather neat trick that explains a condensed initial environment when stars are born, helping to build mechanisms for the kind of chaos often observed. It also allows astronomers to square that aspect with the observed nature of older, more mature systems which are less dynamic. Of importance to us is the very real potential for transient binary companions early in the life of a star system. These then move on when the star cluster breaks up. At least, that's the theory (7).

If the sun formed in a stellar nursery in close proximity to other stars, then there was a good likelihood that one of them passed through the Edgeworth-Kuiper Belt early in the solar system's history. Given what we now know about the formation of brown dwarfs, such a body could just as easily have been a smaller 'failed star', which may have been tempted sufficiently by the sun's greater gravitational influence to have been captured by it, as it moved through the EKB. This capture could have caused the brown dwarf to move through the proto-planetary disc, interacting with the other planets in a similar way to that outlined by Sitchin. His interpretation of the ancient myths thus correlates well with the science we are currently discussing.

Secondly, the Dark Star 'Marduk' may have been born as a binary companion in the first place, and migrated inwards to a new orbit that caused its interaction with the planets. This migration might have resulted from a stellar encounter with another young star in the relatively dense birth cluster. This would prevent us having to worry about the sheer chance of such an object being captured by the sun from interstellar space. In fact, Sitchin's scenario appears to receive tentative support by this mode of thinking.

The astronomer Shigeru Ida describes the point at which a 'binary dissociation' can take place, as about 3,000 years for the binary companion's orbit (7). Zecharia Sitchin's proposed planet Nibiru/Marduk is said to have an orbit of 3,600 years, which would put it on a knife-edge, as far as this effect is concerned. So the Dark Star could be disassociating right now, and at the very least, the implication is that this isn't a terribly stable orbit. Or it may have already dissociated, leaving only a remnant signature on the Edgeworth-Kuiper Belt at about 50AU.

This situation is consistent with my previous claims about migration patterns of the Dark Star, and the consequent effect of changes on the orbital energies of the planets. This is an important point to discuss. If a Dark Star is moving around out there in a migratory way over the lifetime of the solar system, its angular momentum has been changing during that time. Given its distance and mass, such changes would be considerable in relation to the solar system's angular momentum as a whole, which needs to be preserved. So this would imply a counter-active migration of the other planets in response, possibly leading to great climatic changes on Earth, as well as on the other planets during their geological histories.

You see, the more mechanisms that astronomers have to call upon to explain the varied patterns of extra-solar planetary orbits and proto-planetary discs, the more flexible the concepts of planet formation and migration must become. Instead of making the existence of a binary companion less plausible, such variety helps us argue the case for keeping our options open.

It seems quite reasonable to me that the chaos of the early solar system could have left us with a rogue massive planet out there, whose current pattern of migration and movement urgently needs assessing. This is because it is not an isolated body whose effect on the rest of the solar system is negligible. Even though it may be found at a great distance, its sheer size means that its influence on the solar system as a whole may be non-negligible. It may explain a great many anomalies pertaining to our own planet's varied geological history, too.

## Nibiru, Once Again...

The Dark Star may have formed alongside the sun as a bound companion, burning brightly as a young brown dwarf. It may

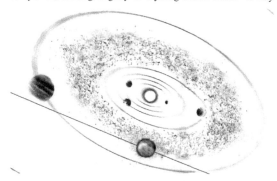

have had an eccentric orbit that brought it into the planetary zone of the primitive solar system, where it interacted with the Water World 'Tiamat' as described by Sitchin. This interaction may have disrupted the natural order of the planetary system, causing the primordial Tiamat to migrate into the inner solar system, where it subsequently lost the vast majority of its water and became Earth.

The Dark Star may then have migrated out of the planetary zone sufficiently to affect only the Edgeworth-Kuiper Belt from then on, despite maintaining a relatively high eccentricity. This encounter with the sun's inner planets early in the life of the solar system might have caused the Dark Star to become rather more attached to the sun than it normally would have, preventing its loss to the system by 'binary dissociation'.

The observed phenomenon of Nibiru's presence is purported to have a cycle of 3,600 years or so. This may vary over time, depending upon how loosely bound the Dark Star is. Science may soon spring the Dark Star from the hat - running through an eccentric orbit which takes it from the edge of the Edgeworth-Kuiper Belt all the way out to the inner Oort Cloud. Such a discovery would explain why the ancients kept watch for this mythological planet (as well as a few modern 'believers' and their rather unorthodox priesthood!). It would explain why the asteroid belt between Mars and Jupiter hasn't been completely 'swept out' by now, as it should have been had Nibiru passed that way every 3600 years. It would stop us from having to worry about the Kozai effect which has been used to criticize a highly inclined perihelion transit through the planetary zone.

It would explain the early migration of the Earth to a location where it should be completely bone dry, yet isn't. It might explain how Neptune and Uranus are found so far away from the sun, where the accretion time for them to form should be prohibitively long. It would explain the Late Heavy Bombardment. Most of all, it would explain the observed phenomenon of the gap in the Edgeworth-Kuiper Belt, that has got the astronomers stumped. In fact, as we have seen, it's the only viable scenario to explain this last issue.

## Planet X As A Moon of the Dark Star?

If we are to consider the possibility that ancient peoples on our planet were intimately aware of the comings and goings of the Dark Star, then we need to understand how they portrayed that understanding. We have looked at the myths of ancient Mesopotamia, but they are not to be held in isolation. This book is primarily aimed at answering the scientific questions raised by a binary companion to the sun, but a lot of my research over the years has looked at its symbolism.

It is beyond the scope of this book to move into that territory in any great detail, but I believe that I have adequately established an association between the Dark Star and seven other stars. These presumably constitute the Dark Star's own system of planets. One of them seems to become visible at some point during the perihelion passage of the Dark Star through the outer solar system.

The appearance of this mysterious and mythical planet is varied, taking on many forms. One of its descriptions is that of 'Phaeton', and in their book "When the Earth Nearly Died", authors D. Allan and J Delair speculate about how the planet's actual appearance could have produced the multitude of mythical image attached to it down the ages. They have created drawings showing how the 4 most significant moons and the tail would change the overall appearance of the Phaeton Phenomenon as it moved through the heavens, and the moons orbited around it (14).

Note the appearance of 4 moons; does Nibiru bring its own entourage? Is it possible that companion moons could be visible at such great distances? Or, is it simply that the incursion of the planet Nibiru through the outer solar system is coincident with a great hail of other cosmic debris; comets from the Dark Star's own sphere of influence.

If the moons/planets/comets orbiting the Dark Star Nibiru were very widely distributed, as the researcher John Lee has suggested in the past, it creates a complex situation which might then explain the sheer diversity of symbolism employed by various cultures. John argues that the Dark Star should not be definitively associated with the myths of Pheaton and Nibiru/ Marduk, as its orbit is likely to be wider and of longer duration than 3600 years, or thereabouts. So there is little need to tie its existence in with myth at all, from John's point of view. This is a valuable opinion, requiring us to bear in mind that although science seems to be moving towards its existence, that doesn't necessarily mean that it must end up being entwined in ancient myth.

However, I believe that the various myths do lead us to the Dark Star, in the same way that the science now being played out in observatories and academic halls is moving in the self-same direction. As such, I think the symbolism, as varied and complex as it is, should be taken into account. But the symbolism can only tell us part of the story; that of the observable, visible phenomenon. There may be more to it than that. We must be cautious of crossing the Rubicon just yet.

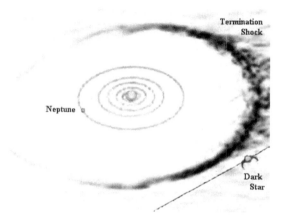

## Perihelion and Heliopause

If we accept that the gap in the Edgeworth-Kuiper Belt is to be attributed to the proximity of the Dark Star at perihelion, then how close does it approach that gap, or indeed the sun itself? According to Quillen, this is heavily dependent upon the eccentricity of the orbit of the binary companion, more so than its actual mass (4). There is a relationship involved called the Lindblad Resonance, where there is a 2:1 relationship between the binary companion's orbit and the inner belt of the primary affected. If, in the sun's case, its belt is truncated at about 48AU, then this implies an interactive planetary orbit at about 70-80AU.

Now, if the orbit is highly eccentric, which the Dark Star's must be, then this value does not apply to a simple circular orbit at this position, or within it (5). Instead, it may apply to the effect over time of a distant planet sweeping through that area over many, many orbits. Does this relationship help us to define the Dark Star's perihelion distance? Can that lead us to an understanding of what effect upon the sun the Dark Star is capable of?

There's not a lot of interesting real estate out at 80AU. The only feature of interest is a boundary known as the heliopause, which lies a little further out than this. At least, that's what the astronomers think anyway. They don't actually know yet, but are hoping that data from several spacecraft might be able to enlighten them. Is the position of the heliopause significant?

The heliopause marks a boundary for the Solar Wind, and is a feature of the extended magnetic field of the sun. At the heliopause, the Solar Wind meets the plasma fields of interstellar space, creating a magnetized bow-shock as the sun moves along. This bow-shock is most likely to reside between 110 - 160 AU from the sun (15). This means that the Dark Star must move through this boundary twice during its perihelion passage, once on the way towards perihelion, and again as it moves away. The

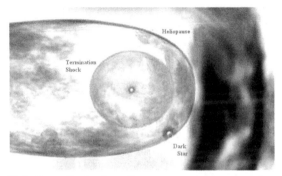

Dark Star will also have its own magnetosphere; a rather substantial one in fact.

The shape of the heliopause is currently not known, but is thought to resemble the planetary magnetospheres surrounding some of the sun's family. The magnetopsheres are created by the interaction of the solar wind with the magnetic field of these planets, including the Earth, and they serve to protect the planets from some of the sun's bombardment of hot, charged particles, or plasma. The influx of these charged particles into the polar regions of the Earth creates the 'Aurora Borealis', or Northern Lights, an effect which is repeated on Saturn and Jupiter on a massive scale.

The Dark Star seems to lie roughly in the direction of the Solar Apex, or the point in space towards which the sun is traveling. If that is the case, then the Dark Star will be in the forward direction of the bowshock of the sun's magnetosphere, or heliopause. Thus, the heliopause will have the lowest distance at this point from the sun.

The heliopause is literally buffeted back from the interstellar medium here, the exact distance of which is determined by many factors, including the current velocity of the Solar Wind and the local density of the interstellar medium. The shape of the heliopause, once known, may also hold clues as to the sun's interaction with the Dark Star's own magnetosphere. The four space probes from the Voyager and Pioneer missions may one day provide some data on this.

The region of the heliopause is an active one, because the sun's charged particles in the Solar Wind encounter resistance at this boundary, and warm up. There is a termination shockwave here, just within the heliopause (16). This is without the action of another massive body, but occurs simply because of the interaction between the sun's magnetosphere and the environment within which it moves.

How much bigger is the likely effect, then, when the extended magnetic fields of the Dark star and the sun interact directly?

## The Cosmic Light Show

Let us consider whether the Dark Star, as an old and small sub-brown dwarf, becomes more active as it interacts with the 'termination shock' of the Solar Wind. Upon arriving at the termination shock, the Dark Star might flare up dramatically, with an auroral and atmospheric light-show several orders of magnitude greater than normal. After all, it will meet a relatively dense and warm layer of highly energized, negatively accelerating particles forming a considerable shock-wave.

One only needs to consider the magnetosphere of Jupiter to realize how strong the interaction between this gas giant's magnetic field and that of the sun is (17). If Jupiter's magnetosphere was visible in the night sky, it would appear about four times the diameter of the Moon. Yet, Jupiter is five times further away from us at opposition than the sun. Its magnetosphere tails back as far as Saturn's orbit.

If the Dark star has an even greater magnetic field, as its greater density implies - then its interaction with the Solar Wind will be proportionately greater. Even if one bears in mind the fact that it is much further away, and the density of the solar wind drops off as a result, the reaction at the actual bow-shock of the heliopause will still create a significant effect.

This begs the question: when the in-bound Dark Star reaches the heliopause would the resultant electro-magnetic interaction create a flaring effect that could actually be visible from the Earth? Would the embers of the sub-brown dwarf ignite once again to shine brightly, even in the depths of the void?

This is a second possibility, which might explain the sudden observable appearance of 'Nibiru'. The effect would be like that of an intruder cutting through a perimeter fence and setting off the alarm. Whilst in the grounds, the intruder would remain in the shadows, only to set the alarm off again upon exiting the perimeter some time later. The actual affect would be sudden and transitory; a bright red glow in the sky centred upon a single light source; that of the excited Dark Star. It would be repeated some years later, in a different part of the sky.

This is speculative, but it might be possible that the sun and Dark Star would cause each other's magnetic fields to charge up dramatically at that boundary crossing near, or within, the Edgeworth-Kuiper Belt. Like a cactus in the desert, the binary companion's flowering would be fleeting, but, under the gaze of the sun, beautiful. Perhaps, the sun would respond in kind with a massive Coronal Mass Ejection, or such like.

There should be no doubts about the exceptionally strong effect of the Solar Wind on a gas giant's magnetosphere. A "pulsating auroral hot-spot" was discovered on Jupiter in 2002, emitting large quantities of X-rays (18,19). How much more activity would be observed on an orbiting brown dwarf, I wonder? It also seems likely to me that the sun's entire, extended magnetic field could be strongly affected by such an interaction, to the extent that some kind of reversal of the solar magnetic field might take place. It's a remarkable thought, and not without precedent.

## Reversal of the Neutral Sheet

It may be that the sun's own field may also be affected by the Dark Star's perihelion passage. Could this be the reason for the alleged reversal of the Neutral Sheet every 3740 years, as proposed by Maurice Cotterell?

The standard sunspot cycle occurs every 11.5 years, a fact that is well known. Cotterell set about examining the relationship between the Earth's orbit, and the sun's different rates of magnetic field rotation at the solar poles and equator. This function he called the "rotational differentiation".

This leads to a fundamental sunspot cycle of 11.4929 years, and a greater recurring cycle of 187 years duration. Further mathematical analysis led Cotterell to conclude that a greater cycle still can be deduced, one that is 1,366,040 days long, or 3,740 years. This represents the complete reversal of the neutral sheet of the solar system. The flip itself is not instantaneous, but would take two of the 187 year cycles to complete (20).

This work fascinated me, because it indicated that the sun's cycles may be affected by an outside agent. A sub-brown dwarf periodically moving through the sun's massive and extended magnetic field would surely be enough to do the trick? How else could one explain such a regular, but momentous change in the sun's complete magnetic field?

But it was not clear from the book that Cotterell co-wrote with Adrian Gilbert, just when such an event would have taken place during the historical period. If this was to be tied in with the appearance of Nibiru, then such a question would be of fundamental importance. An opportunity presented itself to contact Maurice Cotterell, who was very illuminating in his correspondence:

"The sun reverses its magnetic field periodically. We know that ice ages correspond to solar magnetic activity. In effect the sun sucks-in and then blows out every 3,750 years. Charged dust particles would hence sometimes be sucked-in (depending on the polarity of the sun's magnetic fields) and then again blown-away, as the polarity changed…

Now; if the sun's magnetic field twists (the last time was in 3113BC) then planets in close proximity have a propensity to topple as they are magnetically coupled. This happened to Venus in 3113BC, and explains why Venus now spins backwards and why the Maya refer to the event as 'the birth of Venus'. However, the magnetic twist on that occasion, did not topple the Earth...Now 3113BC (minus) plus 3,740 years (one neutral sheet shift) = 627AD, meaning that the last solar magnetic twist occurred in 627AD (clearly neither Venus nor Earth flipped)" (21).

Cotterell's ideas about global catastrophe connected with cosmic events are clearly Velikovskian, although Maurice did point out to me that he did not consider it particularly worthwhile to seek a 'Dark Star' to explain such events. Instead, as our ability to discover data increased scientifically, then so would the chances of finding out causal factors. Until then, we are better off working with what we have got. He links the timing of the last reversal of the neutral sheet to events dated in Mayan myth, rather than specific scientific evidence.

## The Inevitable Question

This seems to me to leave the timing of Cotterell's proposed magnetic change as a rather open question, as I'm personally not convinced by the 'birth of Venus' argument. But the date he refers to is also Day One of the Olmec/Mayan/Aztec calendar, i.e. 13th August 3113BC. I believe that the appearance of Nibiru was of such significance to the ancients, that they started their calendar cycles at that point. This may be true of the South American peoples as much as it is true of the Sumerians of Nippur and, dare I say, Christians.

Richard Day ponders the timing of Nibiru in this South American context, which he finds coincidental with the founding of the first Pharaonic dynasty. Such a timing would also have brought Nibiru back around the time of the birth of the prophet Mohammed (22). Although, by this time the observation records of the heavens were much better than ancient times, particularly among the Arabs, so one would have expected a recorded event in historical astronomy. Of course, if the religion of the Muslims was in some way tied in with the appearance of Nibiru, then this might explain the origin of the Star and Crescent symbol, whose genesis is also very much an open question.

The question as to the exact timing of Nibiru is one that has been long contested by various researchers. The question of the return of the Dark Star is one of the great unknowns in this field of eclectic study, and I am more open to the various possibilities than ever: Particularly, as we consider the perihelion passage to be at the edge of the solar system. This opens things right up. Is the 3750 year cycle due imminently, in 2012, for instance, allowing us to incorporate Cotterell's and Day's Mayan connection? Or, was the last event one that occurred 2000 years ago? Or, is there another possibility entirely?

# Chapter 10 References

1. C. Grady, E. Polomski, "The Disk and Environment of the Herbig Be Star HD 100546" Astronomical Journal, 122, 3396, 2001

2. M. Clampin "HST/ACS Coronoagraphic Imaging of the Circumstellar Disk around HD 141569A" Submitted to The Astronomical Journal, May 2003, astro-ph/0303605v1

3. J. Augereau & J. Papaloizou, "Structuring the HD141569A Circumstellar Dust Disk" Astronomy & Astrophysics, astro-ph/0310732, 2003

4. A. Quillen, P. Varniere, I. Minchev & A. Frank, "Driving Spiral Arms in the Debris Disks of HD 100546 and HD141569A" Astronomical Journal, AJ, 2004

5. A. Brunini & M. Melita "The Existence of a Planet beyond 50AU and the Orbital Distribution of the Classical Edgeworth-Kuiper Belt Objects" Icarus, 160, pp32-43 (2002)

6. Correspondence from Mario Melita, 15th January 2003

7. S. Ida, J. Larwood & A. Burkert "Evidence for Early Stellar encounters in the orbital distribution of Edgeworth-Kuiper Belt Objects" The Astrophysical Journal, 528, 351-356, (2000)

8. A. Quillen, D. Trilling & E. Blackman "The Impact of a Close Stellar Encounter on the Edgeworth-Kuiper Belt" arXiv:astro-ph/0401372v1, 2004

9. J.J. Matese, P.G. Whitman and D.P. Whitmire, "Cometary Evidence of a Massive Body in the Outer Oort Cloud" Icarus, 141, 354-336 (1999)

10. Correspondence from A. Quillen, 18th February 2004,
Reproduced with kind permission


11. Correspondence from A. Quillen, 19th February 2004,
Reproduced with kind permission


12. J. Murray "Arguments for the Presence of a Distant large
Undiscovered Solar System Planet" Mon. Not. R. Astron. Soc.,
309, 31-34 (1999)


13. New Scientist "Rogue star smashed up the solar system" Vol
18, 2433, 7th February 2004, p19, Thanks to Shad Bolling, http:/
/www.amnesium.com.  Here's the paper's on-line abstract:  http:/
/arxiv.org/abs/astro-ph/0401372


14. D. Allan & J. Delair "When the Earth Nearly Died:
Compelling Evidence of a World Cataclysm 11,500 years ago"
pp252-3, Gateway Books 1995


15. B. Arnett "The Interplanetary Medium" 2002, http://
seds.lpl.arizona.edu/nineplanets/nineplanets/medium.html


16. Wikipedia "Heliopause" http://en.wikipedia.org/wiki/
Heliopause


17. C. Kitchin "Aurorae on Other Planets" Astronomy Now, p62,
Mar 2004


18. T. Phillips  "Puzzling X-rays from Jupiter" http://
science.nasa.gov/headlines/y2002/07mar_jupiterpuzzle.htm


19. Gladstone, et al, "A Pulsating Auroral X-ray Hot Spot on
Jupiter" Nature (v. 415) 28th Feb. 2002

20. A. Gilbert & M. Cotterell "The Mayan Prophecies" Appendix 4: 'The Sunspot Cycle' p288-300, Element 1995

21. Correspondence from Maurice Cotterell, 13th September 2002, reproduced with kind permission

22. R. Day "Teotihuacan and the Tenth Planet" Abstracted from the unpublished manuscript 'Nibiru Planet X: Evidence from Antiquity', 1998, pp42-3

## Sedna

So far, we have looked at the historic search for Planet X, and renewed speculation about the potential for a binary companion object orbiting the sun. Work in this field, both academic and alternative has been going on for many years and, under these circumstances, it is natural for a certain

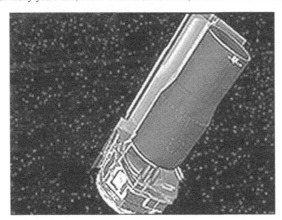

air of despondency to hang over the very concept of Planet X. In times gone by, many astronomers refused to even consider it to be a possibility, despite the growing mass of evidence we have looked at in this book.

So it must have come as a bit of a shock to them when a bona fide Planet X was actually discovered in 2004! Not only has it opened many commentators' eyes to the possibility of yet more planetary objects awaiting discovery, but it has raised questions about some of Science's basic assumptions about the nature of our solar system. Something very odd is going on out there...

"Sedna" is the name given by astronomers for this newest planet to be discovered orbiting the sun. Although the details of the size of the planet are still being sought, it is thought to be about 1,300 miles in diameter and could be of a similar size to Pluto. Given that Pluto is generally accepted to be a planet in its own right, Sedna technically becomes the tenth planet to be found orbiting the sun.

**Quaoar**　　**Sedna**　　**The Moon**　　**Pluto**

NASA had previously hinted about an announcement planned for Monday, 15th March 2004, to be given by Dr. Michael Brown of Caltech (1). His team had recently discovered another large Edgeworth-Kuiper Belt object called 2004 DW, details of which had been released in February 2004 (2). His research team makes use of the recently launched Spitzer Space Telescope. At that time, he made the following tantalizing comment:

"It's now only a matter of time before something is going to be discovered out there that will change our entire view of the outer solar system."

It turns out that Dr. Brown wasn't simply speculating on a remote possibility. His astronomical research team, including Chad Trujillo in Hawaii and David Rabinowitz of Yale University, had discovered the presence of Sedna back in November 2003, and were busy preparing their paper for a public announcement of the find. It had been catalogued as object 2003 VB12.

I had picked up on this development in early March, and I hinted on some astronomical websites that the forthcoming announcement chalked in for 15th March could turn out to be important regarding the Planet X question.

Even so, I was still amazed to hear the news of this announcement on BBC radio on the Monday morning, preceding the actual press conference (3). It enabled me to relay this news onto the Internet through my website, as the USA was waking up in the morning.

I consider the scientific discovery of Sedna to be a major step forward in the hunt for a massive Planet X. It has forced many nay-sayers to rethink completely.

## The Tenth Planet?

Sedna is currently located in the Edgeworth-Kuiper Belt, some 13 billion km from the sun (3). or about 85 Astronomical Units - which is about three times more distant than Pluto. This places it actually within the Kuiper Gap, or Kuiper Cliff, an area unexpectedly devoid of predicted objects. Perhaps it may partially help to explain the lack of companions out at this distance, although it is too small in practice to have swept the Belt clean by itself.

However, although it is located here, it may actually be an object from the distant Oort Cloud of comets. At the moment it is nearing perihelion, which has brought it into the Kuiper Belt. It is the most distant object to have been located orbiting the sun.

It appears to be following an elliptical orbit of between 10 and 12 thousand years duration. Its orbital path is highly eccentric, with a perihelion of 76 AU and an aphelion in the region of 1000 AU (4,5). Thus, astronomers were only able to spot Sedna because it was fortuitously nearing perihelion (which it will actually achieve in 2076). For the most part, Sedna would have been too distant for telescopes to detect. This highly elliptical shaped path is very similar to the kind of orbit envisioned for Nibiru.

However, size-wise, Sedna is too small to be Zecharia Sitchin's Nibiru, and its orbital period is three times as long. Nor is this rocky, icy world anything approaching the size of a 'Dark Star', although it is remarkably red. Whether it is directly connected with Nibiru or not, it is a thrilling discovery, having been confirmed by astronomers at the Tenagra Observatory in Arizona, and then directly imaged by the Hubble Space Telescope (3).

The planet was then named "Sedna", after the Canadian and Greenlandic Inuit Sea Goddess (6). This mythical Sea Spirit partially takes the form of a woman, who sends out her animals to hunt from her lair on the seabed (7). There is certainly some symbolic relevance to this choice of name.

Firstly, the Arctic myth is metaphorically in keeping with the ultra-cold environment of the outer solar system. Secondly, this new planet is readily associated with other similar, but smaller objects in the scattered disc of the Edgeworth-Kuiper Belt. These distant EKBOs also emerge from the darkness of the Abyss during perihelion, appearing like transient hunters from the Void. The name "Sedna" is clearly a perfect choice!

One might argue that the actual discovery of Sedna is not entirely unexpected, in that new technology is helping astronomers to look deeper into the void beyond Pluto to search out dark objects, some of them clearly sizeable. If Sedna turns out to be as large as Pluto, which is still possible, then it would properly be called a planet. However, this is likely to re-ignite debate about what a planet really is, and whether Pluto itself is simply a large, spheroid-shaped asteroid, accompanied by its relatively large 'moon' Charon.

At the moment, it is thought to be smaller than Pluto, but bigger than another substantial EKBO called Quaoar, so it is by no means certain what will be decided for it in time. After all, officially adding to the sun's retinue of planets would mean the re-writing of school books, let alone those of science. Who's to say how many more Sednas are still out there?

Sedna is currently near to its closest approach to the sun, or its 'perihelion'. The outer portion of its highly elliptical orbit falls within the boundary of the inner Oort Cloud, meaning that its entire orbit occupies the substantial gap between the EKB and the Oort Cloud. Because the position of the Oort Cloud is still largely theoretical, findings like this add to the fledgling body of evidence actually describing it.

So the discovery of Sedna, and other 'scattered disc objects' will lead astronomers to reconsider the position of the comet-cloud. For example, Dr. Brown now speculates that the inner Oort Cloud may be closer than once thought, having arisen as a result of the action of a rogue star near to the sun (4). This is reminiscent of the argument for the existence, whether past or present, of a binary companion.

Speculation about the existence of a binary star at the early point in the solar system's history is now bound to grow, as will the possibility that the sun was once subject to a stellar "fly-by". As a result, the outer solar system is starting to look like a very interesting place indeed, fuelling interest and research efforts among the astronomical community.

So what can we expect next; Planet XI, Planet XII, Planet XIII...? Is there an Earth-sized planet out there that might have something to do with this gap in the Edgeworth-Kuiper Belt? Is there something even larger further out, like a binary 'Dark Star', that may still be lurking among the comets?

No one knows for sure, but what is likely is that discoveries will continue to be made, as the ability of astronomers to discover increasingly dark and distant objects orbiting the sun improves. The pace of those discoveries is also likely to accelerate.

## Anomalies Fuel Scientific Speculation

I have hinted above that there are several anomalous aspects to this discovery, not least of which is Sedna's orbit. It is simply not behaving as it should, at least according to the model of the solar system used by astronomers. To have such an elliptical orbit, it would have to have been pulled out of an ancient circular orbit by some other, massive object. Yet no such object is known to exist out there, and the potential existence of an undiscovered massive object has long been dismissed by astronomers.

Sedna's discovery has lead to new speculation amongst some of the biggest names in planetary science. As we have seen, the leader of the team who discovered Sedna, Dr. Michael Brown, has questioned whether the previously accepted position of the inner Oort Cloud is correct - and wonders whether the sun formed in a star cluster whose brethren may have dragged minor planets like Sedna into eccentric orbits (8). Other astronomers, each with their own pet theories about the outer solar system, have contributed other ideas - like the effect of a passing star, or interaction with Gigantic Molecular Clouds.

Perhaps surprisingly, the director of the Minor Planet Centre, Dr. Brian Marsden, has gone on record speculating about the existence of a terrestrial-sized planet, or bigger, several hundred AU away (8). The idea still leaves open the question of how the planet could have formed at that distance, but such a body might provide a mechanism whereby Sedna's own orbit became so eccentric. At some point, Sedna must have interacted with a larger planetary body - flinging it into its now wildly elongated orbit.

It is clear that the notion of a terrestrial-sized planet X is now taking hold within the astronomical community, even though it still faces the same problem encountered before by Brunini and Melita. They argued for an embedded planet in the Edgeworth-Kuiper Belt (9). Their proposed body led to quite a reasonable match for the truncation of the Edgeworth-Kuiper Belt, particularly, as it turns out, with a more eccentric orbit for such a planet (10). But the lingering question of its lack of discovery is an urgent and difficult one.

If the undiscovered planet lies further out, towards the inner Oort Cloud, it must be more substantial in size to create the same effect on EKBO orbits, which is why Dr. Marsden opts for a multiple-Earth-mass planet. But then, how did such a body form in this region of low density of matter? The problem continues to deepen with every turn.

We also have the question of whether the truncation of the Edgeworth-Kuiper Disc was caused by a very massive object. Models of stellar fly-bys can produce some, but not all, of the observed effects (11). In the last chapter, we saw that a Jupiter-plus sized object in an eccentric orbit could create the truncated disc, although Dr. Quillen, who carried out the work, doubts whether one could still be out there. I am not so sure, particularly given Sedna's orbital properties. Sedna seems to call for a more urgent reappraisal of the situation in the outer solar system.

Could a very substantial planet still be out there and have evaded detection? I have argued that that is the case on several occasions (12), and this view seems to have been backed up by Dr. Brown's analysis of previous searches, like IRAS. He has stated that there is an area in the sky covering about 20% of the celestial sphere, which has not been properly searched for a hidden planet orbiting the sun.

This region lies in the direction of the Milky Way - specifically, towards the centre of our galaxy (8). This is, of course, the region that I have already highlighted as being the most probable location for the Dark Star, i.e. in the vicinity of the constellation Sagittarius.

This area is a prime hunting ground for the Dark Star for a number of reasons, not the least of which are textual references to Sagittarius being the direction the mythical planet departs towards (12,13). There are other, more scientific reasons for considering this region for a candidate object, as already discussed in Chapter 4.

One could be forgiven for thinking that things are dovetailing together. Does Sedna's strange orbit give us reason to think that a massive body lies in a region of the sky that previous sky searches simply neglected? Dr. Brown certainly thinks there might be a planet lying in the direction of the galactic core, and his team are actively searching in that region for one (8). This is a much more difficult task than one might imagine.

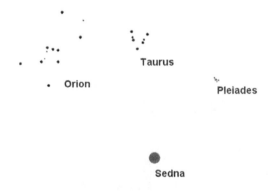

Apart from anything else, the planet's relative motion against the background of the galactic stars will be very slow. It might very much appear as if it's standing still, particularly if its orbit is like Sedna's, and highly elliptical. Under those circumstances, the greatest proportion of its movement will be towards us. Its lateral movement in the sky will be slight, meaning that it is quite possible that it has already been detected, but then incorrectly catalogued as a galactic star.

'Star Wars' fans might wonder whether this missing planet is similar to Kamino; in this case the missing planet may well turn out to have been in the archive all along!

## A Correlation

Sedna, currently moving towards perihelion, has been found close to where I have argued for the sky location of the perihelion transit of Nibiru (near Sirius and Orion). Sedna is currently moving from the constellation Cetus towards Taurus, which is a pro-grade motion across the sky. I think this closely mirrors the likely motion of the Dark Star through the sky when it is close to perihelion. This 'coincidence' seems remarkable, given the other factors involved here. One has to wonder whether the orbits of Sedna and the Dark Star are closely linked.

Such a situation could possibly exist, because bodies in the outer solar system tend to establish orbital correlations between each other. These are called "mean motion resonances" (14). Pluto has a commensurate orbit with Neptune, for instance, in this case a 2:3 mean motion resonance. Many of the Edgeworth-Kuiper Belt Objects have similar resonance ratios with Neptune.

So if the Dark Star is orbiting the sun in the outer solar system, and if it is a substantial planet (and I advocate a sub-brown dwarf, a sub-stellar class of planet that has been theoretically modelled (15) ) then it will interact with the other celestial bodies within the considerable sweep of its eccentric orbit.

Over time, Nibiru would have ejected many so-called scattered disc objects (and the Edgeworth-Kuiper Belt is known to be massively depleted), causing the truncation of the EKB - and those objects that remain in its sphere of influence may have taken on resonant orbits with it. This assumes, of course, that it is still there! So, it is certainly not beyond reason that Sedna is in a resonant orbit with a much larger planet that remains to be found. If so, their orbital periods should correlate in some way.

When discussing the orbit of Nibiru, Zecharia Sitchin proposed that it was about 3,600 years, synchronous with the fundamental number in the Sumerian sexigesimal numbering system of 3,600, or 1 'Sar' (13). Two orbits would thus take place over about 7,200 years, three over 10,800 years. Sedna's orbital period is between 10 and 12 thousand years. So, Sedna may turn out to have a 3:1 mean motion resonance with Sitchin's Nibiru.

This could be an important finding. As astronomers study Sedna's orbit more closely, their data will enable them to work out its actual orbital period more exactly. If I am right, then other scattered disc objects will also be discovered in the future, which will share similar mean motion resonances as Sedna. From the data that amasses over time, a picture will emerge of the orbit of the parent body itself; the Dark Star. In a way, these wandering sheep are moving to the shepherd's tune, and we can start to figure out more about this shepherd by analyzing their trails.

But this will only work if the parent planet is still out there. If it left the solar system long ago, as Dr. Quillen argues, then it could not have created this effect. As such, an emerging pattern of synchronous scattered disc object orbits will determine whether the body is still awaiting discovery, or whether it is now an absent parent.

As Spitzer and other telescopes carry on their work over next year or two, a pattern in the orbits of newly discovered bodies may emerge, which will only increase speculation about the existence of a massive undiscovered body.

## Lagrangian Points

Another possibility is that the Dark Star has attendant clusters of comets, asteroids and minor planets. It is known that there are mathematical locations in a three-body system which are stable regions. These are called LaGrangian points, after the 18th Century mathematician Joseph Louis LaGrange.

If we take the example of the sun and the binary Dark Star as the two main bodies in a 3-body system, we can think about minor objects that could be located at these five stable points. Three of these positions lie along the main axis between the sun and the Dark Star; they are 'co-linear' with the sun and the Dark Star. The two others lie along the path taken by the Dark Star, one of which moves ahead of it, known as the leading LaGrange point; the other is located behind the Dark Star, and is known as the trailing LaGrange point. These positions are really regions, not points, because there are other gravitational influences in the solar system to take into account. The Trojans are more stable regions than the co-linear positions.

An example of bodies located at LaGrangian Points are the Trojans, two clusters of asteroids within Jupiter's orbit, that have a mean motion resonance with the gas giant of 1:1. Is it possible that the Dark Star also has clusters of objects located at its own LaGrangian Points?

John Bagby, a researcher who, several decades ago, considered the possibility that the sun might have a massive companion, offered the thought that immense clusters of bodies at these LaGrangian points might help distribute some of the overall system's mass around the orbital path (16). It seems a reasonable idea, and it would imply that some of these objects in these regions could be quite large; quite possibly as large as Sedna.

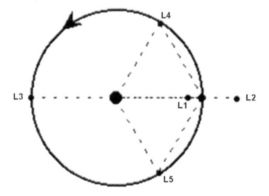

As the Dark Star moves along its orbital path, its LaGrangian Points move with it. If one imagines a roughly circular orbit, like Jupiter's around the sun, one could divide the circle into 12 sections, like a clock-face. If Jupiter was located at 12, then the LaGrangian Points along the circumference of the clock would be located roughly at 10, 2 and 6. If we imagine the clock-face slowly turning about the centre, which would represent the sun, then those LaGrangian Points would also change position accordingly. They would move through the same locations as Jupiter, but at timed intervals.

If we imagine that clock-face to be stretched out into a long ellipse, like the shape of Sedna's orbit, then the same principle would still apply. At given intervals, the LaGrangian Points will move through any given location along the circumference of our weird-shaped clock. Sedna might have minor bodies trapped at LaGrangian Points along its own orbit, that will themselves achieve perihelion over the course of thousands of years, or Sedna itself might even be at the LaGrangian Point of a parent body. Admittedly, this idea is speculative. But let us consider the consequences that would naturally follow from it.

## Multiple Nibirus?

Let us say that Sedna is part of a cluster of minor planetary bodies passing through the Kuiper Gap, in a 1:1 mean motion resonance with the Dark Star. If that is so, then many other bodies contained within that cluster are about to come to light, because Sedna is only 72 years away from perihelion. This might be interesting news to those who believe that comet activity in the solar system is already on the rise. Not only that, but it may explain other phenomena in the solar system at the moment, like the slight warming experienced by all of the planets. We will look more closely at these issues later.

The implication of this speculation is that the Dark Star may turn out to have a much larger orbit than previously thought; possibly in the region of about 10,800 years. The Dark Star would then currently lie about 1,000 AU away, in the exact opposite part of the sky from Sedna. They would forever be chasing each other's tails. In that case, it will achieve aphelion, its furthest point, when Sedna arrives at perihelion in 2076.

So, this scenario would lead us to conclude that the Dark Star's last perihelion was half an orbit ago, around 3325BCE. This is necessarily an approximate date, because the LaGrangian points are in reality sizeable regions, and Sedna could lie anywhere within that region. But, this approximate dating would be around the time of the First Dynasty in Egypt, at the dawn of civilization itself.

It is also worth noting that the Earth experienced some significant changes in solar radiation sometime around 3200BCE. The sun underwent a drop and then a surge in its output 5,200 years ago, leading to a calamitous period of climate change (17). Perhaps this was as a result of the perihelion transit of the Dark Star, whose movement through the solar system may have affected the sun's activity.

We saw last chapter how the sun's magnetic field may have become twisted around this time; Maurice Cotterell places the date at about 3113BCE (18). Is there a connection between this monumental change to the Earth's climate, and the possible perihelion of the Dark Star around 3200BCE? After all, the perihelion transit beyond the EKB would have taken a couple of hundred years, during which the sun's activity would have been subject to change.

For this to be true, we would have to conclude that Zecharia Sitchin's claim that Nibiru's orbit is a Sar in length, or 3,600 years, was not entirely accurate. Instead, the Dark Star itself orbits the sun roughly every 10,800 years, like Sedna, but has associated with it regularly placed pockets of comets and small planets which interact with the outer solar system, perhaps every 3,600 years or so. These correspond with the Dark Star's LaGrangian Points, and their periodic activities are associated in myth with Nibiru. In other words, the phenomenon of Nibiru occurs more frequently than the actual 'appearance' of the Dark Star, because the system is distributed regularly around its orbital path.

If this speculation is correct, it seems like we're living through one of those periods now. This is because the LaGrangian Point which lies exactly opposite to the Dark Star's actual position is currently moving through the EKB, carrying with it bodies like Sedna.

Whether this is the case or not, I suggest that Sedna's discovery draws us ever closer to that of the Dark Star's, and that this parent body will be found somewhere in the sky north of Sagittarius, probably within some of the dense star fields ignored by IRAS. It is quite possible that it has already been catalogued, but incorrectly defined as a more distant stellar object. (It is interesting to note that a faint "red dwarf" star was recently identified as the third closest star to the sun, at a mere 7.8 light years (19) ).

It is heartening that Dr. Brown is now going to turn his attention, and that of the Spitzer Telescope, towards such unexplored regions. He may amaze us all with what he finds there.

## That Red Color

The orbital anomalies associated with Sedna have created a major puzzle for astronomers, and have arguably lead us closer to answers about the Dark Star. But there are other aspects to the discovery of Sedna that have created problems for the scientists. One of them is that Sedna is red.

Organic, volatile, icy deposits on the surface of an outer solar system body tend to make these objects reddish, but none of the Edgeworth-Kuiper Belt objects have the same degree of reddening as Sedna. It has been suggested to me by a research colleague that high speed, collisional interactions could create this kind of coloring effect on the body's surface (20).

EKBOs are thought to collide on occasion, and Sedna is a substantial minor planetary body. But its properties, both orbital and physical, tend to suggest it falls into a new class of scattered disk objects. I have proposed here that this class is related to a massive object, in a similar orbital pattern that currently lies at aphelion. That object is believed to have interacted with the other bodies of the primordial solar system in a catastrophic manner. One can readily see how the red color could tie in with this scenario.

## That Lack of Spin

A further difficulty is the lack of a moon orbiting Sedna. When Sedna was originally discovered, it was thought that it had a moon in tow, rather like Pluto's moon Charon. The reason for that prediction had to do with Sedna's axial spin, which gives it a rather long 'day' - between 20 and 40 Earth days (21). For a solar system body to have such a slow spin, it must have interacted with a moon of about 400 miles diameter, which would have acted as a brake to Sedna's spin over time.

However, Sedna appears to have no such moon. Observations by the Hubble Space telescope have effectively ruled out a moon down to a size equivalent of ten times smaller than Sedna. Any orbiting moon as small as this could not have slowed Sedna's spin down.

The implication of this is that there must have once been a moon, but it is now missing. Yet, Sedna orbits along a trajectory that is relatively empty of other solar system bodies...at least that's the impression astronomers have so far. If a moon is still there, it would have to be the darkest object in the solar system to have escaped detection, a thought put forward by Professor Chandra Wickramasinghe of Cardiff, Wales (22).

How could it have lost a moon? One is led to conclude that Sedna's past was a violent one. This once again fits with the idea of an extended system of objects along Sedna's orbital trajectory, of which Sedna is the first body to actually be discovered. But we must be cautious because this observed rate of spin is only provisional, and may turn out to be erroneous, rather than a real anomaly (23).

Some correspondents have wondered whether Sedna may have been, or still is, a moon of the Dark Star, perhaps dislocated soon after its migration into the outer solar system. This seems an interesting possibility, and makes one wonder whether Sedna's lack of spin might be related to the loss of contact with the original parent planet in a catastrophic episode during the early life of the solar system. However, I am inclined to think that Sedna lies at a LaGrangian Point, and is simply part of the distributed Dark Star system.

## Astronomers Consider Brown Dwarf Solution

There is no doubt that astronomers are becoming more interested in the potential for the involvement of a brown dwarf in the early solar system. This open-mindedness is in marked contrast to the population at large, whose interest in the Planet X phenomenon has waned in recent years. Perhaps that is exactly why astronomers feel more at ease in speculating about the outer solar system's origins now; the feeding frenzy of fringe Planet X conjecture has dissipated. In its wake is the possibility of a real scientific debate about whether our sun became entangled with sizeable objects in the dim and distant past; interstellar passers-by, brown dwarfs and birth cluster companions.

The birth of our sun is no longer being discussed in terms of a lonely appearance in a quiet, unremarkable backwater of the galaxy. The sun may have had siblings; possibly a veritable litter of starlets of all shapes and sizes, whose early presence may not have adversely affected the inner planets per se, but certainly may have played around with the outer bodies orbiting the sun.

Until recently, not enough was known about these bodies, and the assumption was that they would be found to meander around our sun in a more or less orderly fashion.

However, one of the great things about discovery and science is that the unexpected is always what one must expect. In this case, the orbital patterns of some of these outer solar system bodies are quite clearly anomalous, bringing into question the entire issue of the solar system's origins. Something has been creating patterns of change out there, creating bizarre orbits, creating headaches for the boffins. To solve the riddle of objects like Sedna, the astronomers are forced to be more creative with their explanations, bringing Science into the territory of the Dark Star.

New Scientist has published a feature outlining the new thinking being banded about. In July 2004, it reported an "implausible" but nevertheless "cool" suggestion is that Sedna's controversial orbit could be the result of the early presence of a brown dwarf interacting with the sun. The popular science magazine interviewed an astronomer at the Southwest Research Institute in Boulder, Colorado named Harold Levison.

He pointed out that Sedna's orbit could not have come about by any mechanism simply involving all the known objects in the solar system. Instead, the group were speculating that there had been an early passage through the solar system by a brown dwarf. They wondered whether Sedna was once a planet associated with that brown dwarf, and had been captured by the sun into an eccentric orbit, as a result of the fly-by (24).

The group, which included Alessandro Morbidelli from Nice in France, carried out calculations to test this hypothesis, and there was indeed a correlation with observed behavior in the outer solar system. The calculations also showed that about half of the brown dwarf's proto-planetary disc would have been captured by the sun in this way, and would be orbiting the sun in a similar fashion to Sedna (24).

The astronomers have a keen interest in the capture process itself, which is to be the subject of further research. They hope to eventually explain various anomalies in the solar system, like the origin of the Oort cloud and how the outer giant planets came to have such peculiar systems of moons (25). These are the same kinds of issues we have looked at in this book, and indicate the importance attached to them by mainstream astronomers.

But the astronomers fall short of advocating the current presence of a brown dwarf in our solar system. To do so would appear ludicrous to the outside world, perhaps. After all, where is the proof? This is a question that would inevitably be asked by the world's media. It seems highly reasonable from a scientific perspective, to conclude that there is a massive Planet X on the basis of indirect evidence. But the rest of the world demands direct proof.

As time goes on, I suspect that more and more evidence will emerge to bolster their confidence and start open speculation about the existence of a rogue brown dwarf. Already Alessandro Morbidelli has gone on record in France speculating about a hidden tenth planet, stirring up some controversy among some commentators who believe that his arguments reflect even more alternative ideas (26,27). It seems to me that if the sun is capable of capturing half of a rogue brown dwarf's planetary system, then it is also quite capable of capturing the brown dwarf itself! I think it quite likely that a Dark Star awaits discovery, and the minor planet called Sedna has begun the process of unlocking its secrets.

# Chapter 11 References

1. "NASA Schedules News Briefing about Unusual Solar Object"
http://rense.com/general50/mys.htm

2. http://news.bbc.co.uk/1/hi/sci/tech/3506329.stm

3. D. Whitehouse  "Astronomers Discover new planet" 15th
March 2004  http://news.bbc.co.uk/1/hi/sci/tech/3511678.stm

4. Spitzer Press release, 15th March 2004 http://
www.spitzer.caltech.edu/Media/releases/ssc2004-05/
release.shtml

5. Brian Marsden, Minor Planet Center, Harvard Smithsonian
Astrophysical Observatory,interviewed by Linda Moulton Howe
http://www.earthfiles.com/news/
news.cfm?ID=683&category=Science

6. 'Sedna' http://www.rahoorkhuit.net/goddess/goddess_quest/
sedna.html

7. R. Willis (Ed) "World Mythology" p216-7 Simon & Schuster
1993

8. R. R. Britt "Distant Sedna Raises Possibility of Another Earth-
Sized Planet in Our Solar System" 16th March 2004,  with thanks
to David Pearson  http://www.space.com/scienceastronomy/
sedna_earth_040316.html

9. A. Brunini & M. Melita "The Existence of a Planet beyond
50AU and the Orbital Distribution of the Classical Edgeworth-
Kuiper Belt Objects" Icarus, 160, pp32-43 (2002)

10. Correspondence from Dr. Mario Melita, 15th January 2003

11. A. Quillen, D. Trilling & E. Blackman "The Impact of a Close Stellar Encounter on the Edgeworth-Kuiper Belt" arXiv:astro-ph/0401372vl, 2004

12. A. Lloyd "Planet X: Past and Present" UFO Magazine, pp32-7, January 2004

13. Z. Sitchin "The Twelfth Planet" Avon 1976

14. J. Davies "Beyond Pluto" pp94-6 Cambridge University Press 2001

15. A. Burrows, D. Sudarsky & J. Lunine "Beyond the T Dwarfs: Theoretical Spectra, Colours, and Detectability of the Coolest Brown Dwarfs" Jun. 2003 arXiv:astro-ph/0304226v2

16. J. Bagby "Evidence for a Tenth Planet or Massive Solar Companion beyond Uranus" 1982. Many position papers by John P. Bagby were published in several lesser-known journals, nevertheless standing as a substantive public record of his cutting-edge work, including Kronos 1984; Cornell Engineer 1980, v 45, #4, pp32-4; Cycles Journal 1996, and others published as early as 1972

17. Tim Radford "Evidence of 3,000 BC Calamity" 16th December 2004, The Guardian

18. Correspondence from Maurice Cotterell, 13th September 2002

19. Space Daily "New Found Star May Be Third-Closest", 26th May 2003 http://www.spacedaily.com/news/stellar-03a.html

20. Correspondence from John Lee, 18th March 2004

21. R. Britt "Weird Object Beyond Pluto Gets Stranger" 14th
April 2004 http://www.space.com/scienceastronomy/
hubble_sedna_040414.html With thanks to David Pearson

22. "Unique moon may partner Sedna" New Scientist 21
August 2004  http://www.newscientist.com/news/
news.jsp?id=ns99996295

23. The Western Mail "University team's theory causes stir"
30th August 2004, with thanks to David Pearson http://
icwales.icnetwork.co.uk/0100news/0200wales/
tm_objectid=14585326&method=full&siteid=50082&headline
=university-team-s-theory-causes-stir-name_page.html

24. Maggie McKee "Stray Star may have jolted Sedna" 27th
July 2004, with thanks to Lee Covino and Brant McLaughlin
http://www.newscientist.com/news/news.jsp?id=ns99996204

25. A. Morbidelli & H. Levison "Scenarios for the origin of the
Orbits of the Trans-Neptunian Objects 2000 CR105 and 2003
VB12 (Sedna)", submitted to Astronomical Journal 2/4/2004
http://www.boulder.swri.edu/~hal/CR105.html

26. V. Greffos "Planets - But How Many Are There In Our
Solar System?" Science & Vie, Feb. 2003

27. Z. Sitchin "The Case of the French Astronomer", http://
www.sitchin.com, with reference to the February 2003 issue of
"Science & Vie", featuring Alessandro Morbidelli ideas about a
'phantom planet'.

# 12

## The Dark Star System

It might be a good idea to pause for breath at this point, and recap where we have gotten to. We have looked at the history of the search for a tenth planet in the solar system. That painstaking search initially provided science with a new planet called Pluto, but seemed to draw a blank with anything larger, although theoretical work had led scientists to conclude that something else should be there.

Astronomers, building up their theories about how stars and planets form, concluded that another massive planet should not still be out there. They thought this because if it was quite close to Neptune, then it should have been detected by now; and if it was beyond the limits of detection, it should not have been able to form in the first place.

The idea then emerged that a hidden Planet X could have an elliptical orbit. This provided a useful bridge between a previous proximity to the sun's other planets, in turn helping us to explain how it formed, and its current great distance, which would explain why it had not yet been detected. This idea has become the hallmark of Planet X hunters in more recent years, but was generally held in low regard by most "mainstream" astronomers. This idea became entwined in the interpretation of ancient myth, and associated alternative theories, which continue to remain highly controversial to this day.

More ideas emerged about very massive sub-stellar objects called black and brown dwarfs occupying orbits in the outer Oort Cloud of comets. An object at the very great distances involved would be very, very difficult to detect, but its existence might be implied by the pattern of comets that visit us, or by the regularity of catastrophic events on this planet.

My own contribution to this field has been to integrate many of these ideas, to create a coherent whole. Sometimes my efforts in this regard have fallen on stony ground, and I have been forced to re-think. Other ideas have moved things forward.

Throughout, I have been open-minded to new possibilities - particularly when scientific discoveries have created new insights. This flexibility has its downside, however, because my essays and articles down the years have tended to shift their ground. This can easily create confusion among regular readers of the Dark Star material.

It is helpful, then, to present a summary of my current theory about the Dark Star. We will then consider how this integrates with catastrophism and myth, and how the concept of the Dark Star might challenge Science to turn its attention to the peripheries of the outer solar system. As we have already seen, many scientific anomalies can already be explained in this way.

## What Is the Dark Star?

It seems likely that the sun has a companion. It is not a star in its own right, but a Jupiter-sized planet. This planet is much heavier, and therefore denser, than Jupiter, and this creates a certain amount of heat and light generation. Such a world might be called a sub-brown dwarf, and occupies a particular category of planet which is not understood particularly well at the moment.

This Dark Star is not a brilliant object, but it does give out heat. This, combined with gravitational effects, may allow habitable conditions to exist on its nearest satellites, or moons. This allows us to negotiate the problems suffered by Zecharia Sitchin's 12th Planet Theory, through the creation of warm conditions in an environment well beyond that of the other planets of our solar system.

## Where Is It?

The Dark Star is currently lying somewhere close to the ecliptic, or plane of the planets. The constellation Sagittarius is a likely place to search for it. It probably lies in the dense star fields of the Milky Way, an area not properly searched by IRAS, or, indeed, by astronomers searching for Edgeworth-Kuiper Belt objects - who tend to limit their searches to dark regions of the sky.

I think that it is at its furthest point from us, or aphelion. Its exact distance is unknown, but may be as far away as 1,000AU, or 1,000 times the distance from the Earth to the sun. Its lateral movement across the sky is very slow, and this makes it even more difficult to differentiate between an orbiting planet and a distant star. As a result, it is quite possible that it has already been detected and catalogued erroneously as a more distant star in the galaxy.

## Can We See it?

The only chance of directly observing the Dark star without the use of a very powerful telescope is during its perihelion, or its closest passage to the sun. I originally thought that this would occur within the planetary zone of the solar system, coming relatively close to the Earth. However, there are a number of technical reasons why I now consider this to be highly unlikely. Instead, new scientific evidence about the outer solar system implies that the Dark Star moves through the Kuiper Gap at about 70AU distance at perihelion.

There is still a possibility that it would be seen at this distance, but only if there was a significant interaction with the sun's extended magnetic field, as the Dark Star crossed through the Heliopause. This might make the sub-brown dwarf temporarily more active (and the sun, too, might experiences changes to its energy output). Then there might be a visible phenomenon associated with its perihelion passage, which was known to the ancients as Nibiru.

A second, more likely possibility, is that other objects will be seen as the Dark Star crosses perihelion. These might be comets and minor planetary bodies locked into an inner LaGrangian point, that sweeps through the outer solar system. Or, it might be a more substantial planet that orbits the Dark Star at a significant distance. This planet might enter the planetary solar system and quickly move across the sky, seeming to head backwards. This may also be the phenomenon called Nibiru.

If it turns out that the Dark Star does indeed enter the planetary zone at perihelion, then we could expect a very exciting visual phenomenon indeed. It would be a quite spectacular event to observe, and would without doubt become a major religious icon for many of the world's cultures.

When I initially wrote about this subject, I proposed that the actual Dark Star was none other than the Messianic Star of the Christian Nativity. This must remain a possibility, but I now consider it to be more difficult to justify, at least on a scientific level.

## How Many Satellites Orbit the Dark Star?

Astronomers often use the term "satellites" to denote moons. It's difficult to decide whether to call the satellites of a brown dwarf system "planets" or "moons" anyway. For instance, if a brown dwarf was behaving like Jupiter then we would naturally want to call its satellites "moons". But, if we were looking at a brown dwarf free-floating in space with its own planetary system, then we would more likely treat it as a low mass star system. Under those circumstances, we would certainly call the satellites 'planets'.

Our proposed Dark Star is more like Jupiter than an independent star, although it may turn out to have been captured by the sun in the distant past. Its major satellites are likely to be to be substantial planets in their own right, but it seems sensible to call them "moons", because the brown dwarf is itself a planet orbiting a star. Another suggestion has been to call the satellites "planetars", but I think this generally confuses things further. So we shall stick to "moons".

My thinking about the size and distribution of the Dark Star system is based largely upon mythical and esoteric symbolism. Some of that work is derived from Zecharia Sitchin, particularly with respect to his interpretation of Winged Disc symbolism from ancient Egypt and Mesopotamia. But there are many other sources of useful ideas too.

My current thinking is that there are 7 moons orbiting the Dark Star. The closest of them may well have habitable environments; certainly, I think one of them does - with that particular world being of a similar size and character to our Earth. The furthest planet is in a very wide orbit around the Dark Star, and is capable of passing through our solar system during the Dark Star's perihelion. Justification for this interpretation is complex and unfortunately, beyond the scope of this book; it delves heavily into myth and symbolism, and is naturally rather more speculative than the scientific work reviewed in this volume. As such, it would best be looked at in detail in a future book.

But, there is more to the Dark Star system than its major planets. It no doubt has a distributed collection of minor planetary bodies, and probably belts of comets too.

## How Long is the Dark Star's Orbit?

I originally concurred with the general consensus among alternative theorists, that Nibiru's orbit is about 3,600 years in length. This was originally derived from Zecharia Sitchin's original 12th Planet theory. He 'applied' the orbital period to the Sumerian value of 1 Sar, which was equivalent to 3,600 years (1). This was justified because of the centrality of this number within the complex numbering system of the Sumerians, and it seemed to Sitchin that the chronological returns of Nibiru would be a good reason for its importance.

Based on this assumption, I argued for many years that the last visual sighting of Nibiru took place some 2,000 years ago and was in fact the Messianic Star of Christian tradition. This fairly straightforward assertion was actually rather more difficult to prove, and I found myself in a veritable minefield of theological contention. After a great deal of deliberation I considered it probable that the Star of Bethlehem was simply a mythological construct.

That made an association with an actual sighting of the Dark Star problematic. Except, that the Dark Star might not actually be easy to observe at perihelion anyway...and, it was also possible that the ancient expectation of the observation of a Star was more important to our story, than whether one was actually seen at a particular time or not.

You can appreciate the tangle this created in my mind. All that I could really say with any certainty was that the Dark Star was not about to become visible anytime soon - or else, it would have been detected by any number of astronomers, both professional and amateur, studying the stars across the entire face of the Earth.

If the Dark Star's orbital period is Sitchin's 3,600 years, then I still contend that it must have passed through perihelion about 2,000 years ago, because it almost certainly is at its furthest point right now. How else could one explain away the lack of direct detection of such a massive body? So, there is still a reasonable possibility that the phenomenon of Nibiru is closely associated with Messianic prophecy of one form or another.

However, this is another rather complicated subject which requires very comprehensive review. It is unfortunate that I cannot do that argument justice in this volume; to work through the Biblical Scholarship alone would require several chapters. It is best left to a future book more focussed on these particular issues. Suffice it to say, for now, that a potential link between the phenomenon of Nibiru and the Messianic Star is an open one.

However, the Messianic Star thesis would be more difficult to substantiate scientifically than the ideas we are currently looking at concerning a larger Dark Star orbit. If the orbital period was longer - in fact much, much longer - then the Dark Star's current position could be further away still, making it easier to explain why detection had yet to happen. In other words, if we challenge the acquired wisdom that the orbit of Nibiru is just 1 Sar in length, then the science underlying the prospect of a Dark Star becomes more realistic. The question then is how this can be justified, in terms of ancient textual references.

I have occasionally come across passages like this one by Harold T. Wilkins:

*"Censorinus, the Roman chronologist of the third century A.D. said that, at the end of every great year of six Babylonian sars (a period of 21,600 years), our planet undergoes a complete revolution. Polar and equatorial regions change place, the tropical vegetation and swarming animal life moving towards the forbidding wastes of the icy poles...Catastrophes attend the change, with great earthquakes and cosmical throes"* (2).

It seems that it would be legitimate to consider the orbit in terms of multiples of Sars. After all, the length of the reign of gods as described by the ancient Mesopotamians were also set out in Sar multiples. One such multiple, or 10,800 years, is equivalent to the orbital period of Sedna. This points towards a resonant relationship between these outer solar system bodies.

Given all the other anomalous properties of this new minor planet, I wondered whether drawing a analogy was justified. Quite what the exact relationship between the Dark Star and Sedna is, I don't yet know. But it seems more realistic to argue that the Dark Star's orbit is much greater than 3,600 years, and this figure of 10,800 years has real promise, for reasons we shall now consider.

If we work with the premise that the Dark Star's orbital period is 10,800 years, then its orbit is very similar (but exactly opposite) to Sedna. In that case, the Dark Star's aphelion will take place over the next 100 years, coincident with Sedna's imminent perihelion. That means that the Dark Star last encountered the edge of the Edgeworth-Kuiper Belt about 5,300-5,400 years ago, around 3350BCE. This was during Sumerian times, and around the time of the emergence of Dynastic Egypt. There is also strong evidence of severe climate change during that period of time, connected with dramatic changes in the sun's activity (3).

The period between then and now roughly fits in with the current Mayan Age, which will come to an end on 21st December 2012. This date may be associated with changes in the sun's activity, or possibly even a reversal of the solar system's neutral sheet (4). Does that Age coincide with half an orbit of the Dark Star?

## A Distributed System

Last chapter we dealt with the concept of Lagrangian points, or positions in space which were stable for minor bodies in a dynamic three body system. So, for a system with the sun at the centre, with a massive body like the Dark Star orbiting it, regional positions relative to the Dark Star could play host to masses of minor planetary bodies. Sedna may well sit in just such a position; at the co-linear Lagrangian point on the opposite side of the sun to the Dark Star.

If so, then Sedna may be one of many, many bodies clustered together within a particular region of space, made relatively stable by a positional relationship with the sun and Dark Star. Clusters of relatively small objects located at these regions will orbit around the sun just like the Dark Star does, and feel no net acceleration. This works the same for elliptical orbits as for circular ones, with the Lagrangian points being similarly located at 60 degree intervals around the orbital path (5).

I have no idea how many minor planetary objects might be trapped in such a cluster, but it is useful to bear in mind that there may be an effective distribution of total system mass, as described by John Bagby (6). Arguably, such a widespread distribution of the mass of the Dark Star system might help to explain other anomalies, like the apparent slowing down of the Pioneer spacecraft as they move away from the planetary solar system towards the Heliopause. This anomaly has puzzled astronomers and physicists for years.

## Trouble with Pioneer

The earliest spacecraft to leave the planetary solar system, on their way to the stars, such as Voyager and Pioneer, have covered vast distances in the intervening years. They are still able to send small packets of data back to us, but we no longer monitor their weak transmissions. Instead, their positions are monitored by periodically sending them a signal from the Earth, and timing how long the response takes to return.

A few years ago, it became apparent to NASA scientists that the probes were not making the progress expected, possibly indicating they were subject to greater solar system gravity than previously thought. Early in 1999, NASA scientist John Anderson described how Pioneer 10 and 11, as well as the spacecraft Ulysses - which is in a polar orbit around the sun, were displaying anomalous behavior. This anomaly had been picked up by scientists studying the doppler shift of the radio signals from the craft, enabling them to work out the current velocity of the craft (7). Various possible causes have been ruled out, leading some scientists to quite seriously question whether there is some kind of new physical force at work. The fact that this effect is observed in four quite separate cases is exacerbating the issue.

It should be noted that John Anderson is fairly forthright about the possible existence of a tenth planet in the solar system. He was presumably hoping that this anomalous behavior would be a further clue to its existence. Dr. Anderson, a "Celestial Mechanics Investigator" with the Pioneer program, went on record to indicate his belief that Planet X would indeed be found, although no data available at that time supported the notion.

He adhered to the conclusions from nineteenth century astronomical data that the outer planets were being perturbed by a distant gravitational force. He considered it likely that the perturbing influence lay in a plane perpendicular to the ecliptic, and that the orbital period of the planet was between 700 and 1000 years (8). Although this description is not in keeping with the one we are currently considering, it is worth noting the anticipation among the Pioneer team that a breakthrough would one day result.

The two Pioneer spacecraft appears to be slowing down, so much so, that it seemed that they would eventually begin to fall back towards the sun (9). NASA, as an institution, officially denies that these craft are being affected by an unusual gravity effect that was unknown at the time of their launches. Instead, they claim that the phenomenon has been attributed to a mechanical problem with the probes themselves. This is a U-turn from the information presented above, first was made public in 1998. NASA's position at that time was that all mechanical anomalies had been thought of and ruled out.

The scientists who had been studying this behavior could offer no explanation for the slowing down of the probes, and had checked and rechecked their data for years. The results were substantive enough to actually call into question our current theoretical understanding of gravity! Despite NASA's insistence that the problem of this "anomalous gravitational attraction" could be put to rest, the official Pioneer homepage continues to recognize this as a genuine mystery (10).

One must then question whether these gravitational effects might indicate the additional gravitational influence of our unseen brown dwarf? Dr. Carl Sagan once postulated this possibility in 1995, before this scientific anomaly was publicly discussed. He argued that the presence of a massive planet just beyond Neptune would have been given away by variations in the trajectories of the Pioneer and Voyager spacecraft (11).

It turns out that, in the case of the Pioneer craft, such an anomaly has indeed happened. But instead of pulling the craft towards a distant, unseen planet, the effect has been an extra pull form the direction of the sun. It's all very strange.

An interesting footnote to this story occurred one year after the NASA report, presenting a possible explanation that was given about Pioneer 10's weird behavior. It would appear that the craft had been unexpectedly "pushing itself in one particular direction". No explanation was forthcoming about the same behavior in the other probes, and this discussion of Pioneer 10 was made in the context of it having also been "mysteriously knocked off course" by a new, as yet unidentified, object orbiting the sun (12).

The effect occurred in December 1992, when the craft was deflected from its course for about 25 days. The discovery of a Kuiper Belt object was then claimed by researchers at Queen Mary and Westfield College, in London, and the Jet Propulsion Laboratory (JPL) in California.

Would our consideration of a widely distributed Dark Star system help to explain this slowing of the spacecraft? After all, the Dark star is very distant at the current time, and its gravitational influence on bodies nearer to the sun would be fairly negligible. But if we consider clusters of bodies along the orbital path of the Dark Star, which are nearer to the planetary solar system, then we can conceive of a way that they might have some minor, but measurable effect.

This effect would be nebulous, however, because by their very nature these clusters are distributed over space, as is the sum of their gravitational pull. In effect, the known gravitational pull of the central solar system itself is greater taking these clusters into account, and this might explain the observed Pioneer anomaly.

In case you're wondering why the Voyager probes are not similarly affected, Dr. Anderson argued in 2001 that the current trajectories of the Voyager probes could not be analyzed in the same way, because they make use of a different kind of orientation and propulsion system (13).


## 10,800 Years Ago


These clusters of minor planetary bodies and comets are spaced along the orbital path of the Dark Star (which is the same orbital path as Sedna, in effect). One cluster is located alongside Sedna, and is heading towards perihelion at the moment. This is the cluster on the opposite side of the sun, opposite from the Dark Star. A second cluster trails behind the Dark Star and, for the sake of argument, may have moved through its perihelion about 3,600 years ago, around 1600BCE.

There has been a lot of conjecture about catastrophism occurring at that period of time, centred around Biblical texts and other sources. It is beyond the scope of this book to explore them in depth, but one need only browse through the collected works of Immanuel Velikovsky to get the general idea. Such arguments were used to generate the concept of an imminent passage of Nibiru in the very near future. This argument about an extended Dark Star system may help some to reconcile such a scenario with the scientific need to place the actual Dark Star at a very considerable distance.

The next cluster of minor planets and comets would have arrived closer to the known planets during the actual perihelion of the Dark Star, some 5,400 years ago. During this period the sun behaved very strangely, dramatically affecting the Earth's climate.

The date that corresponds with the last full orbital period, when Sedna last achieved perihelion and the Dark Star last reached its furthest point, was about 10,800 years ago. This date is associated with great changes to the climate of this planet; Earth - changes that include the sudden warming of northern oceans over short time periods, leading to the catastrophic melting of ice sheets. For instance, the North Atlantic Ocean appears to have warmed by seven degrees Celsius over a period of just 50 years, bringing in its wake dramatic changes to the climate of Greenland and other land masses skirting the edges of the North Atlantic.

Such changes were not isolated to this region, but were concurrent with other climate shifts in China and across the Himalayas (14). Studies of ancient tree-rings near Lake Superior in North America showed that there was no warning of the sudden flooding of the forests there 11,000 years ago. This dramatic flooding resulted from the melting of glaciers at that time, an event that Theodore Bornhorst, Professor of Geology at Michigan Technological University, thinks could happen again, as our own global warming accelerates (15).

These sorts of changes to the world's climate sound eerily reminiscent of the kinds of Global Warming issues our world faces today. In our present case, the most marked changes seem to be occurring in the Arctic regions where melting processes appear to be accelerating. It is most likely that our industrial output of greenhouse gases is to blame for the problems we now face, but it may also be true that there is a link to the distant past discussed above, spanning 10,800 years. Because, if a celestial body, or its distributed system of accompanying objects, is to blame, then the global effects registered on our planet would be cyclical. Such considerations make the search for the Dark Star and its extended retinue an ever more urgent consideration.

## How Orbital Resonance Started

We have seen that our solar system was not born in isolation, and probably interacted with at least one other star system in the early days (16). Scientists have begun to speculate whether a low mass star, or even a brown dwarf system, may have come so close to the sun that part of its system was captured, leading to the existence of scattered disc objects in the Edgeworth-Kuiper Belt, and other anomalies in the outer solar system (17). Perhaps the low mass star moved close to the sun during the period of the late, great bombardment some 3.9 billion years ago, when the terrestrial bodies in the inner solar system were subject to an unprecedented period of destruction caused by a swarm of massive asteroids and comets.

This would imply that the sun's planetary system was deluged by the other star's outer entourage of comets, perhaps even its planets. Many of them were captured by the sun and fell into distant orbits, like Sedna and 2000 CR105. We don't yet know the scale of this capture of objects, but it seems entirely reasonable to speculate that one of them was the Dark Star Marduk; an extraordinary object of mythic proportions.

Would these bodies become resonant around the rogue planet among them? I believe so. Resonances are important to astronomers, because the repetitive influence of a major planet

**Number of EKBOs**

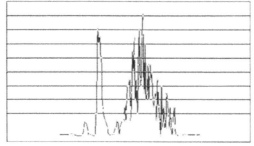

**Distance**

can stabilize or destabilize the orbits of smaller bodies in its vicinity. If the Edgeworth-Kuiper Belt played host to the perihelion transit of the Dark Star then its influence on some of the smaller bodies in the belt should become fairly structured over time.

There are precedents for this in the planetary solar system. Pluto shares a resonant orbit with Neptune that has a three-to-two ratio: Neptune orbits the sun three times for every two circuits by Pluto. This arises because the gravitational effect of the larger body over time, shepherds the smaller one into a stable orbital orientation.

This results in a situation where their orbital paths actually cross in a spatial sense, but they never actually meet, or collide, because they dance around each other in a coordinated fashion. This is the way the dynamics of planetary bodies normally works. The same is also true for three of the four Galilean moons of Jupiter: Io, Europa and Ganymede orbit the mighty gas giant in a 4:2:1 resonance.

## Extra-Solar Planets

The hunt for planets outside our solar system (known as 'extra-solar' planets) is providing a growing data base of planetary behaviors, which will allow scientists to build new models about how the solar system formed. Few expect the current understanding to last for long. Already, many of the new planets exhibit unexpected behavior, indicating that our own sun's planetary system need not provide the blue-print for the entire galaxy.

For instance, brown dwarfs have been discovered orbiting parent stars in very stable systems. The sheer gravitational pull of these massive planets was once thought to rule out such possibilities. It had been thought that they would disrupt the orbits of the other planets in the star system, creating chaotic planetary systems. This is evidently not the case.

The idea was challenged by a discovery by Dr. Geoffrey Marcy's team regarding a star system some 123 light years away. The system, named HD168443, contains a giant planet that is 17 times as massive as Jupiter.

Normally, the astronomers would classify this is a brown dwarf, but this body's close proximity to its star has brought that straightforward classification into question (18). To be circling the star in the relatively close orbit involved, the body should have formed by gas accretion, yet is far more massive than the standard model for planetary formation should allow. The brown dwarf should theoretically have a destabilizing effect on the planetary system as a whole. Yet the HD168443 system is "extremely stable" (19).

To complicate matters still further, another massive planet, this time 7 times as massive as Jupiter, enjoys a circular orbit within the orbit of the first. A planet this size could be termed a "sub-brown dwarf". Even with this second massive planet embedded within the planetary system, the overall system is still 'extremely stable'. This example serves to prove that gargantuan planets such as these, that defy easy classification, can surprise astronomers. They need not be disruptive at all. Instead, they might even create a certain pattern of order within a planetary system.

Further research conducted by Geoffrey Marcy, et al., has shown that planets circling a star can be strongly locked into resonant orbits. A second planet discovered around the star Gliese 876, a small M-type star 15 light-years from Earth, was found to orbit the star in exactly half the time it took for the previously discovered planet to do so. This impressive finding raises questions about how gravitational influence and planetary migration are involved in creating unexpected orbital configurations like this (18).

This last point is important to our investigation into the question of Planet X. Arguments leveled against the existence of Planet X, based upon the current models of the solar system's emergence and development, may be on shaky ground. We simply don't know enough yet to rule anything out. But the other fascinating point about Marcy's discovery is this question of resonance. It's almost as though these two planets are harmonically converged like strings on a musical instrument (20).

This kind of resonance pattern applies to the Edgeworth-Kuiper Belt Objects (EKBOs); small celestial bodies orbiting in an extended belt beyond Neptune. Theo Kermanidis, an engineer with an interest in the existence of Planet X, recently suggested that I study the orbits of the known EKBOs, to see if resonant patterns might indicate the presence of Nibiru within, or beyond, the Kuiper Belt (3). He provided some data and analysis that suggested to him that an undiscovered body may indeed be interacting with some of the EKBOs - but that its orbit would seem to lie well within the parameters normally suggested for Nibiru. He wondered whether a clearer picture would emerge over time, as the database of EKBOs increased, perhaps leading to the discovery of another planet in the solar system. Theo outlined his approach:

"I plotted out the known EKBO distribution and attempted to compare that with the distribution of asteroids. A couple of things to note:

1 The EKBO count could be too low to get meaningful results, but trends in the data could be discerned.

2 Asteroids cluster around specific resonances while avoiding others... because they are dynamically stable.

3 The dynamically unstable resonances can be a more accurate indicator for projecting possible relationships between orbiting bodies, because these notches in the graph are very well defined (otherwise known as Kirkwood gaps). Whereas, stable or semi-stable orbits are shown as broad peaks.

There is a strong Kirkwood gap with resonance 2:1, as well as 3:1, 5:2 and 7:3. Given these resonances, this will then be used to predict the semi-major axis of a possible influencing body" (21).

Intrigued by Theo's suggestion, I contacted an expert on EKBOs at Harvard about the potential for this approach. His reply was encouraging in terms of the application of Theo's method, although in this case, Neptune appeared to be the dominant influence (22).

The EKBO data appears to be consistent with a resonant pattern with Neptune, but it turns out that this generalization is not universally adhered to. The bizarre, highly eccentric orbit of 2000 CR105 is a case in point. Its 'dynamically unstable' orbit is placed well beyond the influence of Neptune, raising questions about the early influences which may have played a part in forming the Edgeworth-Kuiper Belt (23,24).

The Kuiper Belt is classically thought to extend out to about 200AU (25). So an elliptical orbit that extends to 400AU, places 2000 CR105 between the Edgeworth-Kuiper Disc and the inner Oort Cloud (which starts about 2000AU away, according to theorists). If this object had a 'normal' orbit at 400AU, it would circle the sun every 8,000 years or so, yet its actual elliptical orbit achieves a revolution around the sun in less than half the time. In itself, this has important repercussions for the possible orbit of the Dark Star.

Based on the precedent of this eccentric orbit, we can in turn potentially extend the aphelion distance of the Dark Star, perhaps towards the inner boundary of the Oort Cloud. This extreme distance may help explain the difficulties of directly detecting an object whose influence is so keenly felt by the solar system.

To satisfy myself that a more conventional explanation for 2000 CR105's dynamically chaotic orbit had not been established in the meantime, I contacted Dr. Holman, one of the researchers involved in its discovery. Its origins, he noted, still remain a mystery and the subject of much speculation (26).

I think that Theo's proposal about the resonance of the Edgeworth-Kuiper Belt Objects deserves further consideration: there may be more scattered EKBOs, whose perihelion distances lie beyond the point where Neptune's influence can be invoked as an explanation for their behavior. If these more distant objects were also to show a resonance pattern - but this time with an unknown Perturber beyond the Edgeworth-Kuiper Belt - then the position of this planetary body may be readily verifiable in the not too distant future.

This would assume, of course, that Planet X is 'behaving itself'. But, what if its orbit is itself erratic?

## Resonance

The idea of "resonance" is an intriguing one. One assumes that it is an effect that emerges over time as planets 'shepherd' comets, asteroids, or even moons. As we have seen, Geoffrey Marcy's planet-hunting team, from Berkeley, California, have found two planets whose orbital periods resonate together.

Evidently, this effect is a strong one, yet the astronomers seem surprised by this. Presumably, although resonance is noted, it is not predicted for planetary bodies. In other words, our current understanding of celestial mechanics does not lead us to presume that the planets will fall into orbital patterns whose periods become integer ratios of one another. Is that because most of the planets in our solar system quite clearly are not in resonance with one another? Because they are quite evidently more chaotically arranged, we have never assumed that resonance is 'the norm'.

Let's follow this line of thought for a moment. The ancients were not averse to the idea that there was a natural harmony at work in the heavens. Pythagoras, for instance, believed that there was a "dynamic harmony" in the universe, and that the constant movement of the planets and stars created a metaphysical 'music', that was detectable by those with a mystical understanding of the universe (27).

I'm not about to suggest that we could scientifically qualify this belief, but the idea of a celestial harmony at work is an interesting one nonetheless. Perhaps, then, there is a force at work within celestial mechanics that creates harmony between the 'celestial spheres', one that scientists have not discovered yet. But why wouldn't they have? Because, simply, the evidence from our solar system does not immediately support the idea of a universal resonance between the worlds. The planets simply don't behave like that.

But we now know that they can and do behave like that elsewhere. Perhaps our solar system is the exception, rather than the rule. If more double/triple planet star systems are discovered which exhibit the same kind of resonance as that found in the planetary system of Gliese 876, then our understanding of the influence of planets over one another would have to be reconsidered.

I think this could be a distinct possibility. In fact, I would go so far as to say that I would predict such an effect. You see, I think that this harmonic resonance is not found in the solar system as much as it should be, because the solar system has recently been disturbed.

The natural harmony, or resonance, between most of the planets of the solar system no longer exists. Over time, I suspect that the resonance would once more be achieved, but the current relative 'chaos' within the pattern of planetary orbits around the sun indicates the presence of another major planet, one whose distant orbital pattern is a disruptive, rather than cohesive, influence.

## Order from Chaos

To explain the orderly alignments of the planets within the solar system, astrophysicists have traditionally argued that the planets formed in their present orbital configurations, obeying "Bode's Law" right from the word 'go'. This is partly due to the fact that we don't have planets flying around our ears, as one might have thought if things had begun more chaotic in the past. In other words, the accepted physical models are based upon Newton's Laws, that the planets will keep going in a given orbit indefinitely, unless directly perturbed by another planetary body.

But the resonance effect implies a self-regulating principle at work, one that would alter the planetary orbits over time as they harmonize with one another. As such, if resonance turned out to be a common feature of planetary systems, we could no longer surmise a regularity for the early solar system, based upon its current appearance.

Would this be so surprising? After all, other findings from extra-solar planets have already sufficiently rocked the boat for us to question many previously held assumptions (28).

One reason why inner solar system bodies are more haphazardly orientated with respect to each other is because the system becomes increasingly complex. The further out from the sun you go, the more the complexity eases, making it likely, given everything else we know, that the scattered disc objects we are examining are resonant with something massive and unseen.

In which case, we can attempt to find a correlation between what we know about Sedna and 2000 CR105, and what we think we know about the Dark Star. Sedna's orbit is in the region of 10,800 years and 2000 CR105's orbit is about 3,300 years. So, Sedna's orbit is approximately three times that of 2000 CR105. Given that these are approximate values, it is possible that within experimental error the two share resonance. However, better data is needed to say for sure.

Zecharia Sitchin wrote about Nibiru's orbit being 3,600 years, and this has always been taken somewhat at face value. However, there is no piece of Sumerian writing that says 'Nibiru is a planet orbiting the sun whose orbital period is 3,600 years'. His "12th Planet Theory" looked at ancient Mesopotamian myth, and proposed that the cosmogony was based upon real 'creation' events in the solar system. By doing so, one could imply the existence of an undiscovered planet that offered the key to our understanding of the solar system (29).

Sitchin then had to address the issue of its orbit and proposed that it correlated with the Sumerian "Sar" of 3,600, an important component of their unusual and complex sexigesimal numbering system. Well, there is not a great deal of difference between this figure of 3,600 years - which Sitchin has always taken great pains to describe as approximately representing Nibiru's orbital period - and 2000 CR105's 3,300 years. Is there any connection?

We can't know for sure, until more of these objects are discovered and their orbits carefully described. But it would be very interesting indeed if future discoveries of these strange extended scattered disc objects in our solar system showed a statistical correlation of their orbital periods.

One wonders whether their orbits might all be related, with the Babylonian Sar being the basic numerical factor underpinning their relationship! This would make sense of the importance of this number to the ancient Sumerians and Babylonians. From this, we would be able to infer the existence of a distant massive perturbing planet in our solar system, shepherding its widely dispersed flock of planetesimals. So even if we have yet to 'see' the Dark Star, we soon might be able to imply its existence from these companions.

## Chapter 12 References

1. Z. Sitchin "The Case of the French Astronomer"
www.sitchin.com

2. H.T. Wilkins "Mysteries of South America" p32 Rider & Co,
London 1945

3. Tim Radford "Evidence of 3,000 BC Calamity" 16th
December 2004, The Guardian

4. A. Gilbert & M. Cotterell "The Mayan Prophecies" Appendix
4: 'The Sunspot Cycle' p288-300, Element 1995

5. "Klemperer Rosettes", with thanks to Theo Kermanidis http://
burtleburtle.net/bob/physics/kempler.html

6. J. Bagby "Evidence for a Tenth Planet or Massive Solar
Companion beyond Uranus" 1982.

7. D. Whitehouse "Spacecraft pulled by mystery force" BBC,
10th September 1998

8. J. Anderson quoted in "Scientist thinks Tenth Planet may
exist", with thanks to Rick Savard http://www.totse.com/en/
technology/space_astronomy_nasa/10planet.html

9. UFO Magazine "Pioneer Discoveries in Outer Space" Jan/Feb.
1999, Quest Publications International Ltd

10. B. Akins "Pioneer Home: Mission Status" http://
spaceprojects.arc.nasa.gov/Space_Projects/pioneer/PNStat.html

11. C. Sagan "Pale Blue Dot" p143-144, 152 Headline Book Publishing 1995

12. UFO Magazine "Pioneer 10: Still Doing the Business" Jan./ Feb. 2000, Quest Publications International Ltd

13. http://www.cnn.com/2001/TECH/space/05/21/ gravity.mystery/index.html Thanks to Rick Savard

14. D.S. Allan & J.B. Delair "When the Earth Nearly Died" p16, Gateway Books, Bath 1995

15. J. Bone "Ice Age Forest Gives a Global Warning" The Times 25/2/00, with thanks to David Pearson

16. S. Ida, J. Larwood & A. Burkett "Evidence for Early Stellar Encounters in the Orbital Distribution of Edgeworth-Kuiper Belt Objects" The Astrophysical Journal, 528: pp351-6, (2000)

17. A. Morbidelli & H. Levison "Scenarios for the origin of the Orbits of the Trans-Neptunian Objects 2000 CR105 and 2003 VB12 (Sedna)", submitted to Astronomical Journal 2/4/2004 http://www.boulder.swri.edu/~hal/CR105.html

18. J. Foust "Bizarre new planets puzzle astronomers" Spaceflight Now, 10th January 2000

19. Associated Press "We Prefer Not to Call It a Failed Star. We Call It a Specially Challenged Brown Dwarf" 9th January 2001 http://www.aci.net/kalliste/

20. "Planetary Correctness" Associated Press, 9th January 2001 http://www.aci.net/kalliste/

21. Correspondence from Theo Kermanidis, 2nd Feb. 2002, citing data at http://www-hpcc.astro.washington.edu/stawarz/orbres.html and http://ssd.jpl.nasa.gov/a_histo.html

22. Correspondence from Matthew Holman, Harvard-Smithsonian Center for Astrophysics, 10th Feb. 2002

23. B. Gladman "Evidence for an Extended Scattered Disk?" http://www.obs-nice.fr/gladman/cr105.html

24. J. Kelly Beatty "Big-orbit Object Confounds Dynamicists" 5th April 2001, with thanks to Frank Cordell and Theo Kermanidis http://www.skypub.com/news/news.shtml#bigorbit

25. A. Stern "Chiron: Interloper from the Kuiper Disk?" pp26-33 Astronomy August 1994

26. Correspondence from Matthew Holman, Harvard-Smithsonian Center for Astrophysics, 12th Feb 2002

27. M. Baigent "Ancient Traces" p203 Penguin 1998

28. G. Marcy & P. Butler "Hunting Planets Beyond" pp43-7 Astronomy March 2000

29. Zecharia Sitchin "The Twelfth Planet" Avon 1976

CHAPTER

# 13

## The Dark Star and Mass Extinctions

Not so long ago, I was sent a short story by H.G. Wells entitled, "The Star". The story highlights a tradition of catastrophism associated with a returning star moving through the solar system (1). Before receiving this transcript, I was not even aware that H.G. Wells had written about the return of Planet X. The story was written in 1899, and presumably reflects the centennial doom-mongering that anticipates the start of a new century. It describes the unexpected appearance of the Star, a planet from deep space, which collides with Neptune, and then swings towards the Earth when passing Jupiter:

"But near its destined path, as yet only slightly perturbed, spun the mighty planet Jupiter and his moons sweeping splendid round the sun. Every moment now the attraction between the fiery star and the greatest of the planets grew stronger. And the result of that attraction? Inevitably, Jupiter would be deflected from its orbit into an elliptical path, and the burning star, swung by his attraction wide of its sunward rush, would describe a curved path and perhaps collide with, and certainly pass very close to, our Earth. Earthquakes, volcanic outbreaks, cyclones, sea waves, floods, and a steady rise in temperature to I know not what limit - so prophesied the master mathematician" (1).

The story takes on an ever threatening tone, one that becomes Biblical in mythological proportions. Indeed, the advent of the Star's approach brings about a great Flood, perhaps allowing H.G. Wells the literary license to provide his own explanation for the Universal Flood Myth. There is also an allusion to the Earth standing still, reflecting the consideration at that time that there may be truth in the myths of such events across the world:

"And then came a wonder. It seemed to those who in Europe watched for the rising of the star that the world must have ceased its rotation. In a thousand open spaces of down and upland the people who had fled the thither from the floods and the falling houses and sliding slopes of hill watched for that rising in vain. Hour followed hour through a terrible suspense, and the star rose not. Once again men set their eyes upon the old constellations they had counted lost to them forever. In England it was hot and clear overhead, though the ground quivered perpetually, but in the tropics, Sirius and Capella and Aldebaran showed through a veil of steam. And when at last the great star rose near ten hours late, the sun rose close upon it, and in the centre of its white heat was a disc of black" (1).

It would be tempting to read a lot into this story by H.G. Wells. He was a first class science fiction writer, and there was a lot of speculation at the turn of the century that a planet might lurk beyond Neptune. As we have seen in an earlier chapter, the hunt of this planet led to the discovery of Pluto some three decades after "The Star" was written. The story shows how Catastrophism has long been associated with the return of a hidden body of colossal proportions. Can it have any basis in reality?

The possible existence of a hidden planet orbiting the sun is quite often associated with catastrophe on planet Earth. Indeed, the popular consensus that Nibiru - a mythological planet as yet unaccounted for by scientists - is about to appear in our skies, may be intrinsically wrapped up with our common dread of cataclysm. In the same way that many incorrectly anticipated an apocalyptic event prior to the turn of the Millennium, advocates of the Imminent Return hypothesis believe that we are about to face our gravest test since the Flood (which may, or may not, have actually taken place).

Although I believe in the existence of a hidden Planet X, in the guise of a sub-brown dwarf or 'Dark Star', I have been one of the strongest critics of the Imminent Return hypothesis. Yet, there is some merit to the idea that Planet X may be associated with catastrophe, and it is almost certainly connected to rapid climate changes at various points in the Earth's past. In this chapter I will outline a new hypothesis, which seeks to correlate the orbital behavior of this hidden Dark Star with catastrophic events as recorded by geologists and paleontologists.

## A Statistical Threat

To explore this idea, we must immediately get to grips with a problem of time-scale. I am often confronted with e-mails that state that Planet X could not have appeared in our skies on such-and-such a date, because there was no massive catastrophe associated with its arrival. The implication is that every time the Dark Star system was to brush past the planetary zone, the Earth (and presumably some other planets too) would be subject to fundamental change. So, if the Dark Star exhibits an orbit analogous with Sitchin's 3,600 years (2), the implication is that Nibiru causes devastation on a highly regular basis...extremely often, when viewed on a geological scale.

However, I don't accept this argument: it does not fit with the evidence at our disposal. The planetary surfaces in the solar system which are very ancient, like the Moon and some parts of the Martian landscape, show a high incidence of bombardment in the very distant past, during the early period of the solar system's history. Bombardments on this scale are not noted after that time.

One can reasonably conclude that although occasional comets and asteroids do strike the Earth, and the other inner planets too, there is not a regular catastrophic bombardment. Otherwise, more youthful planetary landscapes would also show the kind of cratering patterns obvious to us all when we look up at the rather ancient surface of our Moon. Also, there would be a rather higher incidence of asteroids with Earth-crossing orbits, known as NEOs.

The inner solar system would be a more highly populated environment because far more objects would have been captured into tight orbits around the sun over time. As such, I don't think that associating Planet X Catastrophism with frequent cometary bombardments throughout history is likely to be a particularly fruitful study.

Of course, others differ in their opinions on this subject, but I prefer to find other mechanisms whereby the Dark Star might affect the Earth. The results are less explosive, it is true, but we can readily find ways to account for sudden and dramatic climate changes, for instance. Comet and asteroid bombardments certainly occur, it is true, but I am not certain that a direct correlation between them and Planet X is going to be found, beyond just a greater statistical likelihood of a collision during the Dark Star's perihelion passage.

In other words, when the Dark Star moves past the EKB, a greater number of comets may move through the planetary solar system. That doesn't necessarily mean that we're on collision course with any of them, any more than we would be with 'normal' comets. There would just be more comets for a while, slightly increasing the risk of our crossing paths with one. So whereas observers might report a greater number of comets in the heavens at that time, our world may not face any greater risk of catastrophe.

Catastrophism has come a long way. There was a time when scientists considered the world to be a very stable place, with an evolutionary progression that was slow and steady. This reflected an old-fashioned view of the world embedded in religious and cultural tradition: the World has always been this way.

But we now think that many cataclysms have occurred down the Ages, and that evolution is more of a 'stop-go' affair than one of slow, incremental change. We know that continents drift across the face of the Earth, bringing about the creation of mountain ranges as land-masses lock horns. Further, we know that significant extinction events have blighted our planet, even worse than the heinous acts of mass extinction we are currently responsible for.

Our awareness has been raised about how fragile our world can be, and also how changeable when seen through the eyes of a geologist. We have moved from a theological world-view, that led us to believe that the world was created to meet our needs, to a more terrifying reality. We live in a world whose stability is not guaranteed. Our environment has changed many times in the past, sometimes in orders of magnitude worse than the global warming we have created through the emergence of our industrial power.

We now recognize that our world can also be devastatingly affected by external influence. The chances of this are very remote, occurring on a time-scale that boggles the mind. This reflects the sheer size of the solar system, and the almost negligible proportion of it that is actually occupied by planets, asteroids and comets.

The planetary solar system consists mostly of open, empty space. Even if two objects orbiting the sun have paths that cross each other, the possibility of a collision is extremely remote. So, catastrophic events only become apparent over geological time-scales, when the small statistical danger posed by an Earth-crossing asteroid or comet is actually encountered after countless misses.

So it follows that the regular reappearance of a planetary body that might somehow pose a threat to us would not, indeed could not, always be associated with a cataclysm, even if it passed directly through the solar system..

Only a passing object the size of an actual star could be guaranteed to cause environmental devastation on Earth, and although it is probable that stars have themselves brushed past the solar system in the past (3), the likelihood of a future similar event is minute. As the size of the stellar object decreases, its relative danger threshold quickly falls away.

Large brown dwarfs passing through the planetary zone might pose a problem. Small brown dwarfs probably wouldn't. The danger threshold appears to be 10-20 Jupiter masses (4).

Regular size planets, or even gas giants, passing through the solar system would no more cause a problem to us than the occasional alignment of the known planets. That's how enormous, and mostly empty, the solar system is.

This is why I maintain that for a Planet X to have brought about environmental change on Earth during any of its perihelion passages, it must be nothing less than a brown dwarf, or else it would simply not be massive enough to be remotely effective on a catastrophic scale. According to the scientist Jack Hills, it is quite possible for a small brown dwarf to move through the solar system with impunity. His calculations have shown that it need not affect the orbits of the other planets (4), although this might change with multiple transits as the statistical likelihood of interference with any given planet increases.

I am quite certain that the Dark Star could move through the solar system itself, and leave the place roughly as it found it. However, the evidence from the outer solar system implies that it does not approach closer than about 70AU.

## The Extinction Cycle

In 1984, the paleontologists Raup and Sepkoski argued that there is a cyclical pattern to the extinction events recorded in the fossil record (5). The pattern implied a 26 to 30 million year cycle, itself indicative of an extra-terrestrial cause. There are no known terrestrial causes for such massive and regular extinctions. Could Planet X be to blame, perhaps through showering Earth with comets as it achieves perihelion?

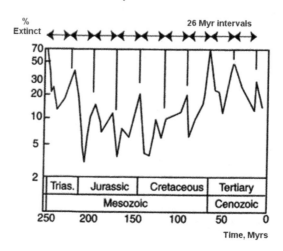

If the cycle of these extinction events is to be believed (and it remains controversial among scientists), then any direct extra-terrestrial cause must be coincident with that enormous time-scale. So it would not be satisfactory, then, to associate a 26 million-year extinction cycle with a planet whose orbit is measured in thousands of years only. The Dark Star's relatively short orbit (Zecharia Sitchin's 'Sar' of 3,600 years, or even a multiple-Sar orbital period of, say, 10,800 years) could only produce a random pattern of extinction events distributed thinly over this time-scale.

Putting this another way, if the Dark Star is directly accountable for extinction level events on Earth, then it must either pass very close to the Earth during a transit actually into the inner solar system, or else it must have brought with it a comet, or swarm of comets, that happened to collide with Earth. Since both these possibilities are statistically unlikely given the sheer size of the solar system, then they could not occur during each perihelion passage. Instead, they might occur very, very occasionally throughout geological history, and the pattern of these events would be effectively random over that timescale, even if it was closely associated with a cyclical event that was more frequent, like the perihelion passage of the Dark Star.

A pattern of extinction-level events, over approximately 26 million year periods, calls for an external cause taking place over a 26 million year cycle. The author Graham Hancock has also considered some of the external influences affecting our solar system when looking at this extinction cycle. Our star rotates around the galactic nucleus over a period of about 250 million years, during which time it bobs up and down through the galactic plane, an oscillation that takes about 30 million years. He has noted the similarity between this 30 million-year 'bobbing' transit through the galactic plane, and the extinction cycle on the Earth.

Referring to the work of eminent astronomers, Hancock, et al. wondered whether the inner solar system is subjected to a periodic bombardment of comets, released by a number of possible cosmic mechanisms, and that comet strikes have brought about these vast extinctions on the Earth. These cometary strikes possibly account for what Hancock describes as the environmental "death mask" currently worn by Mars (6). The factors helping to release the cometary descent from the Oort cloud include the sun's motion through gigantic molecular clouds (GMCs), and the sun's passage through both the Milky Ways' spiral arms and galactic plane. Perhaps these factors could also influence the transit of a distant binary brown dwarf. Certainly, the concept of the proposed extinction cycle being linked to an orbiting dwarf has been a controversial one within science.

## Nemesis

In the 1980's, the idea emerged that the binary companion takes the guise of an extremely remote "black dwarf" star, orbiting the sun at the very limit of its influence. This theoretical body was called "Nemesis", and was put forward by Professor Daniel Whitmire, amongst others. Its orbital period at such a great distance (about 90,000AU!) would then be analogous with an approximately 30 million-year extinction pattern.

This extinction pattern occurred because Nemesis would bombard the planetary zone with a massive shower of comets at a given point of its orbital cycle, by ploughing through the inner Oort Cloud (7). This would release a deadly shower of comets without Nemesis ever approaching the planetary zone itself, or so the theory goes.

Here's the problem: if the Earth was successfully subject to a cometary bombardment with every orbital completion of Nemesis, then to guarantee a comet strike on little old Earth, each comet shower must have been truly massive. After all, the shower of comets must get past Jupiter first!

The black dwarf would have had to have literally peppered the sun with comets every 26 million years, like a Chicago mob catching up with one of their old buddies. In which case, there would have to be ample evidence of renewed and regular cratering of other planets in the solar system too.

But instead, the solar system cratering patterns show little activity in recent epochs, implying a different mechanism for the 'cyclic' extinction patterns. Lone killer asteroids perhaps, but not massive comet swarms. One or two of these catastrophes (like the K/T boundary devastation) may have been caused by an asteroid strike, but the alleged 26 million-year extinction cycle cannot be accounted for by a routine act of cosmic pummeling.

It is also not clear to me why comets should be released by Nemesis at a given point in its orbit. Surely there would be a sustained 'drip, drip' pattern of long-period comet activity associated with the extremely slow and distant sweep of Nemesis around the sun. Advocates of the Nemesis theory might argue that there is an interaction with the galactic tide, or an association with the sun's 30 million year motion through the galactic plane, that triggers such a catastrophic release of comets.

But one might as well simply look to the motion of the sun around the galactic centre, and miss out the middle-man (or middle-dwarf, in this case). The bottom line is that a cosmic Nemesis is simply too distant, and irrelevant, to periodically facilitate such a devastating extinction level event.

On the face of it, it would seem as though the Dark Star's orbit is not in keeping with this cycle of catastrophe. The cyclical nature of catastrophism still remains controversial amongst scientists. Robust and pains-taking new research by Richard Muller, who is a professor of physics at the University of California, Berkeley, has revealed further clues to extinction events occurring with uniform regularity over the last half billion years.

His cycle is characterized by a 62 million year periodicity (8). It includes the asteroid impact 65 million years ago, near the Mexican Yucatan peninsula that seems to have destroyed the dinosaurs. It also includes the 'Great Dying' 250 million years, which we shall look at shortly.

But this careful research still has its critics. Professor Muller is puzzled by the cause of the cycle, and has exhaustively addressed problems with each proposed scenario. He remains convinced that an astronomical cause will eventually be found to explain his version of this controversial extinction cycle.

## The Planet that Thinks Like a Comet

I have already described how a brown dwarf could, on the one hand, create a non-random pattern of comets from the distant Oort Cloud, and, on the other, actually move through the outer solar system. That explanation hinges on the possibility that the Dark Star's loosely-bound orbit around the sun was subject to change in a manner not often considered by astronomers. Astronomers are used to thinking about planets behaving themselves in an orderly manner, with only minor bodies like comets becoming perturbed from their restful canter around the sun. But why couldn't a planet among the comets also be perturbed?

As it turns out, theoretical models show that 25,000AU happens to be a rather unstable place for a planet to reside. A planet or brown dwarf at this distance would be subject to a number of forces from outside the solar system, and could readily be nudged into a new orbit.

Indeed, one of the more scientifically-minded Planet X researchers, a professor of physics named Dr. Matese, has calculated orbital paths for a massive planet at this distance that seem to necessarily bring it close to the planetary zone on occasion (9). Those occasions would be rare, of course, but then so are mass extinctions! It is possible that such a connection exists.

We also touched upon the work of another physicist, Jack Hills, who made calculations about the effect of passing stars and black or brown dwarfs traveling near to or through the planetary zone. Although passing stars would likely sail on past (given their considerable size and momentum), the dwarfs run a very real chance of becoming captured by the sun. Indeed, his calculations showed that a subsequent temporary orbit of the captured dwarf could be highly eccentric, possibly degrading over time (4).

This is in contrast to the general assumption that such a body would be quickly expelled from the solar system. It should also sound very familiar by now. It seems as though such a sub-stellar body could actually be captured by the sun, and its natural inclination then would be to fall into a highly eccentric, but relatively unstable orbit.

## Binding Energies and System Expansion

Hills worked for the Los Alamos National Laboratory at the time he wrote this paper in 1985. He conducted computer simulations modeling the effect of an intruder on the sun-Jupiter system. The planetary intruder would either originate from interstellar space or the Oort cloud. He discusses a minimum radial distance of 5AU, which corresponds to the orbit of the sun's largest known planet, Jupiter.

Although Jack Hills may not have intended to, he has simulated the orbit of Sitchin's Nibiru. His computer simulations show that a massive object, which is as far away from the sun as the Dark Star, is subject to external forces that can cause it to behave erratically.

Hills showed that if the sub-brown dwarf had less than 10 Jupiter masses, then its temporary infringement into the planetary zone would not necessarily cause the other planets to fly off into interstellar space, or to become unrealistically chaotic. But there would be a different, but remarkably important effect, one that is well understood by astrophysicists - but takes a bit of getting used to for the rest of us.

There is an energetic relationship between the orbits of the sun's children. The 'planetary binding energies' are not fixed, but intertwined. Introduce a new, maverick element to the solar system (particularly one of considerable mass) and those binding energies are subject to change, even if the planets are tightly bound in stable, circular orbits.

Hills indicated that the overall energy of the orbits of the known planets would alter, if the interloper's own orbit around the sun changed. This might happen if the interloper came from interstellar space and was captured by the sun, or if it was an Oort Cloud object that had trespassed into the planetary zone and taken on a new, more tightly bound temporary orbit.

What exactly would be the physical manifestation of such a change in the binding energies of the planetary orbits, as the interloper falls under the influence of the sun gravitationally? Simply put, the solar system would be subject to possible contraction or expansion, dependent upon the particular event. The very distances of the planets from the sun would be subject to change! The dwarf would not need to directly interact with the planets, either…simply the changing relationship with the sun would be enough to affect other bodies in the solar system.

Jack Hills described these effects in a theoretical way. His interest was in studying whether a body the size of Nemesis, a proposed black dwarf, could have become captured by the sun. He concluded that it would have caused too much chaos in the solar system. But below 10 Jupiter masses, an interloper would not create the same devastation. In other words, a Dark Star in the form of a sub-brown dwarf might just have been captured by the sun in the remote past, and the solar system would still appear as stable as it is thought to be today.

A brown dwarf which had migrated inwards from the comet clouds would enter the planetary solar system at nearly parabolic speed. If it subsequently interacted with the other planets, as in Sitchin's thesis, then two things might happen according to Hills' calculations. One scenario indicates that the Dark Star might have attained greater orbital energy, and thus would have been flung out of the solar system altogether.

The other possibility is that its orbital energy decreases, and it becomes bound into a much tighter orbit around the sun. As it turns out, the chances are about 50:50 between the two scenarios. In his paper, Hills describes the planetary system 'binding energies', and how the orbital radii of the planets are affected by the incursion of the intruder (4).

During this devastating event in the early history of the solar system, there would have been massive changes to the climates of the planets, particularly in the inner solar system. This reflected massive changes in the orbital energy of the Dark Star. Now, if the Dark Star's orbit is still subject to some fluctuation, then there could be on-going changes over time during the life of the solar system.

Indeed, changes in the binding energy of the Earth may then have had significant effects upon our world's climate down the ages. Venus and Mars may have experienced similar climate changes during similar periods of time. That might explain why the existence of water on Mars is so odd, or why Venus became trapped into its runaway greenhouse gas effect (10). Venus has had its share of extreme climate variation in the past as well, leading to extensive changes to its surface about 700 million years ago (11).

So, the paper by Hills shows us that if Planet X is a small brown dwarf, then physical mechanisms have been modeled that can actually account for its existence within the solar system. Furthermore, those calculations show that the interaction between this dwarf and the rest of the solar system might have fundamental physical ramifications. The distance between the Earth and the sun might have been altered, for instance. Not just once; but every time the temporary orbit of the loosely bound cometary dwarf changes. Such changes would readily account for planetary migration.

Which leads me to ask…has the Earth's distance from the sun altered? Was the distance between the Earth and the sun a variable that changed with respect to the incursion and subsequent capture by the sun of a brown dwarf? What if the unstable nature of the orbit of our Dark Star meant that, over time, several such changes occurred?

Perhaps the Dark Star's orbit altered because of other external influences, like the gravitational attraction of other passing stars, or of giant molecular clouds found within interstellar space. If so, then the Earth's relative position with respect to the sun might have changed several times. If so, how would we know?

Such changes would have had catastrophic environmental effects on this planet, leading to the coming and going of Ice Ages and inter-glacial periods, dependant upon the altered distance between the sun and the Earth. Additionally, the actual physical displacement of our planet would have brought about sudden, catastrophic Earth-changes. What happens to the oceans, for instance, when the Earth suddenly falls away from or towards the sun? Would they not be swept over the land, accompanied by titanic volcanic and seismic activity?

We now know that Ice Ages are global in nature, and not confined simply to one hemisphere (12). This implies changes to the Earth's entire climate system, possibly drawing us towards the conclusion that an external factor is at play here. There is certainly a substantial question mark hanging over the previous received wisdom that Ice Ages resulted from a redistribution of heat via the world's oceans. Instead, the entire atmosphere of the Earth appears to cool during the glacial periods of Ice Ages.

# Early Permian 260 Myr ago

Might our lack of understanding of the causes behind the ebb and flow of Ice Epochs (13), or of mass extinctions, find an extra-terrestrial explanation - in the guise of a maverick brown dwarf occasionally lurching from one unstable temporary orbit to another? Let us look at this possibility. I have chosen three examples of periods of sustained catastrophic damage to our world, to illustrate how this hypothesis might work. They start with the most recent, and work backwards to the early solar system.

## The Permian-Triassic Boundary

A great extinction event occurred around the Permian-Triassic boundary, some 245 million years ago. The scale of the destruction of life on Earth was an order of magnitude greater than the wiping out of the dinosaurs 65 million years ago. The destruction of the dinosaurs at the end of the Cretaceous period is now thought to have been caused by a single impact event off the coast of Yucatan, Mexico (14). This asteroid or comet impact led to the deposition of extra-terrestrial iridium, forming the famous K/T boundary in the rock strata of that period. Can we look to a similar cause for the more catastrophic P-Tr boundary mass extinction?

Well, the problem is that the extinctions at the P-Tr boundary did not occur instantly during a single boundary event (as would be expected if the mass extinction had been caused by an asteroid impact). They were associated with multiple events, including the overturning of the oceans, and massive volcanism. One of these events was a major asteroid or comet impact that created a 130 kilometer crater at Woodleigh in Australia, discovered in

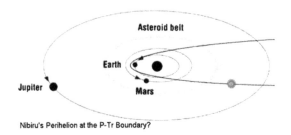

Nibiru's Perihelion at the P-Tr Boundary?

April 2000 (15). This one event, however destructive it may have been, was simply one of several which occurred over a relatively short period of time.

Paleontologists have recorded 4 distinct extinction episodes during the Permian, over a 10 million-year period. At a loss to explain such a bizarre extinction pattern, paleontologists considered the coalescing of the continents into the super-continent 'Pangea' to somehow be the likely cause (16). Ice caps were also forming at that time. However, this is an unsatisfactory theory, as it fails to come up with an explanation for the pulsed nature of the extinction events in the geological record (5).

How did the world's entire ocean become overturned, driving multiple extinction events over a 10 million-year period? The devastation of the P-Tr boundary is so great that internal environmental readjustments simply don't provide a satisfactory answer. Instead, an extra-terrestrial cause is necessary to meet the fundamental and sustained changes affecting Earth during the Permian. An isolated asteroid impact is insufficient. What else could there be?

I suggest that this pattern of extinction and environmental change is readily explained by the perturbation of the Dark Star into a temporary tightly bound orbit. If the brown dwarf migrated close to the planetary zone at the beginning of the Permian, and became captured into a new, much tighter orbit, then the Earth would have been subject to a number of tremendous pressures. This is because there must be a conservation of energy within the overall orbital system of the planets. If the Dark Star were to be dragged into a closer orbit, then there would have to be an adjustment made among the other planets, resulting in them feeling less tightly bound to the sun. Their orbits would expand accordingly.

Earth's lurch into a new orbit might provide the mechanism for the over-turning of the oceans, the coalescing of the continents, and the formation of ice caps. What's more, repeated passages of the brown dwarf through the solar system during, say, its 10 million-year long temporarily tightly bound orbit, would endanger Earth again and again. At the end of the Permian, the unstable temporary orbit might have naturally degraded, expelling the Dark Star back towards a more familiar orbit beyond the Edgeworth-Kuiper Belt. This reversal of fortunes would mean that the Dark Star's binding energy would decrease, and the binding energies of the other planets would subsequently increase. The Earth would move back to an orbit closer to the sun, warming the world environment and ending this temporary period of instability.

Such a sustained pattern of orbital change and planetary interaction with a brown dwarf within the planetary solar system would certainly have destroyed far more life on this planet than the single asteroid strike of the K/T boundary. For about 10 million years, the days of the early solar system would have been relived - bringing about the string of extinction events at the P-Tr boundary.

This model presupposes that the perihelion distance of the Dark Star is a variable over time and, as a result, the Permian may have witnessed its closest and most devastating series of passages through the solar system. The massive asteroid or comet impact recorded by the 250 million year old crater in Woodleigh, Australia may have been part of this wider phenomenon.

## The Cambrian Explosion and 'Snowball Earth'

New advances in molecular biology have allowed scientists to back-track through the record of evolutionary change and date the various points when great divergence in life on this planet occurred. The Precambrian-Cambrian boundary of 540 million years ago represented a colossal sea-change in the development of life on this planet. The sudden emergence of an immense diversity of life forms at that time is known as the Cambrian

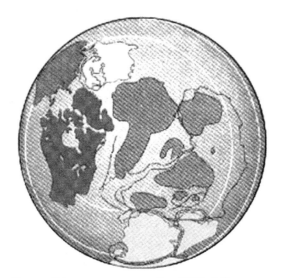

## Late Neoproterozoic 550 Myr ago

Explosion, but paleontologists now consider it likely that life was already highly variable before this boundary. The boundary itself indicates a massive carbon isotope shift, implying profound extinctions among late Proterozoic life (4). Severe cooling would have accompanied such changes as carbon dioxide was catastrophically removed from the atmosphere.

In fact, such was the severity of the glaciation during the late Proterozoic, that some scientists have theorized that our planet became completely covered in ice...the so-called "Snowball Earth" effect (17,18). Again, there appears to have been a multiplicity of events over a period of several million years, rather than a single "Snowball Earth" event. But what could account for such a fundamental climate shift which saw glaciers forming over the equator?

It is thought that the break-up of the then super-continent 'Rodinia' may have contributed to this effect, spreading the broken up continents around the equator. This increased the global ratio of sea to land and brought about increased rainfall which, in turn, scrubbed out the carbon dioxide from the atmosphere. A positive feedback cycle then led to a series of glaciations around the globe.

But surely this is not a satisfactory explanation. After all, the current continental distribution is also located in a band around the globe, and the last Ice Age was very mild in comparison. It is not clear what preconditioned the Earth to go into such a calamitous freeze, the likes of which have not been experienced again for 600 million years.

The 'Snowball Earth' scenario prior to the Precambrian/Cambrian boundary is an extreme environmental condition, calling out for a bold explanation. Again, I suggest that the precondition to this series of catastrophic global glaciations was nothing less than a temporary expansion of Earth's orbit. The Earth's greater distance from the sun would readily explain the freezing over of the whole planet, and the orbital expansion of Earth would be consistent with the variables associated with the orbit of the Dark Star.

# The Late, Great Bombardment

Our third catastrophic series of events in the geological record involves a massive bombardment of the solar system by comets and/or asteroids, and possibly even minor planets. The cratered appearance of the Moon is largely due to this intense bombardment of space debris that spiked between 3.8 and 3.9 billion years ago, and the Earth similarly suffered the most cataclysmic bombardment in its history (19).

What puzzles astronomers is why this occurred so long after the birth of the solar system. Once again, the bombardment appears to have been a somewhat dragged out affair, implying intensely chaotic activity in the solar system over a period lasting tens of millions of years. Then it all stopped.

This puzzle has recently been resurrected to form the basis for the one-time existence of an additional planet, which initially formed between Jupiter and Mars. Somehow, this planet took on an unstable orbit and crashed into the sun, at least according to the "Planet V" theory (20). Another theory holds that the bombardment was the result of a late formation of the outer planets Neptune and Uranus (19).

This late formation might have been the result of the more thinly spread material in the outer planetary zone, causing a longer accretion period. But such a bombardment from outside the planetary solar system should have catastrophically affected the Jovian moons as well. Once again, this period of sustained catastrophe in the inner solar system calls for a radical solution from 'outside the box'.

Sitchin's account of the Celestial Battle fits this 'lunar cataclysm' event very well, as the missing planet located between Mars and Jupiter (Tiamat; the primordial Earth) was bombarded by the planet Nibiru. This was said to have occurred about 4 billion years ago, some time after the solar system had formed (2).

It seems reasonable to me to speculate that this 'late, great bombardment' was the work of a brown dwarf, from the sun's birthing stellar nursery, moving catastrophically through the early solar system. The subsequent interaction with the planets and the sun resulted in its capture, and a then sustained bombardment of cosmic debris. But this is where I think Sitchin's account is itself insufficient, because the very nature of the cataclysm was a temporary one, lasting at most 100 million years. Something happened after that point to draw the cataclysmic activities to an end.

Returning to the calculations by Hills regarding the effect of a captured dwarf on the planetary solar system (4), the intruder brown dwarf and its retinue would be first captured into a temporary orbit of some eccentricity. This is consistent with Sitchin's model, and for tens of million years Nibiru appears to have actually returned to the inner solar system, bringing repeated catastrophic effects to the inner planets. During that time, the Earth was pummeled by thousands of asteroids, many far larger than the one that killed off the dinosaurs.

Then it all stopped. Why? If Nibiru's orbit was a stable one that continues to this day, then surely the cosmic melee would have been a constant feature of the solar system for the last 3.9 billion years?

The answer lies in the notion that the Dark Star orbit calculated by Hills is a temporary one. If the logic of astrophysicists like Matese and Whitmire is to be applied (7), then this captured brown dwarf underwent massive orbital expansion, eventually locating it safely into the outer Oort cloud. In other words, as time went by, the highly eccentric orbit that had arisen as a result of its capture by the sun loosened.

The Dark Star slowly migrated out beyond the EKB. Its binding energy decreased, and the other planets in the solar system would have then been pulled closer to the sun. As part of that process, the Earth itself migrated towards the sun, bringing its anomalous body of oceanic waters with it.

The Dark Star ended up outside the planetary solar system about 3.8 billion years ago. At that distance it could do no more than shower down a few long period comets, most of which would be intercepted by the solar system's sweeper, Jupiter. The bombardment had ended after about 100 million years, and the brown dwarf had taken on a slow, distant orbit around the sun. But, as we have seen, this was not the end of the story. More extinction events were to manifest themselves in the geological record, taking on peculiar attributes, like the ones we have considered above.

# Physical Mechanisms

There is a common adage in science that the more you study a phenomenon, the more confusing it becomes. I think it is self-evident that the material I have presented here is complex and by no means clear-cut. Each of the three examples I have offered provide their own mystery, but taken together they lead to even greater obfuscation.

The common thread between them is that they all involve unusual or unique activity over a period of some millions of years. Then the activity stops. A careful analysis of the bombardment events 3.9 billion years ago seems to vindicate Sitchin's claim about a cosmic interloper of extraordinary significance. Yet, the effect disappears as quickly as it occurred, and this turns out to be a significant issue. The theoretical models for such a planetary intrusion predict eccentric orbital properties, but for only a limited number of orbits.

Where some might argue that a planet in such an unstable orbit might fall into the sun, or be ejected outright from the solar system, I would argue a middle position between these two extremes. The Dark Star orbit simply changes from one phase to another as a result of various external influences over time, and these phase changes are what brings about the cataclysms we have seen on Earth at some of the Epoch boundaries described above. This is a rather straightforward conclusion that arises from a chaotic and often confusing collection of data sets, which makes it a rather thrilling possibility because science generally prefers to seek out a simple solution to a complicated problem.

Drs. Murray and Matese both point to their non-random data sets of long-period comet orbits (21,9), and claim the existence of a small brown dwarf/giant planet slowly meandering around the sun among the comets. Yet they struggle with the problem of how the sun ended up collecting such an object into its family.

It could not have accreted normally among the comets, as the material available at that distance was too scant. So it must have been captured, and such an event would most likely have occurred early in the lifetime of the solar system. This is because the stellar nursery where the sun was born was relatively dense with stars and dwarfs during that period of time. An inter-stellar passer-by, entering the fray later on, is much less likely to be a candidate for capture by the sun.

In either event, the capture of a Dark Star surely would have taken place reasonably closer to the sun itself, or else this brown dwarf would have continued past, oblivious to Sol's influence. Dr. Daniel Whitmire, a leading scientific thinker in the Nemesis debate, suggests that comets expand out into the Oort cloud from an initial location closer to the sun and that the giant planet would have done the same. As such, the binary brown dwarf would have started life located between one and ten thousand astronomical units from the sun - when the solar system formed - before its orbit became affected by external influences like passing stars (22). He hypothesizes that this influence led to the planet's orbit expanding into the outer Oort cloud, but it's possible that the planet could just have easily been swung into the direction of the sun, thereby entering the fray of Sitchin's Celestial Battle. After all, that's also what happens to comets.

The Dark Star would have been captured, and then pursued a series of violent bouts of destruction in the planetary zone, before then drifting out into a wider orbit. It will be evident to the reader that the patterns of change in the outer solar system have built into them far more flexibility than the planets closer to home. This is because the sun's stranglehold on these denizens of the peripheries of our system is so much less. We are therefore quite entitled to talk about migrating orbits and changing trajectories for bodies like the Dark Star, and it is this factor that creates the potential for the binary brown dwarf to shape and re-shape the planetary solar system.

In the next chapter, we will look in more detail at how the Dark Star might well be the mysterious factor behind the coming and going of Ice Ages, and how this should give us pause for thought about our current predicament regarding global warming.

## Chapter 13 References

1. H.G. Wells "The Star" 1899 With thanks to Rob Astor

2. Z. Sitchin "The Twelfth Planet" Avon 1976

3. J. Hills "Comet Showers and the Steady-state infall of comets from the Oort Cloud" Astron. J. 86, 1730 (1981)

4. J. Hills "The Passage of a "Nemesis"-like Object through the Planetary System" Astron. J. 90, 1876 (1985)

5. R. Corfield "Architects of Eternity" Headline Book Publishing 2001

6. G. Hancock, R. Bauval & J. Grigsby "The Mars Mystery" Ch 23 Penguin 1998

7. R. Muller "Nemesis - The Death Star" Weidenfield & Nicholson, 1988

8. J. Roach "Mystery Undersea Extinction Cycle Discovered" National Geographic News 9th March 2005, with thanks to Lee Covino

9. J. Matese, P. Whitman and D. Whitmire, "Cometary Evidence of a Massive Body in the Outer Oort Cloud" Icarus, 141, 354-336 (1999)

10. C. Sagan "Pale Blue Dot" Ch 11 Headline 1995

11. M. Heil "Math Program Cracks Cause of Venus Climate Change" 12th March 2001 http://www.jpl.nasa.gov

12. M. Edwards "Glacial Records Depict Ice Age Climate In Synch Worldwide" National Science Foundation 24/3/04, with thanks to James Monds

13. Illinois State Museum "Ice Ages" http://www.museum.state.il.us/exhibits/ice_ages/

14. W. Alvarez "T. Rex and the Crater of Doom" Penguin 1998

15. "Report on the Task Force on Potentially Hazardous Near Earth Objects" September 2000, British National Space Centre, London citing L. O' Hanlon "Killer Crater Found" http://www.discovery.com/news/briefs/20000419/geology_crater.html

16. I Dalziel "Earth Before Pangea" Scientific American, Aug 1994

17. P. Hoffman & D. Schrag "Snowball Earth" Scientific American, Jan 2000

18. Horizon "Snowball Earth" Shown on BBC2, 22nd Feb 2001

19. I. Semeniuk "Neptune Attacks" New Scientist 7th Apr. 2001

20. G. Birdsall "Tenth Planet Did Exist Claims NASA" UFO Magazine Jun. 2002

21. J. Murray. Mon. Not. R. Astron. Soc., 309, 31-34 (1999)

22. Earthfile "A Mysterious "Perturber" at the Edges of Our Solar System?" Linda Moulton Howe interviewing Dr. Daniel Whitmire, http://www.earthfiles.com/earth086.htm 1999

C H A P T E R

# 14

# Ice Age

It is sometimes tempting to try and use a new idea to answer just about everything, and take things a little too far. We have to tread carefully when attributing significant events to the Dark Star. Obviously, we cannot for certainty say that it exists, or accurately describe anything about its orbit. However, the new scientific evidence in the outer solar system is consistent with its presence, but the fact that such a body remains undetected prevents scientists from sticking their necks out on this issue.

In the last chapter, we looked over periods in the Earth's history when mass extinctions took place. But instead of looking at events that were seemingly sudden, like the asteroid impact that probably drove the dinosaurs to extinction, we considered other, larger events that occurred over extended time periods. The causes of these events remain mysterious, but if a Dark Star were to be discovered, it could readily account for them through orbital fluctuations and related mechanisms.

I believe that the same holds true for another problem faced by Science, and that is the coming and going of Ice Epochs. Simply put, the Earth's distance from the sun is not cast in stone, but is a variable.

## Expansion and Contraction

This will strike many as being quite unthinkable. However, I have corresponded with many astronomers and astrophysicists over the last few years and they all confirm this fact, which I first became aware of through reading Jack Hills' 1985 paper (1). For instance, here is an extract of my correspondence with Dr. Daniel Whitmire, which not only confirms the general idea that the companion's orbital changes would have knock-on effects with other planets, but also indicates that such changes are significant enough to limit the initial distance of formation of the brown dwarf companion:

**Andy Lloyd:** If the brown dwarf is pumped out over billions of years, does its binding energy to the sun alter over time?

**Daniel Whitmire:** Yes.

**Andy Lloyd:** If so, does this have a knock on effect on the orbital radii of the known planets?

**Daniel Whitmire:** This is a constraint on how close it could have formed. Must be at least hundreds of AU.

**Andy Lloyd:** Given that a great circular orbit at 20,000 AU is inherently unstable…,

**Daniel Whitmire:** Not "inherently". It's statistics. Maybe there's a ~50% chance it would have survived passing stars until today if it started at 20,000 AU.

**Andy Lloyd:** …according to the 1999 Matese/Whitmire paper, and Hills (1985), the as the brown dwarf attains this distance from the sun in its slow spiral outwards, would it not be in danger of being perturbed back into the solar system by, say, a passing star?

**Daniel Whitmire:** Odds of that are small, but it would be expected to be perturbed into the planetary region (or within ~100 AU) a few times in 4.5 Gyr [the lifetime of the solar system] due to the galactic tidal force. No problem however, at least according to a study by Hills. I believe he concluded even a 0.1 solar mass passing star need not significantly disrupt planetary orbits.

**Andy Lloyd:** Can we not envisage, then, a cyclical orbital pattern whereby the brown dwarf is pumped up until it reaches an unstable orbital configuration, and then perturbed like a comet back into the planetary zone to start all over again?

**Daniel Whitmire:** Once its orbit is greater than about 30,000 AU the tide will accomplish this on times scales less than the age of the solar system, but still measured in hundreds of millions of years. Stellar perturbations alone result in only a tiny fraction of comets coming into the planetary region (2).

So, we can see how a substantial planet beyond the EKB is a rogue element in more ways than one. Not only could it push comets into the inner solar system, but its orbit could readily be subject to change over time. Its sheer size then, has a knock-on effect for our planet's orbit. The same holds true for the other planets in the solar system as well. The whole system is subject to expansion or contraction at the whim of this rogue body.

This is a difficult concept to grapple with, because we are all so used to thinking of planets behaving like billiard balls. The Planet X catastrophists generally describe the potential for catastrophe in blunt terms, having to do with planetary collisions and bombardments by comets. But for me, the real problem is that our planet's orbit is inherently linked to the fate of a massive hidden planet, which is subject to forces outside the solar system. There need not be any bombardment or in-coming planet to directly affect our planet's orbit and global climate. Yet, this physical situation is not even considered for the most part, and for obvious reasons.

## A Planetary Spanner in the Works

If the number of planets in the solar system is simply nine, as is generally accepted at the present time, then there would be absolutely no reason to think that these orbits should change through the life of the solar system. That is why this fact is never discussed, because it is irrelevant under the conditions we think are prevalent in our solar system. The problem only arises when we consider the additional existence of a binary solar companion like our Dark Star.

This situation is a bit like the argument for Einstein's special relativity (3). 'normal' common sense physical laws apply for most situations, but they break down when objects are accelerated towards the speed of light. But the very fact that this happens indicates that there is something about the how the Universe works as a whole that we missed before considering the relativity problem. In our case, every object in the solar system can affect all of the other objects, when the energy of its orbit changes.

So we can legitimately state that if a comet changes its orbit because it moved close to a planet and was perturbed by it, then that change in the orbital energy of the comet will change the entire system. However, that change would be so infinitesimally minute that it is effectively negligible. For all intents and purposes, the subsequent effect is unobservable. So, the common sense physical laws still apply.

However, this situation alters dramatically as the comet we are considering starts to get larger in mass. The bigger it gets, the greater the overall orbital energy it carries with it. How about a comet whose mass is greater than that of a gas giant? Would the same effect of a change in its orbit be measurable then? Absolutely. One physicist I have corresponded with about this, put it very succinctly:

"The inner planets are pretty tightly bound to the sun. The binding energy scales like M m / r, where M is the solar mass, M the planetary mass, and r the orbital radius. It is, therefore, hard to see how a shift in orbit of a lightly bound outer planet would significantly affect any of the inner planets (e.g. Earth), *unless the outer planet was very massive*" (4). [my emphasis]

So, if Planet X is simply a Mars-sized object, then the binding energies of the inner planets would not be significantly affected by any given change in its orbit. However, if we consider a binary companion, such as a small brown dwarf, then there would be a measurable effect. If the brown dwarf's binding energy changed, due to a perturbation of its loosely-bound orbit, then the Earth's orbit would alter. It could contract or expand, depending upon the change to its binding energy (1).

The Dark Star's mass is presumably several times that of Jupiter, which in turn is more massive than all the other planets in the system combined. So the entire mass of the planetary system becomes multiplied upwards from what we normally work with, and the Dark Star itself accounts for the majority of that total planetary mass. This means that the relationship between the Dark Star and the other planets is important, in terms of the overall energy of the solar system: it becomes our "speed of light" issue. Alter the energy of the Dark Star orbit, and the rest of the planets will feel a significant and observable jolt as a result!

Because the Dark Star's orbit lies beyond the planetary solar system, it is only loosely bound to the sun, and is thus more likely to be affected by outside influences. Although we should not say that its orbit is necessarily 'unstable', it is clearly subject to change, like the comets.

Assuming that any given perturbation, or change in its orbit, is not extreme enough to hurl the Dark Star into the sun or out of the solar system completely, the fact is that the rest of the planets would still be affected by any given change. This is because the Dark Star's mass is so great, that even though its orbit is relatively distant it will still play a major part in reshaping the orbital energies of the other planets, in order to conserve the overall energy of the system.

In that way, we can legitimately talk about the planetary orbits collectively expanding and contracting as a response to the perturbation of the Dark Star. So, if the orbit of the Dark Star were to migrate away from the sun, the Earth's orbit would expand, the length of the Earth year would increase, and the world would become colder. This would happen to all the other planets, asteroids and comets at the same time as well, as the whole system changes in response to the Dark Star's orbital contraction. There would be a small, but collective, mass migration.

Conversely, if the Dark Star was nudged into a more expanded orbit, then the orbits of the known planets and other solar system objects would collectively contract. All of these worlds would become a little warmer, and their years would be shorter. Readers acquainted with myths about the year gaining or losing days from the calendar will no doubt raise an eyebrow at this point. As much as I'd love to delve into this subject at this juncture, a careful examination of such mythology is best left to a future book.

Now, we know that the Earth's global climate system is complicated, and possibly rather fragile. I suggest that even a relatively small orbital change that, say, saw the Earth year expand or contract by just a few days, would be sufficient to trigger major climate change as a response. This is why I think that the Dark Star could be responsible for certain aspects of the phenomenon called Ice Ages.

## Ice Ages and Interglacials

We are all familiar with the term "Ice Age'" The normal understanding of the term relates to a prehistoric time when much of the Northern Hemisphere was covered in continental sheets of ice. This Ice Age slowly wound down over the course of several thousand years, leading to the extinction of many species which had become specially developed to cope with the extreme conditions of cold prevalent during the glacial period. This, then, is the extent of common knowledge about Ice Ages.

It turns out that the last Ice Age was one in a series of such Ice Ages, which have been coming and going over the course of the last four million years. The fluctuation between these Ice Ages and the warmer Interglacial periods seems to follow an approximately 100,000 year cycle. Evidence emerged in the 1960's which persuaded scientists that the Pleistocene era had been dominated by this cycle (5). Such a cycle required an explanation.

The first ideas about the possibility of Ice Ages were written about in the 18th Century, but received little attention. The idea was put forward to explain the phenomenon of erratic boulders strewn across the landscape of Europe. It was taken more

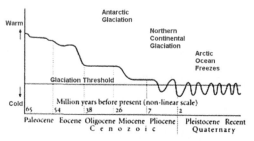

The onset of the current Ice Epoch 3.5-4 Myr ago may have been triggered by changes in the orbit of the Dark Star. If so. the question whether we are emerging from this Ice Epoch or simply living through a temporary Interglacial is tied to the sub-stellar companion's very existence.

seriously in the 19th Century, when it was promoted by the Swiss Louis Agassiz.

Almost immediately, the idea started to become associated with astronomical cycles, but this was within the context of great controversy about the subject as a whole. It took a long while for the concept of Ice Ages to become acceptable, and even longer for the link between the fluctuations of Ice Ages and Interglacial periods to be established. This may be because the cycle itself is a rather complex one, containing other minor patterns of climate change.

# The Milankovitch Model

The link to Earth's movement through the solar system was made by a Serb engineer and mathematician named Milutin Milankovitch. He looked at how variables in the Earth's tilt, precession and orbital eccentricity might fit in with climate change over periods of many thousands of years. He created a theoretical model for establishing a link between climate and astronomical influences, but the detail of this model could only be put to the test when dating techniques were developed to provide a detailed picture of climate change over the millennia.

This took many, many years and, in the meantime, the Milankovitch Model was widely dismissed by scientists. In the 1970's, experimental techniques were developed which were able to provide sufficiently detailed quantitative data to properly test the Milankovitch hypothesis. As a result, the dating of climate change was found to fit with the complexity of his proposed astronomical cycles (5).

The major 100,000 year cycle, connected as it is with changes in the Earth's eccentricity, is peppered with periods of dramatic change. These can be sudden and extreme. The Earth's geological record has helped us to realize that the world's climate changes dramatically, often without warning.

For example, ice cores examined in Greenland show that, when the last Ice Age was coming to a close some 15,000 years ago, there was one occasion when continent-sized ice sheets melted and fell apart within just one decade. Then the climate cooled again, going through a fluctuating pattern of change before the Ice Age finally completely receded (6).

Work carried out in the Antarctic has shown that the weight of the continental Ice Cap changed dramatically about 14,000 years ago, leading to Tectonic deformation in the western Marie Byrd Land and the Ross Embayment area. This may have been brought about by separation and crustal uplift, caused by isostatic rebound following the last glacial maximum (7). As we can see, massive climate changes took place in both hemispheres over a similar time-frame, and scientists now accept that the coming and going of Ice Ages occurs on a global level (8).

The Ice Age/Interglacial cycle fluctuates with a complex rhythm dependent upon the Earth's variable eccentricity in its orbit, as well as its tilt and precession. There is even a relatively minor effect attributable to variations in the gravitational pull of the other planets felt by the Earth over time! One can see how fragile the world is, if such seemingly inconsequential variables can have such dramatic effects on the global climate. It should now be clear why I can argue that orbital changes of the Dark Star could cause such a system to unbalance even more dramatically.

I need to make it clear that the Dark Star does not influence this Milankovitch Cycle. I am not proposing that it is another causal variable in an already well-established pattern of climate change connected with the Earth's movement in the solar system.

What I am attempting to establish is whether the Dark Star might be the causal factor behind why these Ice Ages occur at all.

## Ice Epochs

For the vast majority of geological time, the Earth has had no ice caps. In effect, the whole planet was an ice-free zone during immensely long periods of time, spanning hundreds of millions of years.

During those ice-free eons of time, the Earth was presumably still undergoing the same rotational and orbital changes. Its orbit's eccentricity was presumably just as variable. Its angle of tilt still changed over time. Its precession, the wobble about its own axis, still took place, presumably. Even the gravitational influence of the other planets must have still played a part. In other words, the multiple factors governing the Milankovitch Cycle were still very much at work.

Yet, for some reason no one can fathom, the Earth saw no ice for hundreds of millions of years at a time. However, the global warmth experienced by this planet during those extended periods would occasionally be exchanged for periods of intense cold known as Ice Epochs.

The most recent Ice Epoch, which lasted for about four million years up until about 10,000 years ago, was fragmented into a number of periods of glaciation with intermittent warmer periods, associated with the Milankovitch Cycle. When we casually talk about the last Ice Age, we are simply referring to the last in a series of Ice Ages that made up the Ice Epoch.

It's possible that the Ice Epoch has not actually ended at all, but that our world could yet be dramatically plunged back into a new Ice Age, as part of the Ice Epoch's internal cycle. We may simply be living through a warm interglacial period at the moment, which may be an unsettling thought.

Scientists are still unable to offer a definitive solution to the reason why long-period Ice Epochs occur at all, bearing in mind that during most of the last billion years this planet had no permanent ice. In fact, it appears that the Ice Age that occurred 600 million years ago was so extensive that the whole globe may have been affected, leading to what some scientists have termed "Snowball Earth". On either side of this extreme period of almost total global glaciation, there was no ice whatsoever. Yet, the reasons behind these massive fluctuations in the terrestrial climate remain elusive (9).

We are currently four million years into one of these periods of cooling, which sometimes lasts a hundred million years or more. Our current era appears to be a period of glacial retreat, a process which we are accelerating due to our own environmental destruction. The reasons for the advance and retreat of the glaciers during an ice age is quite well understood, dependant as they are upon various orbital factors. But why these extremely long, cool periods occur at all is just not understood.

In the last billion years, long periods of glaciation have occurred during these geological periods:

**1** During the late Protozoic (800-600 million years ago).

**2** During parts of the Ordovician and Silurian (between about 460 and 430 million years ago).

**3** During the Pennsylvanian and Permian (between about 350 and 250 million years ago).

**4** During the late Neogene to Quaternary (the last four million years) (10).

When trying to understand why these long periods of glaciation should be occurring, scientists look at a number of contributory factors, including changing continental positions, uplift of continental blocks, reduction of $CO_2$ in the atmosphere and changes in the Earth's orbit. The mechanisms of plate tectonics contribute to the formation of extensive ice caps by intermittently providing large land masses at high latitudes for the ice to build upon. The subsequent formation of large ice-sheets appears to be catalyzed by positive feedback mechanisms due to reflection of sunlight away from the Earth, and thus general cooling of the planet. Changes in the orbit of the Earth around the sun are also alluded to, particularly with respect to the Earth's eccentricity, tilt and the direction the North Pole points towards (10).

But these explanations are simply the same ones that are used to explain the Milankovitch Cycle. They simply become overextended when being brought to bear on the problem of Ice Epochs. The problem of this particular variation takes us to a new level, calling for an external influence that is simply missing.

There does not appear to be any known mechanism that could explain why the Earth is wrapped in ice for hundreds of millions of years, then completely free of ice for similar periods of time: It's almost as though the Earth has moved into a new orbit.

## Thinking the Unthinkable

Towards the beginning of this chapter, we looked at the orbital binding energies and noted that both astronomers and physicists are well acquainted with the idea that planetary orbits are reliant upon inter-dependent energetic relationships, rather than simply gravitational interactions. In this way, a large rogue body shifting its orbital path would necessarily cause orbital shifts in the other planets in the same system.

The fact that theory called for the Earth's orbit to actually migrate seems to have created artificial limits on the starting point of the binary companion's orbit, at least in the minds of the scientific advocates of the Nemesis theory. Yet, what we are seeing in the evidence presented in this book is that the migration of the Earth is not impossible at all; in fact, it is absolutely pivotal for a proper understanding of our planet's history.

The fact that there is way too much water on this planet compared with the theoretical situation implied by its current location is a major clue. Then there are the mysterious comings and goings of these Ice Epochs. I am quite sure that scientists looking at these problems must have at least considered the possibility that the Earth's orbit has shifted at times during the lifetime of the solar system.

But because there is currently no rational mechanism to allow this to occur, this common sense solution is shelved in favour of more elaborate ones. Yet, the existence of the Dark Star creates a viable and dramatic causal factor. It should allow us to think outside the box.

I suspect that more evidence to support this hypothesis will emerge, as our knowledge of planetary science increases over the coming years. Future study of the other terrestrial planets' geology will provide further evidence for other cataclysms on other worlds, and my bet is that the same boundary chronologies will be discovered. After all, if the planetary binding energies change as a result of a 'phase change' in the Dark Star's orbit, then all of the planets will be affected. Local planetary conditions might alter the physical manifestation of the effect, but the timing would necessarily be the same.

In this I can make a scientific prediction based upon my hypothesis. Epochal boundary changes on Mars and Venus will be synchronistic with the P-Tr boundary event, the Precambrian-Cambrian explosion and the late, great bombardment, or 'lunar cataclysm'. Other huge changes in the geology and climate of these worlds will be found to be synchronistic with changes on this planet too, including extra-terrestrial geological markers commensurate with the sudden onset of long-period terrestrial Ice Epochs.

Will the patterns of glacial advance and retreat over Epochs be the same on Mars as it is on Earth, for example? Was Mars similarly warm over 4 million years ago, only succumbing to a long period of severe glaciation, as the Earth became similarly gripped by the 4 million year long Ice Epoch? As the Earth steadily warms will we see a similar pattern emerge on Mars, leading slowly towards a more habitable climate on the red planet?

## Changing Poles

Other researchers have considered other radical ideas to explain anomalous patterns of Ice Age fluctuation.

For instance, in Graham Hancock's book "The Fingerprints of the Gods", he discusses the theories of Charles Hapgood regarding "Earth-crust displacement". Evidence of sudden global climate change in our pre-history is not new, but some people may not be aware of the many anomalies that have been found, indicating extremely sudden change. For instance, "flash-frozen mammoths in Northern Siberia and Alaska, and the 90ft tall fruit trees locked in the permafrost deep inside the Arctic Circle at a latitude where nothing grows" (11).

Further evidence for cataclysms occurring during periods of dramatic climate change is attested to elsewhere (12). Essentially, Earth-crust displacement encapsulates a theoretical spinning of the thin crust around the Earth, known as the lithosphere, around the rest of the body of the planet. It's sudden occurrence would be cataclysmic, and the Canadian researchers Rand and Rose Flem-Ath have cited geological and mythological evidence to support their proposition that the last Ice Age finished, suddenly, in the 11th Millennium BC (12,13,14). The idea that the entire crust of the Earth slips catastrophically is, of course, a radical one. Now, it may be that the Milankovitch Cycle offers a more robust solution to the problems addressed by Hancock and others, because the Milankovitch model fits with the patterns of cyclical change between Ice Ages and Interglacials within the last Ice Epoch. However, do all of these changes involve such apocalyptic changes as those recorded about 11,000 years ago? Does this date mark a quite different transition into a new permanently warmer period, or was it simply one of many incremental adjustments to the world's climate, as the Earth's wobble and eccentricity predictably shifted into a different phase of the Milankovitch Cycle?

## The Big Question

The area of real concern for me is whether the catastrophic end of the last Ice Age some 11,000 years ago marked a shift into a new Interglacial period, or whether it catastrophically plunged the Earth out of the long-standing Ice Epoch. If it is the latter, which seems likely, given the scientific evidence cited by many catastrophists, as well as in the traditions recorded by many ancient peoples in their myths, then the complete recession of the 4 million year old Ice Epoch should eventually lead us towards a point where all of the world's ice disappears over time, and global warming gets a firm grip on the entire planet.

The ice caps will become a thing of the past once again, and the planet's global climate will return to the sort of warmth that allowed the dinosaurs to thrive, even at the poles of the Earth! It's an alarming thought.

These complex issues are not new. Before the realization dawned on the scientific community, and our wider society, about the consequences of accelerated global warming, the consensus was that the Earth would likely cool again. This was because the interglacial period currently enjoyed was simply one of a number of such warm intermissions, set within a three to four million year long Ice Epoch. Those interglacial periods were determined solely by orbital considerations, in other words, the Milankovitch Cycles. Because previous interglacial periods had begun to wind up after about 10,000 years, then it was expected that glaciers would start to grow once again during this modern period.

However, more recent research has indicated that this is by no means a 'normal' interglacial period. In fact, our world has continued to slowly warm long after it should have started to cool. It has been suggested that this shift from the normal climate-change pattern, associated so closely with the Milankovitch Cycle, began as long ago as 6000 BCE. Concentrations of carbon dioxide and methane in the atmosphere are already starting to appear anomalously high 8,000 years ago, and have continued that trend since then.

Although the cause is not known, it seems clear that the general principle of the Milankovitch Cycle, that has dominated our global climate for 4 million years, has been broken. Such a change is coincident with the ascendance of human civilization, and has been linked to the invention and early promulgation of agriculture [16]. But it should also be remembered that Ice Epochs have drawn to a close before. Humans were not around at those points in time. Such major shifts in global climate call for solutions related to the Earth's place in the Cosmos.

The scientific community has a fairly detailed record of Earth's geo-history that shows that it is incredibly unstable as far as climate is concerned, and that breath-taking changes can occur in just decades. This adds uncertainty to an already chaotic picture regarding the Earth's present global climate changes. That uncertainty means that science cannot predict whether the Earth will warm steadily towards a runaway greenhouse effect, or whether the balance of climate regulation on the planet will be self-correcting, or whether we will eventually be plunged back into a new Ice Age.

This is why it is so vital to discover whether there is a Dark Star orbiting the sun. If there is, as I firmly believe, then I contend that its presence is the causal factor between the comings and goings of Ice Epochs. Put simply, the Earth's distance from the sun should no longer be considered a constant, but is instead a variable. During periods of hundreds of millions of years, it was close enough to the sun to banish all ice from the surface of this planet.

We may now be returning to those times. During the Ice Epochs, the Earth orbited slightly further away from the sun. This caused the inter-continental glaciers to form, broken up occasionally only by the vagaries of the Earth's wobbles and eccentricities.

The reason why the Earth's radius of orbit varies is because of the instability of the Dark Star's own loosely-bound orbit. The energies of the orbits of all the planets in the solar system are necessarily inter-woven, and the Dark Star holds the key to them all. If the Earth is now warming up out of a four million-year old Ice Epoch, then it reasonable to assume that Mars is similarly warming from its own Ice Epoch. Maybe that explains recent evidence of water movements on the red planet.

Venus should also be warming catastrophically, perhaps implying that during its own "Colder Epoch" conditions on this inner planet were once not so extreme. (It would be quite wrong to associate the word "ice" with Venus. A colder period on this hellish planet would simply amount to turning the oven temperature down a notch.)

If we have fully emerged from the last Ice Epoch, rather than simply enjoying a warm inter-glacial interlude, then this is directly attributable to a fairly recent shift in the orbit of the Dark Star. The consequences of this shift are significant.

It would mean that the complete ice caps of the planet Earth are under considerable threat. This threat has been massively added to by our own industrial activities of the last few hundred years. The coastal and low-lying areas of the Earth's landmasses will become permanently flooded as the caps melt, probably catastrophically at some point...maybe soon.

Our planet as a whole is going to be getting a lot warmer - whether we inadvertently contribute to that effect or not - through our emissions of greenhouse gases. This is a very serious situation, one whose understanding rests completely upon the detection of the sun's binary solar companion. There is simply no time to waste.

# Chapter 14 References

1. J. Hills "The Passage of a "Nemesis"-like Object through the Planetary System" Astron. J. 90, 1876 (1985)

2. Correspondence with Dr. Daniel Whitmire and Dr. John Matese, 5th March 2001, reproduced with their permission given at the time of correspondence.

3. B. Greene "The Elegant Universe" Jonathan Cape 1999

4. Correspondence with Dr. R. Fitzpatrick, 29th January 2002

5. J. Gribbin & M. Gribbin "Ice Age" Allen Lane, the Penguin Press 2001

6. Grayson (Ed) "Equinox: The Earth": 'Ice Warriors' by P. Simons, pp126-7, Channel 4 Books, 2000

7. Jet Propulsion Laboratory "Scientists see Earth Move in Antarctica" http://geodynamics.jpl.nasa.gov/antarctica/mblproject.html 14th December 2000

8. M. Edwards "Glacial Records Depict Ice Age Climate In Synch Worldwide" National Science Foundation 24/3/04, With thanks to James Monds

9. Horizon "Snowball Earth" Shown on BBC2, 22nd Feb 2001

10. Illinois State Museum "Ice Ages" http://www.museum.state.il.us/exhibits/ice_ages/

11. G. Hancock "Fingerprints of the Gods" p490-495 Mandarin 1995

12. D.S. Allan & J.B. Delair "When the Earth Nearly Died" p16, Gateway Books, Bath 1995

13. R. & R. Flem-Ath "Atlantis and the Earth's Shifting Crust" http://www.flem-ath.com/dell.htm

14. R. & R. Flem-Ath "When the Sky Fell" Stoddart, Canada 1995

15. R. Flem-Ath & C. Wilson "The Atlantis Blueprint" Warner 2001

16. W. Ruddiman "How did Humans First Alter Global Climate?" Scientific American, Vol. 292, No. 3, p34-41, March 2005

# 15

## Is This Our Nemesis?

In this book I have set out my own particular view of the Dark Star. I have placed this within its proper historical setting, drawing upon the various other ideas about Planet X, which have been talked about by scientists and members of the general public alike. My Dark Star is very similar to the concept of Nemesis, at least in terms of its stellar qualities. However, my Dark Star is right at the bottom of the range of objects that might constitute Nemesis.

In the mid 1980s, the concept of a binary companion called Nemesis was big news. Discussion about whether it could be a real possibility filled serious scientific journals of the day. It even made the front cover of Time magazine (1). Media coverage was not always particularly kind, probably because the idea seemed so speculative, yet awesome in its magnitude.

I wonder whether people are all that comfortable with the thought that scientists might be able to predict apocalyptic events through their study of astronomy. Perhaps it drags Science into the realm of Religion, especially the controversial Christian vision of "Armageddon". This is an area that many scientists themselves feel less than comfortable delving into. So, it is little wonder that scorn was also poured upon the "Nemesis" theory by many scientists at that time.

Dr. Richard Muller, one of the scientists who first proposed "Nemesis" (2), still thinks that the hypothesis remains viable, despite a widespread misconception that the case for Nemesis had been disproved. He concedes that the orbital path of Nemesis would be currently unstable. However, its variability over time answers this problem because, as his astronomical colleague Piet Hut showed, its initial lifetime at the beginning of the solar system was 6 billion years (1).

I think that Dr. Muller is quite right to argue that the case for Nemesis is still an open one. Indeed, our more up-to-date knowledge of brown dwarfs has re-ignited the debate. I think that Nemesis is a very small brown dwarf, not a significantly larger red or brown dwarf as initially envisioned. That makes questions about its current lack of detection easier to counter.

But, that's where my agreement with the Nemesis theorists ends. I don't think that an orbit of 26, or 30, million years is the answer. Instead, I see a much closer bound object as a more viable prospect. An orbit of thousands of years, rather than millions, makes more sense.

It seems to me that the extinction cycle, proposed by Raup and Sepkoski (3), remains unproven, because the data it relies upon is too narrow in its scope. It may turn out to be correct in time, perhaps as our knowledge of cratering patterns on other worlds adds to this data. However, I would argue that we should not pin the whole of the Nemesis/Dark Star argument onto the back of this particular beast. The alleged cyclical pattern of comet bombardment may be a statistical illusion. Profound changes to our planet over time are not.

In Chapter 14, I proposed that the variability of the Dark Star was itself the causal factor for catastrophe. The nature of its loosely bound, eccentric orbit leads to change over time that has momentous implications for climate and life on this planet. I hope that this concept may help to move the debate about Nemesis onto a new footing. After all, the stakes could hardly be greater. There are changes afoot on planet Earth which urgently require an explanation.


## A Modern Catastrophe


Mankind has an amazing propensity for self-inflicted wounds, but our appetite for destruction sometimes pales into insignificance, when placed against the kinds of disasters occurring in Nature. The tsunami unleashed by the shifting of tectonic plates below the Indian Ocean on 26th December, 2004, killed thousands along many stretches of coastline in the area. The plight caused by this catastrophe seemed to capture the sympathy of our entire global population: billions of dollars were raised by the general public, shaming governments whose initial reactions were less then forthcoming.

The cause of this tragedy is a reminder of the fragility of our life on this planet, and how close we may all be to potential disaster. For decades, Catastrophists have argued the case for there having been repeated devastation of our world in pre-historical times. They wonder whether our emergence from caves to civilization may not have been the smooth and relatively recent transition alluded to in the history textbooks. Many have wondered whether our progress has been less graduated, more stop/start; that our human predecessors may have repeatedly fallen afoul of natural disasters that have affected our planet and environment.

This latest disaster affected coastal areas peripheral to the epicenter of the sub-oceanic earthquake, which measured 9.0 on the Richter scale. A collapse of the sea bed caused a ripple effect across the Indian Ocean that culminated in 30 foot waves in shallow waters: these waves then crashed into islands and coastal areas causing devastation. It seems difficult to imagine a worse scenario.

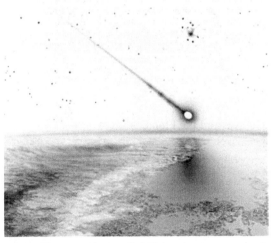

Yet, similar events in recorded history have seen tsunamis substantially greater, culminating in the movement of oceanic waters deeper into land areas.

It is a fact that human settlements have always preferred coastal areas to inhabit. Such areas are richer in good soils and wildlife, and generally enjoy less extreme climates than more inland, continental lands. But the risk associated with a substantial fraction of the human population living near coastal areas is that the sea might one day unleash devastation commonly affecting them all.

Many have wondered: is it possible that a worldwide disaster might have been caused by a global tsunami? It would have to be a very substantial wave indeed, one that originated from a devastating catastrophe in oceanic waters. Not only that, but the epicenter of such an event would have to have been positioned in such a way, that the wave was able to access all oceans and seas without having its momentum broken by a substantial landmass. This could only have taken place, then, if the epicenter was in the Southern Oceans in the vicinity of Antarctica. And the most likely source of such an event would be an oceanic comet strike.

2.15 million years ago, an asteroid greater than 1 kilometer in diameter, crashed into the South-East Pacific Ocean. Scientists have been able to draw this conclusion from evidence from the ocean floor, which shows damage over hundreds of square kilometres (4,5,6). The devastating impact created a massive tsunami that, after only five hours, was about 70 metres high. It continued from the impact point to move at the speed of an aircraft across the Pacific and South Atlantic Oceans, devastating coastal areas from Australia and Asia to South-West Africa.

## Comets and the Flood

In the U.K. Government-funded "Report of the Task Force on Potentially Hazardous Near-Earth Objects" (7), which was published in 2000, discusses the threat posed by tsunamis which are unleashed by asteroid impact. The tragic events of Christmas week, 2004, underline the potential catastrophe we all face.

There are many, many Flood myths from around the globe. The Biblical account of Noah is not just a story popular in the Levant, but one whose telling spanned the ancient world. The Book of Enoch identifies seven burning stars with the Flood (8). Perhaps these were part of a comet swarm, or perhaps they were part of the observable phenomenon of Nibiru, or the Dark Star. Such an association sets off alarm bells in my head.

However, scholars seem unwilling to give any credence to the idea that a world-wide catastrophe of this nature may actually have occurred in pre-historical times, leading to the extinction of many species. Yet, it is such a common myth across disparate cultures, that there is surely some truth to it. Scholars counter that such an event could not have occurred across the whole face of the planet, without some kind of evidence being left behind.

However, it is the very nature of such sudden flooding, that little trace of the devastation remains long after the event. The damage is literally washed away, or left buried in a chaotic state.

One of the surprising stories to emerge from the terrifying tsunami of 26th December, 2004, was the reaction to it by an undeveloped tribe of hunter-gatherers living on North Sentinel Island, among the Andaman Islands. The entire tribe of 500 or so people survived the tsunami, having evacuated the coastal areas immediately following the initial earthquake. Madhusree Mukerjee, a researcher and author working among the Andamanese, spoke with tribesmen, who explained that their evacuation of the coastline before the tsunami struck happened because of warnings given to them by their forefathers. Their folklore advises the tribe to head for the hills, or out to sea in boats, when an earthquake occurs (9). The tribe clearly took that advice very seriously, saving many lives.

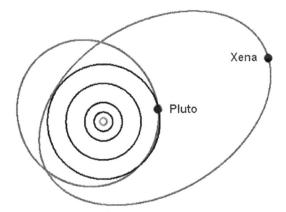

This remarkable tale indicates the importance of orally transmitted folklore and teachings within any culture. Tsunamis are examples of rare catastrophic phenomena, yet this undeveloped tribal society held onto the warnings of dire consequences for many years following an earthquake. Our modern thinking has long since rubbished the warnings of the ancients about catastrophe. By ignoring the ever-present dangers – our modern society -- through its misplaced scepticism, has foolishly turned its back on the wisdom handed down to us from the past.

We should learn from this. There is great wisdom to be found in the writings of the ancients, and the orally transmitted tribal teachings. These teachings cannot replace our science, but they can, and should, complement our modern framework of knowledge.

## Running Out of Myths

This loss of interest in our pre-historical roots, and the myths which abounded in those times, finds another analogy in the modern hunt for planets beyond Neptune. When astronomers began to catalogue the minor planets and asteroids in the solar system, they gave each a name. These names were derived from the pantheons of classical gods and goddesses, much like the more familiar names of the planets like Mars and Jupiter. However, as the number of known minor bodies in the solar system has expanded over time, the pool of available gods and goddesses to which they could be dedicated has dried up.

This problem is worsened if one considers the possible requirement of a name of a major god for a potential major planet. This problem has been recently tested by the discoveries of various Edgeworth-Kuiper Belt Objects whose sizes have begun to compete with Pluto itself. Names of gods from pantheons of other religions have been used, of which the Inuit "Sedna" is a good example. But if the discovery was of a planet bigger than Pluto, then shouldn't that planet be named after a classical god or goddess from Greek or Roman mythology?

The discovery of a 'real' tenth planet has recently highlighted this problem, as well as raising some further controversy for the Planet X debate. The planet, officially designated 2003 UB313, was found by Dr Mike Brown and colleagues using the Samuel

Oschin Telescope at Palomar Observatory near San Diego, California (10). It is the most distant object yet found in the solar system, currently lying almost 100 times the distance from the Earth to the sun.

It is incredibly difficult to spot a planet at this distance. Indeed, this new world still cannot be picked out by the powerful Spitzer telescope, despite a good knowledge of its whereabouts. Its fortuitous discovery results from the high reflectivity of its icy surface, without which it would certainly have remained hidden. Again, this very large scattered disc object has an elliptical orbit, falling in line with several other lesser objects discovered recently. Have these eccentric scattered disc objects have been affected by an influence beyond that of mighty Neptune? It seems reasonable to think so.

This emerging trend also suggests that larger bodies almost certainly await discovery, each with its own remarkable degree of eccentricity. The elliptical orbits of these scattered disc objects seem to be the reason why such large planetary bodies have been so difficult to spot. This, of course, is why the Dark Star has remained undetected, for the moment at least.

2003 UB313 is not just bigger than Pluto, it is also a planet of similar character. One would expect it to be justly called the solar system's Tenth Planet.

At the moment, 2003 UB313 does not have an official name. It appears that the planet's discoverers have offered up the name 'Xena', after the character from the fictional television series of the same name (11). This suggestion breaks the mould of planetary nomenclature, and will certainly provoke controversy among professional astronomers. Personally, I quite like the name. It has a certain ring to it, and gives the impression of moving off in a new direction, which Planet X research does, of course. But I'm not sure that it will be very acceptable to the authorities charged with a final decision.

Quixotically, they may even decide that, although 'Xena' is a planet larger than Pluto, it is not really a 'tenth planet' proper after all, and that giving it a rather trivial name symbolically down-grades its importance. So, dependent upon the philosophical stance taken over how to categorize planets, the non-classical 'Xena' might prove to be useful nomenclature after all...

The name eventually attributed to 2003 UB313 will depend upon whether it is actually classified as a major or minor planet. Given that it is larger than Pluto, one would have thought that should be incontrovertible. Pluto, after all, doggedly remains a 'major planet'.

However, this discovery may be the first among many. If every round chunk of rock and ice larger than Pluto in the Edgeworth-Kuiper Belt were to be classified as a major planet, then one could imagine a situation where the science books need to list literally dozens of 'planets' in the solar system in a just few years time! You can see why astronomers have a dilemma on their hands.

## Secrecy And Astronomy

You might have wondered why astronomers would announce the discovery of a brand new planet without being in a position to give it a proper name. Its technical name implies initial discovery in 2003, actually before Sedna whose designation is 2003 VB12. The realization that this new Edgeworth-Kuiper Belt Object was actually a planet in its own right did not occur until 8th January 2005, however. From that point onwards, Mike Brown and his team worked with at least two different telescopes to collect the cast-iron evidence needed to make the discovery public.

During this time, they kept their discovery secret. However, technical information about 'Xena' was being held on computer databases by the research team, and it transpired that this 'secure' data was actually available over the Internet for anyone with sufficient technical knowledge to find their way around the databases.

Dr Mike Brown then discovered to his horror that someone had clandestinely accessed that database, which meant that someone with an astronomical background could work backwards through his data and 'discover' Xena independently, before his team made their planned announcement. Mike Brown was forced to release his findings prematurely, which inevitably stole some of his thunder (12).

Given that 'Xena' had been catalogued for over 18 months prior to the public announcement of its planet-hood, could one argue that all such astronomical discoveries are being deliberately kept from the public? Does Nibiru appear on a database somewhere, quietly mulled over by a research group somewhere? Are we being kept in the dark about Planet X?

Such considerations are far from fanciful, but the issues involved are admittedly rather complex.

Releasing information about the discovery of new EKBOs is fraught with difficulties. Spotting new dots of light on CCD camera images, and capturing enough data to actually specify orbits and sizes of new objects are two entirely separate things. Sometimes it proves difficult to re-find objects that have previously been identified.

This might seem difficult to believe, given the technical power of the instruments used nowadays. However, these objects are being resolved at the very limits of the instruments' power, and the quality of scans over a period of time will vary with atmospheric conditions, and such like. Some potential objects are simply seen once, and then never seen again. Without a history of sightings mapping out an actual trajectory for the object over time, there is no discovery to speak of. An entire planet might blink in and out at the edge of resolution.

In addition, the more distant the object, the slower is its procession across the sky. This is because its orbital period is that bit longer. This perhaps explains why a Nemesis object is so difficult to pinpoint. Its lateral motion across the sky is so slow that it is readily mistaken for a stationary background star, and catalogued as such.

After all, the stars themselves are dynamic, revolving around the galactic core like celestial carousel horses. Nothing in the universe is truly at rest. So establishing what is distant, and what is relatively nearby is not as straightforward as one might imagine. As we have discussed in a previous chapter, even the heat signatures of objects located on an infra-red search might be less easy to verify than one might think, with many objects being pinpointed but never properly identified or researched.

So an object might be initially classified in 2003, but it may take a couple of years of painstaking work to establish enough factual data to allow other scientists, and the general public, to accept this object as a new planet. Scientists who rush through this kind of process are liable to find egg on their faces.

That said, the issue of secrecy remains. Even if we can appreciate the complexities of the scientific work being undertaken here, and the need to verify the work before writing up a paper for a journal, the fact remains that discoveries of new planets in the solar system will be kept secret temporarily. This may be fine if the discovery of Planet X is merely of academic interest.

However, there is an aspect to this work that transcends the science involved. There are so many different ideas about the significance of Planet X that it's difficult to cover all of them in detail here, but it's worthwhile appraising the possibilities briefly.

## The Consequences of Discovery

During the heady days of the 2003 Planet X controversy, many researchers claimed that the imminent threat of a perihelion passage of this object could bring about global devastation. The most likely cause of such cataclysms, it was argued, would be comet showers of Biblical magnitude. Planet X carries with it an entire system of comets, asteroids and even moons and planets. Despite the vast distances over which the solar system is laid out, such an enormous retinue of potential impactors offers us a phenomenal threat.

If the comets don't get us, then another possibility is that the sun's activity will shift into a different gear as a result of the presence of Planet X amongst the planets. Massive solar super-storms would destroy communications globally and send our climate into meltdown. Perhaps the magnetic poles would reverse, or at least shift dramatically, bringing along unknown consequences for life on this planet. Another possibility is that the incoming swarms of comets might bring with them viruses which descend like a deadly plague through our atmosphere.

For these reasons, argued the doomsayers of Planet X lore, we should take due precautions against the end of the world.

If you place the secrecy of the discovery of Planet X into this context, then it is easy to see how a major conspiracy theory can emerge. Let us entertain the possibility that the Government is well aware of the existence of Nibiru, the Dark Star, Nemesis...call it what you will. Let us say that they also recognize the threat posed by such an entity, and are charged with keeping our society free from the kind of panic which could emerge if the worst case scenarios listed above were, in fact, for real. Well, it seems plain to me that full public knowledge of the discovery of Planet X and its terrifying implications would be actively suppressed, with all necessary force.

In which case, astronomers hunting for this object would be in a rather precarious position. Their data would be collected and placed into computer files. Diligent agents of the Government would then monitor activity on these computers, looking for the Big One, and have plenty of time to act on it before a public announcement was made. After all, the scientists themselves are not about to release their news without verifying it, which would take months. This would provide the authorities with the intelligence needed to act in time to prevent panic.

If one was to go to these extremes of paranoia, then one could suggest that Dr Mike Brown's 'hacker' may have been official in nature...

Of course, this all reads like the screenplay of a bad science fiction movie. Is this really very likely? Well, that depends on the nature of Planet X. If it is a terrestrial planet which moves through the asteroid belt during perihelion, as Zecharia Sitchin argues, then it is potentially dangerous in its own right. But it must be far enough away from perihelion at the moment to give us many, many years of warning between its discovery and its actual perihelion. Such an object takes its time moving around the sun - it is not going to suddenly turn up on our doorstep.

If Planet X is a bigger object, more in the Nemesis genre, then it is less likely to be a direct threat. However, its indirect impact on our planet might be just as bad over a longer period of time. The sheer magnitude of this Dark Star in relation to the other planets of the solar system means that it holds the balance of power among the worlds of the sun.

Even at great distances, it may affect us through orbital diversification, or its movement through the various layers of the solar magnetic field. It may even send us comet swarms by sweeping through parts of the solar system dense with such objects, like the Edgeworth-Kuiper Belt. The gap in the EKB might be due to such cosmic vacuuming in the past, with our planet having been the sufferer of previous cataclysmic cometary fallouts. The late, great bombardment 3.9 billion years ago would be an example.

My own opinion is that this Dark Star holds the key to long-term shifts in the climate of the Earth, and that the changes we are currently experiencing here on Earth may be symptomatic of adjustments in that cosmic balance of power. In itself, this may not seem too threatening to our world, at least compared to the threat of cometary bombardment. However, there is another balance of power at stake here.

The world's energy needs have been met by petroleum for decades, and the need for oil steadily increases as more of the world develops industrial muscle. This inexorable rise in the emissions of greenhouse gases means that we fear that we may start to get the taste of what it's like to live on Venus. This is a divisive political and environmental issue.

But the climate of the world is not a stable commodity, and never has been. It oscillates between great extremes, from Snowball Earth to poles inhabited by dinosaurs. These changes weren't a result of the over-use of fossil fuels. We know that for certain, at least.

Other more natural mechanisms dictate the Earth's terrifying swings in climate, and the same seems to be true for other planets in the solar system too. If the key to this mystery is the Dark Star, then its discovery would have a great impact on the debate about climate change itself. We might start to see the bigger picture for what it is.

There is a final consequence of discovery which would interest Governments. If the Dark Star is indeed an integral part of ancient mythology, then its discovery will pose deep questions for all of the world's religions. It will change the way we look at ourselves and our place in the Cosmos.

This may take many years, possibly even generations, but there would be a fundamental shift in our understanding of our own origins, and the source of our beliefs. The myths which we have all been systematically fed throughout our lives by society, and the religious and secular organizations we hold dear, might finally be dispelled. But they would not be given up easily, that's for sure.

This consideration, finally, may be more important to our futures than any considerations about comet clouds or global warming. In our paranoid times, the resultant instability may not be entirely welcomed by our already twitchy Governments, or communities.

Like the scientists who innocently toiled away on the Manhattan Project, our present day astronomers may be playing a game whose consequences entirely transcend their own hopes and fears. Perhaps their scientific caution and secrecy provide them with useful buffers, allowing them to consider the wider consequences of their discoveries.

## Myth and Reality

In this book, we have looked at the science that supports the concept of a hidden binary companion. I have put forward a new formulation of the older Nemesis theory, one that brings such a body closer to the solar system. My Dark Star theory is a compromise between the Nemesis concept and the more traditional considerations regarding a Planet X beyond Pluto.

This has allowed us to consider scientific evidence from the Edgeworth-Kuiper Belt, which shows something massive has moved around beyond the Kuiper Cliff. That evidence is mounting. It seems from the work of Alice Quillen, that the truncation of the EKB relates to the activity of a Jupiter-sized, or more massive, planet at some point in the past. I argue that that planet is still orbiting the sun.

If I am right, then the Dark Star is not just another planet found in the depths of the solar system. Its sheer size, mass, and the bizarre nature of its orbit mean that it has a profound effect upon our world. It may turn out to be the key to understanding the massive changes in our planet's climate over the eons. It may help us to explain why the planets of the solar system, including ours, seem to be warming up. This may lead us to revise our entire understanding of global warming, and the imminent fate of our planet's climate.

Furthermore, if the Dark Star becomes visible during its perihelion passage - through some kind of intensification of its activity as it passes through the sun's extensive magnetic field - then its appearance in the sky might provide us with a missing link in understanding many of the world's oldest myths and legends. The discovery of the true nature of the visible phenomenon named "Nibiru" would help to give credence to the other ideas generated by Zecharia Sitchin.

At the beginning of this book, I highlighted my desire to successfully blend myth and scientific reality. As far as interpretation of myth is concerned, I have concentrated upon the work of Zecharia Sitchin in this book, and gone on to explore how his theories might find a scientific mandate as our knowledge of the solar system develops. It is beyond the scope of this particular book to comprehensively explore the various other mythical sources that might indicate the existence of an unseen planet in our system. There is certainly plenty of fascinating material to consider, particularly in the more eclectic realm of esoteric studies.

Such an investigation is a major undertaking, requiring a diligent study of the complexities of myth and reality. But it is a study which shows considerable promise, and I hope to provide my findings in a future book. For instance, I have a great deal of interest in the association between esoteric symbolism and the existence of a hidden binary companion. Studies in this direction have revealed many potential insights about the secret knowledge of the Dark Star.

Zecharia Sitchin's claims are interwoven with the proposed existence of a substantial tenth planet, moving along a highly elliptical orbit. Sitchin postulated that our species was bio-engineered by flesh-and-blood gods, who travelled to Earth from Nibiru. They allegedly found our ape-like ancestors and modified them to produce, in effect, intelligent slaves capable of doing their bidding. We are the descendants of those experiments, it would seem, abandoned to our fate after the Deluge failed to entirely destroy our species.

It seems to me that the evolutionary development of our species over the last few million years ran hand in hand with the last Ice Epoch, which may or may not have now finished entirely. Arguments about the evolution of the human species are complex, and often antagonistic (13,14,15). One could argue that the evolution towards humanity represented a natural change, when confronted with the environmental onset of an Ice Age.

After all, the onset of 'modern' humans over the past 100,000 years is coincident with the last Ice Age - with civilization sprouting during the current interglacial (if that's what this warm period really is).

But it is also interesting to consider the following thought. If the Ice Epoch began 4 million years ago because of a change in the orbit of the Dark Star, then that might also have brought the Anunnaki to the planetary solar system. This is because as the Earth and other planets moved slightly further away from the sun, the Dark Star must have been migrating inwards. That means that the planet Nibiru might have entered the planetary zone of the sun for the first time in many millions of years.

This is a rather fantastic claim, and readers more focussed upon the science contained in this book may balk at such a suggestion. One can quite understand such a reaction, and it is probably why the Planet X debate is avoided by mainstream scientists for the most part. This association between the potential physical reality of a massive Planet X, and questions about our own origins, would become more profound should the Dark Star actually be discovered. These are high stakes indeed.

# Chapter 15 References

1. P. Dauber & R. Muller "The Three Big Bangs: Comet Crashes, Exploding Stars and the Creation of the Universe" Chapter 8, Addison Wesley 1996

2. R. Muller "Nemesis - The Death Star" Weidenfield & Nicholson, 1988

3. D. Raup "The Nemesis Affair, A Story of the Death of the Dinosaurs and the Ways of Science" W.W. Norton, 1986

4. R. Grieve in Ann NY Acad Sci, vol 822, p338, 1997; Kyte et al "New evidence on the size and possible effects of a late Pliocene oceanic impact", Science, 241, 63-65, 1998

5. S. Ward & E Asphaug "Asteroid Impact Tsunami - A Probabilistic Hazard Assessment", submitted to Icarus 2000

6. S. Ward & E. Asphaug "Impact Tsunami - Eltanin", submitted to Deep Sea Research - Oceanic Impacts, 2000

7. U.K Government "Report of the Task Force on Potentially Hazardous Near Earth Objects", p18, British National Space Centre, September 2000

8. C. Knight & R. Lomas "Uriel's Machine" pp95-100, Arrow 2000

9. M. Mukerjee "The Scarred Earth" Scientific American 292, No. 3, p8-10, March 2005

10. David Tytell "Astronomers Discover "Tenth Planet"" Sky and Telescope, 29th July 2005 http://skyandtelescope.com/news/article_1560_1.asp

11. Robin McKie "The Little Rock Causing a Galactic Storm" The Observer, 31st July 2005

12. Michael Brown, Caltech "Astronomers at Palomar Observatory Discover a 10th Planet Beyond Pluto", with thanks to Mattia Galiazzo http://www.gps.caltech.edu/%7Embrown/planetlila/index.html

13. M. Behe "Darwin's Black Box" Touchstone 1996

14. A. Walker & P. Shipman "The Wisdom of Bones" Weidenfield & Nicholson 1996

15. L. Pye "Everything You Know is Wrong" Adamu Press 1997

# INDEX

Timeless Voyager Press

Made in the USA
Monee, IL
20 September 2021